Plant Physiology

A TREATISE

EDITED BY

F. C. STEWARD

Department of Botany
Cornell University, Ithaca, New York

Volume I A: Cellular Organization and Respiration

1960

ACADEMIC PRESS, *New York and London*

United Kingdom edition published by
ACADEMIC PRESS INC. (London) Ltd.
17 Old Queen Street, London, S. W. 1

Library of Congress Catalog Card Number: 59-7689

PRINTED IN THE UNITED STATES OF AMERICA

CONTRIBUTORS TO VOLUME I A

WALTER D. BONNER, *Department of Botany, Cornell University, Ithaca, New York**

R. BROWN, *Agricultural Research Council Unit of Plant Cell Physiology, Department of Agriculture, Oxford, England*†

DAVID R. GODDARD, *Division of Biology, University of Pennsylvania, Philadelphia, Pennsylvania*

BIRGIT VENNESLAND, *Department of Biochemistry, University of Chicago, Chicago, Illinois*

* Present address: The Johnson Foundation, University of Pennsylvania, Philadelphia, Pennsylvania.

† Present address: Department of Botany, University of Edinburgh, Edinburgh, Scotland.

Preface to Volume I

Since Volume II of this treatise actually preceded Volume I, it is desirable to recapitulate certain general aims and objectives of the whole work.

The aim of this treatise is to *say* what Plant Physiology is about and to do this in sufficient detail and with sufficient analysis of, and even extracts from, the ever expanding literature, so that each volume will be in large measure self-contained.

Plant physiologists will find that the treatment is sufficiently detailed to benefit their research in their own specialized fields and that the scope is broad enough to make reading of all portions of the work both stimulating and profitable. This treatise is, therefore, designed for the use of advanced and postgraduate students, teachers, research workers, and investigators in other fields of knowledge who need information about the present status of plant physiology. While such a synthesis of current knowledge is well justified by the great advances that have been made, especially in the last quarter of a century, its accomplishment requires the knowledge and mature experience of many authors who are aware of the trends in their often rapidly advancing fields of interest. Upon these authors, therefore, rests the quality and value of the work and to each the editor acknowledges his debt.

Although the treatise is now arranged in six volumes, each has been planned as a distinct unit and consists of a group of related chapters which, together, cover a major segment of the subject. Each chapter has been written by an authority in the field and analyzes the present status of its subject matter, giving pertinent references to the literature. The chief emphasis is on a synthesis of current knowledge, but consideration is also given to significant accomplishments of the past and, where possible, an insight into the problems of the future. Thus the reader may acquire an informed outlook on each topic.

While full advantage is taken of recent advances which accrue from the application of physical and biochemical techniques and the study of subcellular systems, the need to see the subject of plant physiology in terms of the morphology and organization of living plants is recognized throughout.

The treatise is intended not solely for use as a work of reference but is to be read by those who wish to obtain a reasoned analysis of the status and development of each subject which is discussed. Admittedly, and rightly, each chapter is affected by the author's own opinions, but, so far as possible in a work of this kind, an attempt has been made to achieve a measure of integration between the different chapters. Indexes make it possible for information to be traced by reference to an author's name, to the plants used, or to the subject matter in question. For this volume the Index of Plant Names was prepared by Dr. W. J. Dress, and the Subject Index was compiled by Dr. H. Y. Mohan Ram. For this help the editor is grateful.

Volume I consists of two parts, A and B, each of which is complete with its own table of contents, separate pagination, indexes, etc. The consecutive numbering of Chapters 1 through 5, however, links these together as a single volume within the over-all plan of the treatise.

Even though Volume II has in fact preceded Volume I, it is still appropriate that the subject matter of Volume I should be considered first, for it concerns problems raised by the cellular and subcellular levels of organization within which physiological events occur, and it also deals with mechanisms by which cells store energy only to release it later for useful purposes.

While any of the subjects dealt with in Volume I could have been expanded beyond the limits of the present treatment, there were special reasons for the more extensive treatment of photosynthesis in Chapter 4 of Volume IB. The subject of photosynthesis, distinctive as it is of plants, has advanced so rapidly in recent years that an adequate treatment of all facets of the problem required a longer chapter. This plan was adopted even though it necessitated the division of Volume IA and IB into separate books. These parts now represent separate but closely related works on cells and cellular respiration in one unit (IA) and photosynthesis and chemosynthesis in the other (IB), and the hope is that the two parts will be the more useful because of their separate publication.

In both the treatment of cellular respiration, i.e. of energy release and utilization, and of photosynthesis, or energy storage, the attention is focused upon these physiological functions as they occur in cells. Other problems are to be raised at the level of organs or organisms, and these will be dealt with in Volume IV, along with other aspects of organic nutrition and of intermediary metabolism: this may account for some seeming gaps in the present treatment.

The separate acknowledgment to all those who have helped the authors and the Editor by permitting the inclusion of their published or unpublished material would be too great a task in a work of this kind. It should be understood, however, that both acknowledgment and thanks are conveyed by the form of citation in the text. The Editor wishes especially to acknowledge the helpful cooperation of the personnel of Academic Press.

F. C. STEWARD

Cornell University
April, 1960

PLANT PHYSIOLOGY

The Plan of the Treatise

The treatise is planned in three main sections, as follows:

Section on *Cell Physiology and Problems Relating to Water and Solutes*

The purpose of this section is to present the properties of cells, their energy relations (Volume I) and behavior toward water and solutes with the closely related problems of the movement of solutes within the plant body and the economy of water in plants (Volume II).

The underlying theme of Volumes I and II is the basis of plant physiology in cell physiology.

Section on *Nutrition and Metabolism*

In this section the detailed facts and knowledge of nutrition and metabolism are presented, first with reference to the need for, and utilization of, inorganic nutrients (Volume III), and second with respect to the processes of organic nutrition (Volume IV). The treatment of organic nutrition leads to a reconsideration of photosynthesis and respiration at the level of organs and organisms. Volume IV describes the intermediary metabolism of carbon and nitrogenous compounds and presents a brief comparison of plants in health and in disease.

The main theme of Volumes III and IV is the nutrition, organic and inorganic, of plants and the biochemical steps by which these processes are achieved.

Section on *Growth and Development*

The purpose of the last section is to present the problems of plant physiology as seen through the analysis of growth and development, mainly with reference to flowering plants. This entails (Volume V) a reappraisal of the main events of growth and development from the standpoint of morphology and leads to a consideration of growth of cells and of organs. Tropisms and the role of hormones and the effects of synthetic growth regulators are discussed. In Volume VI the attention is focused upon the quantitative analysis of growth and development, the physiology of reproduction, the development of fruits and seeds, the problems of dormancy and perennation. The role of environmental factors in the control of growth and development merits separate treatment. Finally the problems of growth and development are examined from the standpoint of genetic control and from the interpretation of abnormal growth as seen in the formation of tumors. Throughout this treatment the controlling mechanisms of growth are evaluated.

Thus the last section of the work provides a synthesis of knowledge about plants since all their physiological processes converge upon growth and development.

The fulfillment of these objectives is possible only through the cooperation of many authors. The scope and treatment of individual chapters reflects the special interests of the contributors. While each volume is a complete unit, with its own table of contents and indexes, it is also an integral part of the whole plan.

Outline of the Plan

Section on *Cell Physiology and Problems Relating to Water and Solutes*

Volume IA. Cellular Organization and Respiration
Volume IB. Photosynthesis and Chemosynthesis
Volume II. Plants in Relation to Water and Solutes

Section on *Nutrition and Metabolism*

Volume III. Inorganic Nutrition of Plants
Volume IV. Organic Nutrition and Metabolism

Section on *Growth and Development*

Volume V. Analysis of Growth
Volume VI. The Physiology of Development

NOTE ON THE USE OF PLANT NAMES

The policy has been to identify by its scientific name, whenever possible, any plant mentioned by a vernacular name by the contributors to this work. In general, this has been done on the first occasion in each chapter when a vernacular name has been used. Particular care was taken to ensure the correct designation of plants mentioned in tables and figures which record actual observations. Sometimes, when reference has been made by an author to work done by others, it has not been possible to ascertain the exact identity of the plant material originally used, because the original workers did not identify their material except by generic or common name.

It should be unnecessary to state that the precise identification of plant material used in experimental work is as important for the enduring value of the work as the precise definition of any other variables in the work. "Warm" or "cold" would not usually be considered an acceptable substitute for a precisely stated temperature, nor could a general designation of "sugar" take the place of the precise molecular configuration of the substance used; "sunflower" and "*Helianthus*" are no more acceptable as plant names, considering how many diverse species are covered by either designation. Plant physiologists are becoming increasingly aware that different species of one genus (even different varieties or cultivars of one species) may differ in their physiological responses as well as in their external morphology, and that experimental plants should therefore be identified as precisely as possible if the observations made are to be verified by others.

On the assumption that such common names as lettuce and bean are well understood, it may appear pedantic to append the scientific names to them—but such an assumption cannot safely be made. Workers in the United States who use the unmodified word "bean" almost invariably are referring to some form of *Phaseolus vulgaris;* whereas in Britain *Vicia faba,* a plant of another genus entirely, might be implied. "Artichoke" is another such name that comes to mind, sometimes used for *Helianthus tuberosus* (properly, the Jerusalem artichoke), though the true artichoke is *Cynara scolymus.*

By the frequent interpolation of scientific names, consideration has also been given to the difficulties that any vernacular English name alone may present to a reader whose native tongue is not English. Even some American and most British botanists would be led into a misinterpretation of the identity of "yellow poplar," for instance, if this vernacular American name were not supplemented by its scientific equivalent *Liriodendron tulipifera,* for this is not a species of *Populus* as might be expected, but a member of the quite unrelated magnolia family.

When reference has been made to the work of another investigator who, in his published papers, has used a plant name not now accepted by the nomenclatural authorities followed in the present work, that name ordinarily has been included in parentheses, as a synonym, immediately after the accepted name. In a few instances, when it seemed expedient to employ a plant name as it was used by an original author, even though that name is not now recognized as the valid one, the valid name, preceded by the sign =, has been supplied in parentheses: e.g., *Betula verrucosa* (= *B. pendula*). Synonyms have occasionally been added elsewhere also, as in the case of a plant known and frequently reported upon in the literature under more than one name: e.g., *Pseudotsuga menziesii* (*P. taxifolia*); species of *Elodea* (*Anacharis*).

Having adopted these conventions, their implementation rested first with each contributor to this work; but all outstanding problems of nomenclature have been referred to Dr. W. J. Dress of the Bailey Hortorium, Cornell University. The authorities for the nomenclature employed in this work have been Bailey's *Hortus Second* and Bailey's *Manual of Cultivated Plants* for cultivated plants. For bacteria Bergey's *Manual of Determinative Bacteriology*, for fungi Ainsworth and Bisbee's *Dictionary of the Fungi* have been used as reference sources; other names have been checked where necessary against Engler's *Syllabus der Pflanzenfamilien.* Recent taxonomic monographs and floras have been consulted where necessary. Dr. Dress' work in ensuring consistency and accuracy in the use of plant names is deeply appreciated.

THE EDITOR

CONTENTS

INTRODUCTION TO THE TREATISE

Plant Physiology—The Changing Scene

F. C. STEWARD

The origins of Plant Physiology merge in antiquity with those of primitive agriculture. "Consider the lilies of the field how they grow" could well have evoked a primitive observational plant physiology in Biblical times. It is a matter of some pride that a landmark along the centuries-long road from Aristotelian dogma to modern experimental science was the famous seventeenth century experiment of Van Helmont, which was performed during five years with a rooted willow twig and was designed to test whether the substance of plants was of the earth.

Whether the experiment of van Helmont was in fact both the first recorded one in natural science and the beginning of plant physiology as an experimental science, the events of which it was the herald were slow to unfold. Following Francis Bacon, a spirit of enquiry, in protest against the ancient voice of authority, found its expression in the motto "*Nullius in Verba*" of the Royal Society of London (1662). Even more, the newly formed Society helped, in no small measure, to create the climate in which the works of Stephen Hales, Robert Hooke, Nehemiah Grew, and Marcello Malpighi were so soon to flourish, and later also those of Joseph Priestley. The eighteenth century was ushered in by what is commonly regarded as the first attempt at water culture by John Woodward (1699) and, in the newly awakened spirit of observation and experimental enquiry, such classics as "Micrographia" (1665) by Hooke, "The Anatomy of Vegetables" (1676) by Grew, "Anatomes plantarum" (1675) by Malpighi, and "Vegetable Staticks" (1727) by Stephen Hales appeared in rapid succession. By the close of the eighteenth century, through the great works of Joseph Priestley, K. W. Scheele, Jan Ingen-Housz, and Antoine Lavoisier, not only was the elementary nature of oxygen understood, but the foundations were laid for an understanding of combustion and of the nature of its relations to what we now recognize as photosynthesis and respiration.

If the early eighteenth century produced in "Vegetable Staticks" what many would regard as the first research monograph in plant physiology, the dawn of the nineteenth century gave the subject its first comprehensive work, based on the new knowledge which was gained by chemical experiment and by measurement. By many Nicolas Théodore de Saussure is regarded as the one who is best entitled to be recognized as the founder of modern plant physiology. To de Saussure's great work "Recherches chimiques sur la végétation" (1804) the history of so many of the physiological functions may be traced and there seen, clearly stated, while they become diffuse in the mists and maze of earlier days. Whereas van Helmont marks the approaching end of the period of dogma and alchemy and the beginning of experiment, de Saussure marks the opening of a period of careful investigation based on a rational system of chemistry and a logical appeal to experiment. As he said in his preface, "I attack the problems that can be decided by experiment, and I abandon those that can give rise only to conjecture." Whereas van Helmont really belongs to the middle ages, de Saussure ushered in an era of enlightened understanding in plant physiology.

The march of events in the nineteenth century is impressive indeed. The discovery of the cell nucleus by Robert Brown (1831); the crystallization of ideas about cells into the cell doctrine usually attributed to M. J. Schleiden and Theodor Schwann (1838–1839), which paved the way for the emerging science of cell physiology; the recognition of plant protoplasm by Von Mohl (1846) as the essential ingredient of living cells; the observations on plasmolysis (1855) by Karl von Nägeli and Wilhelm Hofmeister, and later by Hugo De Vries (1877), which heralded the knowledge alike of water relations of cells and of the nature of solution, are but a few of the great landmarks of the developing science. From the discovery of asparagine in 1806 to the mounting knowledge of nitrogen compounds; from the carefully conducted field trials and experiments of J. P. Boussingault (from 1834) and J. B. Lawes and J. H. Gilbert (from 1843) to the emerging science of plant nutrition; from the water and sand culture experiments of Julius von Sachs (1860), W. Knop (1860), and others, to the mounting knowledge of mineral requirements; from the early work of Louis Pasteur in 1857 and 1858, which furnished early knowledge of fermentation, to concepts both of respiration and of microbiology; to trace all this and more is to risk losing the dramatic sweep of events in the nineteenth century in the repetitive details of a tale that is often told.

But the nineteenth century saw the subject of plant physiology pass from the scattered writings of a dedicated few to a well-documented body of knowledge equally important to scholars and practical men of affairs. While the subject made its own response to the questioning vigor and turmoil of the mid-nineteenth century, it doubtless profited much from the general spirit of the times. It is significant that Charles

Darwin, the author of "The Origin of Species by Means of Natural Selection," one of the provocative works around which the nineteenth century intellectual stimulus centered, also addressed himself in such works as "Insectivorous Plants" (1875), "The Movements and Habits of Climbing Plants" (1875), "The Power of Movement in Plants" (1880) to some challenging problems of plant physiology. Had Darwin's reputation not rested firmly on his better-known works, his accomplishments as an observer of phenomena in plants would still have given him a secure historical place.

The mid- and later nineteenth century was a period in which sweeping biological generalizations were embodied in now familiar aphorisms. "*Omnis cellula e cellula*" (1855); "*omnis nucleus e nucleo*" (1882); "protoplasm is the physical basis of life" (1868)—which led on to concepts of the nucleus, chromosomes, and now the genes as "the physical basis of heredity." If we become obsessed by such phrases and carry them down to modern times, there are emerging their modern equivalents such as "the mitochondria (or the microsomes) are the physical basis of metabolism" and "the nucleoproteins are the physical basis of specificity." However, although plant physiology in the late nineteenth century did not produce such resounding generalizations, it did emerge as a coherent body of well-documented, scientific knowledge. For this we owe a great debt to the scholarship of Sachs and Wilhelm Pfeffer.

By the end of the nineteenth century the student of plant physiology had at his disposal, amongst other works, Sachs' great "Lectures on the Physiology of Plants" (1887), (the 1882 edition of which was, translated in 1887). In this work the problems of botany were considered by a mind attuned to think in terms of the physics and chemistry of the day. The student of plant physiology also had Pfeffer's monumental three-volume work, "Physiology of Plants," the 1887 edition of which appeared in English translation in 1899. Until the twentieth century turned, it was indeed possible reasonably to comprehend the subject of plant physiology through such works as these, which were made available in English translation by the Oxford University Press.

But something of deeper significance had occurred. Tracing the history of botany from ancient times, Sachs, in his indispensable "History of Botany" (1875; English translation, 1890), paused at the year 1860. About this time plant physiology became, not merely a part of botany, but a discipline which could hardly be treated only as a part of the whole. Indeed the march of events subsequently described in Reynolds Green's sequel (1909) to Sachs' History, which comprehends only the years 1860–1900, amply justifies the year 1860 as the time which marks the divide between plant physiology as a modern discipline and plant physiology hitherto pursued as but one of the many interests of the well-rounded botanist.

Whereas in earlier times plant physiological findings were adequately communicated through the correspondence of investigators and the scholarly interchange made possible by the learned societies, and were eventually documented in such collected works as those of Hales and de Saussure, this now proved to be inadequate. First, the scientific journals appeared and proliferated, and they continue to increase to the present day. Then came the attempt of the Royal Society to list by title and reference all scholarly scientific works in The Royal Society Catalogue of Scientific Papers. Ambitiously conceived, and started by 1867, the work was issued in successive volumes only to fall farther and farther behind the march of current events until, by 1926, the project was abandoned when the papers published up to 1900 had been compiled. Even so, this catalogue is a valuable source of bibliographical information prior to the advent of the abstracting journals.

First the *Botanisches Centralblatt* (1891), then other abstracting journals such as the *Experiment Station Record* (1890), *Botanical Abstracts* (1918), and others testify to the increasing pace of scientific and plant physiological work in a period in which the output of scientific work increased exponentially with time. Now, although other aids exist, the student of plant physiology, often baffled by the task of assimilating knowledge that may appear in any of several hundred different scientific journals, published in any of several languages, turns perforce either to *Biological Abstracts* (from 1926) or to the American *Chemical Abstracts* (from 1907) for a first account in English of much of the world's current output of plant physiological work.

But a further literary development occurred, first by the appearance in increasing numbers of journals devoted solely to reviews of broad areas of subject matter, and finally by the annual appearance of volumes of reviews which attempt to summarize in one work the march of events. In the English-speaking world the issue in 1925 of a journal, *Plant Physiology*, devoted solely to that field, marked an event and, with the appearance of the *Annual Review of Plant Physiology* in 1950, in response to the widespread developments of the second quarter of the twentieth century, the subject may be said to have come of age. If plant physiology was born in the early seventeenth century, it made its first tentative strides in the eighteenth, approached its rapid formative growth in the nineteenth, reached adolescence around 1860, and emerged into full adult vigor by the mid-twentieth century!

But, with the changing times and the scope of the subject, the way in which the plant physiologist does his work has also changed, and, inevitably, the manner of man that he is. The dedicated scholar who sought knowledge as an avocation, often sheltered by a way of life that is now available only to a few, has been supplanted by the professional scientist, for whom the pursuit of knowledge is a vocation and, perhaps too often, an acceptable means of livelihood. To read the accomplishments of the great pioneers, who had not the resources of modern laboratories, and whose work was carried out with tools that they personally improvised, or acquired, prompts one to approach the problems of today, with the impressive tools and techniques of today, in a new spirit of humility and with respect for the accomplishments of the leaders of long ago. Perhaps it is not inappropriate to quote again some of the words which show with what exuberance the founders of the subject addressed themselves to their self-appointed tasks:

In John Evelyn's Diary, 9th August, 1661, we read, "I tried several experiments with the sensitive plant and *humilis*, which contracted with the least touch of the sun through a burning glass, though it rises and opens only when it shines on it."

Stephen Hales in the Preface to "Statical Essays" (1726–1727), Volume 1 ("Vegetable Staticks") described how he wished after his observations on the "force of the blood in the arteries" of dogs and horses to "discover the force of the sap in vegetables." However, Hales "despaired of ever effecting this" till some years later "by mere accident, I hit upon it." In this way Hales describes his method of attaching a glass tube to the cut stem to measure the "ascending force of the sap in that stem" and, since this "succeeded according to my expectation . . . I have been insensibly led on to make farther and farther researches by variety of Experiments."

And again on page 171, Hales expresses his faith in the experimental method in the following words, "It is consonant to the right method of philosophizing, first, to analyze the subject, whose nature and properties we intend to make any researches into, by a regular and numerous series of Experiments: And then by laying the event of those Experiments before us in one view, thereby to see what light their united and concurring evidence will give us. How rational this method is, the sequel of these Experiments will show."

In Joseph Priestley's "Experiments and Observations on Different Kinds of Air" (1775), Vol. II, there are numerous passages which reflect, in the phrases here quoted, his eager enthusiasm for discovery and observation: "At the time of my former publication I was not possessed of a burning lens of any considerable force; and for want of one, I could not possibly make many of the experiments that I had projected . . . But having afterwards procured a lens of twelve inches diameter and twenty inches focal distance I *proceeded with great alacrity* to examine by the help of it, what kind of air a great variety of substances, natural and factitious, would yield."

"I cannot at this distance of time, recollect what it was that I had in view in making this experiment, but I know that I had no expectation of the real issue of it. Having acquired a considerable degree of readiness in making experiments of this kind, a very *slight and evanescent motive* would be sufficient to induce me to do it. If, however, I had not happened, for some other purpose, to have had a lighted candle before me I should probably never have made the trial; and the whole train of my future experiments relating to this kind of air might have been prevented."

And again, "I have been so happy as by accident to have hit upon a method of restoring air which has been injured by the burning of candles, and to have discovered at least one of the restoratives which Nature employs for this purpose. It is *vegetation*."

The modern plant physiologist could well recapture some of the enthusiasm of long ago and the ability to state the vital issues in the majestic, simple words often used by the great pioneers. Two passages from F. F. Blackman's celebrated paper of 1905 (*Ann. Bot.* (*London*) **19,** pp. 281–295) admirably illustrate this facility. One concise passage enunciates Blackman's famous axiom, the other is remarkable for its prophetic vision of modern cellular studies at a time when enzymology and the knowledge of intermediary metabolism were in their infancy. On page 289 of his paper Blackman wrote, "When a process is conditioned as to its rapidity by a number of separate factors, the rate of the process is limited by the pace of the slowest factor"; and on page 294 the following passage occurs: "Regarding the cell as we now may, from the metabolic point of view, as a congeries of enzymes, a colloidal honeycomb of katalytic agents, as many in number as there are cell functions, and each capable of being isolated and made to do its particular work alone *in vitro*, we look for light on the action of chemical stimuli in the cell to their effect on the action of isolated enzymes *in vitro*. Here too law and order is now known to reign, and while enzymes only 'accelerate' reactions without being incorporated into their end products, yet the acceleration produced is proportional to the mass of the enzyme present, minute as it is, and the effects of 'activators' and 'paralyzators' of this action are also in proportion to their masses."

Plant physiology, now a modern, professional discipline, is equipped as never before with the "tools for the job." However, the subject can ill afford to lose that dedicated personal search for truth, out of which the great discoveries of the past emerged, and which were so often expressed in eloquent, clear, and forceful language.

Belatedly we may ask what plant physiology really is? By derivation physiology means strictly "a discourse about nature"—and a discourse about the nature of plants is a title embracing enough so that hardly any botanical topic will be irrelevant. Like all branches of natural knowledge, the subject passed through its early observational phases, in which often the problems could only be recognized; it became a science through quantitative measurement and the assembly of the knowledge so gained into generalizations. But it is evident why plant physiology attained maturity later than some other, more observational, branches of botanical knowledge; for it is largely founded upon the application of physics and chemistry to the interpretation of plant behavior. Not only were the physics and chemistry even of the mid-nineteenth century inadequate to the task, but, at many points, subsequent progress in what are often called the more basic sciences was inspired by the quest for knowledge about plants and plant cells. Much of the rise of organic chemistry—regarded as the chemistry of carbon compounds—drew its stimulus from the need to understand and eventually to synthesize naturally occurring compounds, and, if pride of place as a natural product from the animal kingdom goes to urea (1828), it was followed by asparagine (discovered 1806, synthesized 1887) from plants. From the Abbé Nollet (in 1748) through the membrane experiments of M. Traube (1867) and of Pfeffer (1877), and the observations of De Vries (1871–1888) on cells, to the theoretical concepts of J. H. van't Hoff and S. A. Arrhenius (1887), one recognizes parallel and mutually complementary lines of development in which plant physiology and physical chemistry were interdependent. And the history of diffusion and membrane equilibria is fraught with examples in which major advances in physicochemical theory have come in direct response to the work of, and problems posed by, the students of plants and plant cells. All this is as it should be.

However, the plant physiologist is concerned with more than the chemistry and physics which his problems present. Plants and plant cells are highly organized systems; indeed, in their very complexity of organization lies much of the challenge of the task. At each point in time the physiologist has been engrossed with interpretations and observations which were limited by the level of organization at which he could work. Plant physiological problems were first considered at the level of whole plants and organs, then at the level of cells, but now there is an increasing awareness of the heterogeneity of cells and the importance of their several inclusions. The subject has thus moved rapidly into the current trend. It is now almost axiomatic that plant physiology is considered in terms of the behavior of organelles and in relation to the intimate submicroscopic structure of cells and their inclusions.

Indeed a dramatic development of modern times is the bridging of the erstwhile gap between genetics, on the one hand, and physiology and biochemistry on the other, through the fast-growing subject of biochemical genetics (foretold by J. B. S. Haldane in 1937, but stimulated by the works of G. Beadle, E. L. Tatum, and others principally since the Second World War). No longer is it possible to deal complacently with physiological responses as though the organism responded only to the environment, to its stimuli and nutrients, for in an increasing measure its response is also seen to be conditioned by its inheritance. This vigorous branch of biological research has brought to plant physiology the means to dissect pathways of metabolism and stages in development into discrete steps, which are subject to hereditable control through the gene-enzyme relationships. So intimate has this connection become that geneticists, enzymologists, physiologists, and biochemists often now operate busily in a sort of "terra incognita" in which the problems range from the origin of life, and how protein is made, to the nature of the gene and of virus particles and the ultimate action of these, as well as of enzymes, in their regulatory control of development and metabolism. In this still relatively uncharted area a few landmarks have now become recognized and bear such hitherto unfamiliar signs as RNA, DNA, nucleoprotein.

Thus, in a variety of ways, the asymmetry of complex molecules and structures, with their characteristic molecular architecture, creates the milieu in which physiological processes occur. Hence the direct observations of Hales, the early use of the microscope by Hooke, Naegeli, Hofmeister, and De Vries now give way to the use of the electron microscope and such techniques as X-ray diffraction and electron density measurements, which permit organic structure to be comprehended even at the molecular level.

Whereas the early students of nutrition and metabolism necessarily thought in over-all terms, the modern plant physiologist is conditioned to think in terms of the graduated, often gene-controlled, and frequently cyclical, stages of intermediary metabolism. Moreover, by chromatography, by the use of isotopes and the techniques of radioautography, it has now become possible to discern steps which, because of their short duration or of intermediates which are present only in small amount, would earlier have passed unnoticed. However, because information is now gathered not merely at the cellular but at the subcellular level, there still remains the task of resynthesizing from this now often astonishing array of detailed and intimate knowledge the behavior of the entire cell, of the organ, or the whole plant body. As General Smuts, soldier, statesman, philosopher, and botanist, maintained in his doctrine of holism (1926), the whole is here, indeed, more than the sum of its parts.

Therefore, the plant physiologists of the mid-twentieth century work in a period of unparalleled challenge and opportunity. The knowledge, the tools, and the skills of the biophysicists and the biochemists, combined with the instrumentation of today, are, as never before, proving able to carry our knowledge down to the molecular level in cells. Because this is so dramatically true, the need to retain the knowledge of plants as living entities, with a morphology and development all their own, remains evident; for the intermediary chemical reactions, the enzymes and the coenzymes, the organelles, etc., are but the working parts of the whole complex, but beautifully integrated, biological machine. Plant physiology has not outgrown morphology and plant anatomy, for it now requires that these older disciplines shall be interpreted at the submicroscopic, and even at the macromolecular, level.

Here then lies the challenge of the mid-twentieth century. As whole new areas of subject matter have appeared in response to new avenues of experimental approach, even old problems assume a new guise. Although Sachs and Pfeffer and their contemporaries could, with consummate scholarship, comprehend their subjects as a whole and present them, individually, in their full scope but in the necessary detail, that is now no longer feasible. Therefore, in this Treatise, as in science increasingly, it has only been possible to cover the wide range of subject matter by the help of specialists versed in its several parts. Also, biological investigation, like that in physics, becomes increasingly a matter for the carefully directed efforts of workers who combine their respective skills as a team. One can even visualize that there will eventually emerge a specialty of theoretical plant physiologists who may, like the theoretical physicist, concentrate on interpretations and on synthesis of ideas rather than upon experimentation. Increasingly, plant physiological experimentation moves into areas in which attempted standardization of all but one of the separate variables is neither feasible nor perhaps wise. Thus, comprehensive interpretations now involve the ability to elucidate many interlocking variables and to analyze observations which involve so many parameters that new methods will need to be applied to the data. Increasingly it becomes clear that no single physiological function can be fully understood if it is considered in isolation from the rest.

The science of plant physiology today is therefore responding to the challenge to apply every modern aid to experiment, and all modern knowledge of biochemistry and biophysics to the interpretation of the behavior of plants. In so doing, events have moved with gathering speed in the twentieth century. From the concept of enzymes, literally meaning "in yeast" (W. Kühne, 1878), and the general ideas of "organized" and "unorganized" ferments current toward the end of the nineteenth century, to the prophetic ideas of the cell as a "congeries of enzymes, etc. . . . " of Blackman (1905), and the first crystalline enzyme of Sumner (1926), the vast edifice of modern enzymology has now emerged, as seen in the comprehensive work edited by J. B. Sumner and K. Myrbäck, "The Enzymes" (1950–1952). Metabolism is now conceived in terms of interlocking, cyclical, systems taking place reversibly in a system which is rarely static, but which, in life, is intensely dynamic. Physiology has thus moved from the earlier and more rigid concepts of true physicochemical equilibrium, to the dynamic, steady state and to the contemplation of processes in which, because free energy is increased, there is essential coupling with energy-yielding, or exergonic, reactions. Activated or dynamic transfers or movements of solutes have now become familiar. Moreover, in cells, now no longer regarded merely as heat engines, the means by which such metabolically released energy may be coupled to do useful work in the organism can be discussed in terms of the various molecules through which the energy may be transmitted and directed to specific ends. Just as energy is discrete and "particulate," consisting of indivisible units such as photons and quanta, so the energy which is usable by cells comes in discrete packages which can be located in certain chemical configurations or linkages. For this purpose nature has elaborated upon a number of anhydrides which, unlike many such compounds, can exist in aqueous solutions to perform these functions. These are notably the ribose-containing nucleotides of adenine, uridine, and cytosine in the form of their compounds which contain the pyrophosphate group and probably many other anhydrides, some containing sulfur, which can perform similar functions. All this, stemming from the pioneer work of F. Lipman (1941, see *Advances in Enzymol.* **1**, 99), is the distinctive product of modern times and now furnishes the means to link respiration, as the source of energy, with specific energy-requiring functions.

In short, plants are no longer regarded merely as systems passively responsive to equilibrium. To quote from Erwin Schrödinger's challenging book on "What is Life" (1947), "it is by avoiding the rapid decay into the inert state of 'equilibrium,' that an organism appears so enigmatic." . . . "How would we express in terms of the statistical theory the marvelous faculty of a living organism, by which it delays the decay into thermodynamical equilibrium (death)? We said before: 'It feeds upon negative entropy,' attracting as it were a stream of negative entropy upon itself to compensate the entropy increase it produces by living. . . . These [i.e., plants] of course have their most powerful supply of 'negative entropy' in the sunlight." Orderliness of molecular structure and arrangement, the inevitable concomitant of morphological complexity goes hand in hand with the production and maintenance of that "low level of entropy" to which Schrödinger refers and which is the antithesis of that state "in which no observable events occur" for "differences of electric and chemical potential have been equalized . . . and temperature becomes uniform by heat conduction." Thus it is now seen that work may be done and a positive change in the free energy ($\Delta F = +ve$) effected, even when the over-all heat change (ΔH) is small and negative, or zero, if the entropy change, the measure of orderliness, is negative ($\Delta S = -ve$); this follows because $\Delta F = \Delta H - T.\Delta S$, where T is the absolute temperature. This gives to the alternating sequences of synthesis and breakdown, folding and unfolding of macromolecular chains and fibrils, orderly arrangement of molecules in thin surface films, and their disorderly arrangement in solution an importance far greater than their heat change alone might imply. To quote Schrödinger's aphorism again, "nature feeds on negative entropy," and negative entropy is inherent in the creation of the orderly patterns and restricted molecular movements which biological structure and organization present.

But by no means all of the outstanding developments have been along the lines of cellular physiology. This century has seen great strides in the understanding of, and control over, growth and development. It is now to be recognized that the very coveted constancy of experimental conditions may conceal information because of those plant responses which are essentially due to periodic fluctuations in their environment. The seasonal cycles of seed time and harvest, rest and dormancy, like the asymmetric growth of plants under unilateral stimulation of light or gravity have long excited curiosity. But this hardly prepared plant physiologists for either the range, or the frequency, of the effects on growth and development of plants which are caused by such periodic fluctuations as in the phenomena of photoperiodism or of day and night temperature. To obtain the necessary degree of control over these variables and to permit research in these areas, the conventional greenhouse must needs give way to the highly controlled plant growth chamber, which in itself presents an engineering problem.

In this challenging period, therefore, more than fifty years after Pfeffer's classical work, it is fitting to try again to express what the subject of plant physiology is about, and to do this with respect for the great accomplishments of the past but recognizing that the advances of the present now permit old problems to be attacked with new tools. These new tools permit work with plants at ever lower levels of their organization, on the one hand, and, on the other hand, they also give sensitive control over the external environment for work on whole plants.

But the over-all task is still to describe and explain how plants work. After the particular substances, reactions, or processes are separately described, the modern plant physiologist must still endeavor to comprehend all this knowledge in terms of the organization of plants—in terms of the organelles, the cells, the tissues, the organisms in which the physiological processes occur. Thus plant physiology, which, with its modern counterpart of cellular physiology and biology investigated at the molecular level, has prospered with the developments in biochemistry, has increasing need of those who will experimentally study structures and relate them to function. Therefore, the old problems of structure and function remain, although they are now being examined more intimately at different levels of organization.

CONTENTS OF VOLUMES I B AND II

Volume I B. PHOTOSYNTHESIS AND CHEMOSYNTHESIS

Volume II. PLANTS IN RELATION TO WATER AND SOLUTES

PREAMBLE TO CHAPTERS 1 AND 2

The plant physiologist should ultimately comprehend the behavior of the whole organism. Indeed there is much to be said for an approach to the subject, first in terms of those features which apply to the whole organism, through the more familiar processes of growth and development and the responses of plants to external stimuli. Proceeding in this way, the discussion would pass later to the underlying processes of nutrition and metabolism as these may be revealed in organs, tissues, and cells, or even in cellular inclusions. This plan is however here reversed, following a now well established practice, which seeks first to comprehend the general and fundamental properties of cells as the units of which the whole organism is composed. Chapters 1 and 2 of Volume IA are, therefore, concerned with organization and its consequences. Chapter 1 describes the essential features of cells and their inclusions and presents the considerations which follow from their degree of organization. Chapter 2 describes the molecular properties of enzymes as proteins and so deals with a different level of organization but one at which the chemical reactions of cells are catalyzed.

CHAPTER ONE

The Plant Cell and Its Inclusions

R. Brown

I. Historical

The decisive event in the history of cell biology was the development of the microscope. The first instruments were built in the early seventeenth century, and these, although primitive, were nevertheless effective. They did provide access to a hitherto unexplored realm of structure and with them the investigation of cellular phenomena could begin. At first microscopes were used with the same exuberant and indiscriminate enthusiasm with which electron microscopes are being used now, and their use led to the same accumulation of sporadic observations. Within a few decades, however, from the wealth of fragmentary descriptions two dominant themes of research emerged. These were, the character of minute and ubiquitous organisms that were called infusoria; and the nature of the complex pattern that could be seen in tissues which were homogeneous to the naked eye.

The study of microorganisms made an important contribution to the development of the concept of the cell, and it begins with the work of Antony van Leeuwenhoek (1632–1723). This investigator was a devoted microscopist, who, in the course of a long life, examined the structure and behavior of a bewildering variety of organisms and tissues. He was the first to describe bacteria and the first to observe in any detail the structure of certain protozoa and of certain unicellular algae. The observation and description of these organisms was an event of great importance. Clearly, until they had been observed, the nature of each unit in cellular terms could not be defined. Nevertheless it is important to notice that Leeuwenhoek himself did not recognize that each unit he observed was an entity of the same status as each unit in a tissue—that in fact it was a cell. Leeuwenhoek also examined the structure of a number of multicellular organisms, but in this he was not as successful as a distinguished contemporary Robert Hooke (1635–1703), whose "Micrographia" is one of the classical texts of scientific literature. This volume contains a figure showing the structure of cork which has frequently been quoted and as frequently reproduced. It is certainly an important illustration since for the first time it shows a tissue that is composed only of rows of radially disposed cells. Hooke was the first to use the word "cell," and he invoked it in connection with the microscopic structure of tissues such as cork. It may be emphasized that in seventeenth century terms the cell was both simple and incidental. It was simple in the sense that it was an object that had only a wall; and incidental in the sense that it was recognized only in certain structures. The recognition of the cell as the unit of biological structure did not come until later, and just how far the anatomists of the seventeenth century were from this concept may be gauged from the work of Nehemiah Grew (1641–1712), who was another contemporary of Leeuwenhoek. Grew used the word cell and in a series of beautiful and meticulous diagrams he figured outlines which were unquestionably those of cells. On the other hand he wrote: "The most unfeigned and proper resemblance we can at present make of the whole body of a plant is to a piece of fine bone lace, when the women are working it upon the cushion; for the pith, insertions and parenchyma of the bark are all extreme fine and perfect lace work; the fibres of the pith run horizontally as do the threads in a piece of lace . . . "

Two diagrams prepared in the seventeenth century are reproduced in Fig. 1. They are the first of their kind and incontestably important. They were made, however, with crude instruments, and they may be compared with the recent electron micrographs of Figs. 9, 14, and 16, which are in the same tradition. The differences between the two sets of illustrations mark the technical achievements that span three centuries.

The further elaboration of the structure and status of the cell was the work of the nineteenth century. The instruments available to the observers of the seventeenth century had not been sufficiently powerful to reveal more than the simple outlines of cells. During the succeeding hundred years the resolving power of microscopes improved, and by the beginning of the nineteenth century the structure of the content of the cell could be explored. This phase in the development of cell biology opens with the work of Lorenz Oken (1779–1851), who was interested amongst other things in the same sort of unicellular organisms that had caught the attention of Leeuwenhoek. In relation to these in a work published in 1805 he refers to cells as "mucous vesicles" and as being composed of an "*Urschleim*." Clearly, in this phraseology there is the first intimation of the presence within cells of the viscous material that is subsequently described as protoplasm. Thirty years later an important detail was described by Robert Brown (1773–1858), who was interested in the structure of a peculiar group of dicotyledons, the Asclepiadaceae. He examined the surfaces of these plants microscopically, and in so doing he noticed that each (epidermal) cell was equipped with a small, frequently spherical, body which he called the nucleus. Other structural features of the plant cell were described still later by Hugo von Mohl (1805–1872), a gifted microscopist who devoted himself to the examination of plant tissues. This observer described in the middle years of the century a thin mucilaginous layer within the outer wall to which he gave the name of protoplasm and which he asserted is separate from a watery sap in a central cavity. At this stage the major components of the plant cell had been recog-

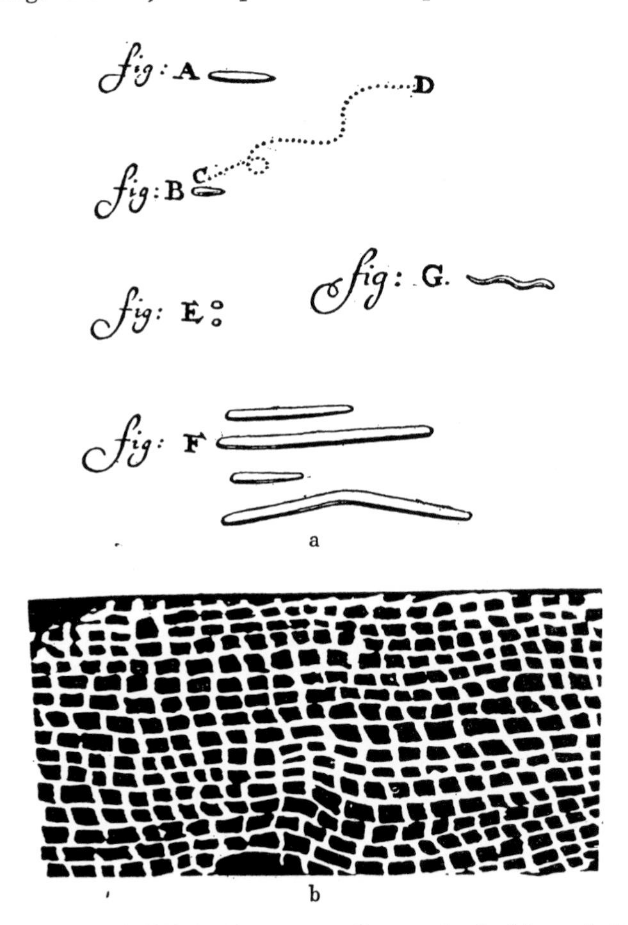

FIG. 1. a. Drawing (1693) by Antony van Leeuwenhoek of bacteria from human mouth. Dotted line from *C* to *D* shows the track observed with a motile form. b. Drawing (1665) of cork cells by Robert Hooke ("Micrographia," 1665).

nized, and it was thus only a little over a hundred years ago that the plant cell emerged as a structure composed of a limiting wall, peripheral cyptoplasm, a nucleus, and a central vacuolar system.

Finally, when the main components had been recognized, a further important structural concept could be formulated. It was noticed by several workers that the wall always survived death. From this observation it was concluded that the essential features of the cell as a living system were the cytoplasm, the nucleus, and the vacuole. These components could therefore be recognized as together constituting a distinctive entity—the protoplast.

While the structure of the cell was being elaborated, the status of it was also being defined. At the end of the seventeenth century the connection between unicellular "Infusoria" and multicellular organisms had not been established. Oken, who first identified protoplasm, also provided the suggestion on the basis of which all organisms could be assimilated to the same cellular pattern. He suggested that "all organic beings originate from and consist of vesicles or cells. These when detached and regarded in their original process of production are the infusorial mass or *Urschleim* whence all larger organisms fashion themselves or are evolved. Their production is therefore nothing else than a regular agglomeration of infusoria" (78).

This statement carries the implication that the individual so-called infusoria are single cells and that the higher organisms are aggregates of such cells. This is clearly a generalization of great importance, since if it is valid it follows that the unit of biological structure is the cell in the same sense as the unit of chemical structure is the molecule. More than this, however, is involved. If the cell is the primary structural unit and the higher organism does not contain units of any other category, then the cell must also be the structure from which the dynamic properties of the aggregate are derived. This aspect of organic structure was explored further first by Schleiden (1804–1881) and later by Schwann (1810–1882), and from the speculations of these two the cell theory emerged as one of the decisive generalizations of biology. According to Schleiden, "The vital processes of the individual cells form the first indispensable and fundamental basis for both vegetable physiology and comparative physiology in general"; and according to Schwann, "The question as to the fundamental power of organized bodies resolves itself into that of the individual cells." Both, however, added an important qualification. In the words of Schleiden, "each cell leads a double life; one independent pertaining to its own development alone; the other incidental as an integral part of a plant." In other words, that the activity of a cell is modified by the environment created by the other cells in the aggregate and that the activity of the integrated organism is not simply the additive expressions of individual cells.

Since the cell theory has had such a profound influence on the development of biology—and, since incidentally, it provides the justification for this chapter—it is important to notice the precise assertions that it makes. It claims that all organisms are composed of cells, that these exist as independent units, and that the dynamic properties of the whole are derived from the isolated activities of cells sustained in an environment created by the aggregate. The emphasis is on the independent activities of the units, and the stress on the influence of the aggregate does not imply that the group of cells form a connected interdependent system which reacts as a single protoplasmic mass.

To the contemporary sophisticated mind there is perhaps nothing alarming or challenging in the cell theory. It has indeed become an integral part of hallowed doctrine. When it was formulated, however, it was treated by many with some scepticism, and it is perhaps worth noting that even now it is not beyond reproach. The early criticism had, and still has, some validity. It was argued that the integrated character of a tissue indicated that its activities were due to a continuous protoplasmic system, the localized segments of which could be seen in the cavities of cells. The suggestion was that the coordinated activity of a differentiated system could be due only to a continuous protoplasmic network that permeates the whole. It is of some interest that this objection can now rely on the support of the observation that cells are connected by plasmodesmata. It has been known for some time that in certain exceptional situations protoplasmic strands can be seen connecting one cell with the next. This evidence was frequently disregarded since for various reasons the strands might have been artifacts. Recently, however, the presence of plasmodesmata in a large variety of cell walls has been confirmed in studies with the electron microscope and it is now beyond dispute that a tissue, although composed of cells, is nevertheless a system of connected protoplasmic units.

At the same time it is clear that this does not invalidate the cell theory. Although the significance of the structural connections between cells is not known, nevertheless, considerable evidence has accumulated showing that cells are in many respects independent of each other. The evidence shows conclusively that the protoplasts of different cells retain their identity and that even the characteristic products of separate protoplasts may not be available to adjacent cells. The situation in variegated plants is particularly instructive. In these a cell with colorless plastids may be attached to another with normal green chloroplasts. The plastids are the products of the protoplasts to which they belong, and if the protoplasts both belong to the same system then they might both be expected to have the same products. The case of variegation which is due to different pigments in the vacuole is perhaps even more significant. In this situation adjacent cells may contain different soluble pigments which are produced in the respective protoplasts and an exchange of at least pigment molecules along connecting protoplasmic strands is clearly incompatible with the diversity observed. [For further historical details consult Singer (78).]

II. General

This chapter is mainly concerned with the general biology of a representative type of mature plant cell. It will facilitate subsequent discussion if the main structural features of this system, as at present known, are outlined and if at the same time the terms that are used in the description of it are defined with some precision. It may be urged that a glossary such as that given below is necessary. Many of the terms that have to be used in describing the cell are regrettably ambiguous since different authors frequently use the same term with a different meaning. Unfortunately, cellular biology is still not equipped with a universally accepted terminology, and if the use of some familiar terms here seems peculiar, the author can only plead that it is perhaps no more exotic than it is in many other texts.

Some of the structural features of the hypothetical representative mature cell, which are seen with the resolution of the light microscope, are shown in Fig. 2.

The two primary components of the cell are the wall and the protoplast.

The *wall* (*w*) is that part of the system which is external to the protoplast. It is often relatively thick, inert, elastic and provides a supporting envelope for the whole cell.

The protoplast involves three components: the cytoplasm, the nucleus, and the vacuole.

The *cytoplasm* (*cy*) is a hyaline viscous fluid material which is present as a thin sheet immediately within the wall, and which separates the wall from the vacuole. Cytoplasm may, however, traverse the vacuole in the form of discrete strands.

The *nucleus* (*n*) is a dense opaque body which may be spherical, and when it is, has a diameter of about 8 μ. It may be suspended in the center of the cell or it may be embedded in the peripheral cytoplasm. When in this latter position it may be flattened into a disklike shape. The nucleus and cytoplasm together are commonly regarded as the "living" components of the cell. They are the structures which carry the metabolic and hereditary characteristics of the organism.

The *vacuole* (*v*) is a cavity or cavity system within the protoplast which is normally occupied by an aqueous fluid. It may be considered as a reservoir of metabolites, and although probably essential to the maintenance of metabolism in the cells in which it occurs, it cannot be classified as part of the metabolic system itself. In the diagram of Fig. 2 the vacuole is shown as a single central cavity. Frequently, however, it may (as in growing cells) consist of a group of separate cavities and the different cavities may carry different metabolites.

The cytoplasm is itself a heterogeneous system. It consists of a series of particulate inclusions embedded in a ground component which

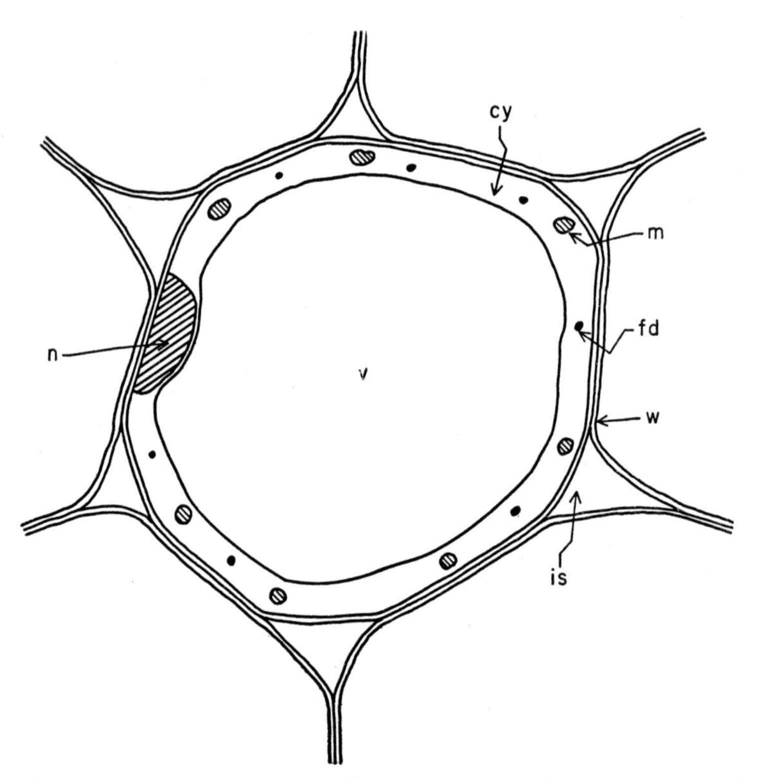

Fig. 2. Schematic parenchymatous cell; *n*, nucleus; *m*, mitochondrion; *w*, wall; *cy*, cytoplasm; *fd*, oil droplet; *is*, intercellular space; *v*, vacuole.

consists of three phases, the mesoplasm, the plasmalemma, and the tonoplast.

The *mesoplasm* is the central zone of the cytoplasm and consists of a *ground phase* and particulate inclusions. The ground phase is optically homogeneous and constitutes the continuous medium in which the inclusions are embedded.

The *plasmalemma* is a membrane probably 100–150 A thick on the external surface of the mesoplasm.

The *tonoplast* is a membrane 100–150 A thick on the inner surface of the mesoplasm, and it separates this from the aqueous fluid of the vacuole.

The particulate inclusions of the cytoplasm, which are mostly embedded in the mesoplasm, may be classified into three groups: those which are integral components of the metabolic system and therefore of the protoplast; those which incorporate by-products or end products of metabolic activity; and, those which may be precursors of the other two types of inclusions.

The metabolically active inclusions are the mitochondria, the microsomes, and the chloroplasts.

Mitochondria (*m*) are spherical or cylindrical bodies which stain with Janus green B. When spherical they are about 1.0 μ in diameter, and when cylindrical they may be as much as 2.0 μ in length.

Microsomes are spherical bodies beyond the limit of resolution of the light microscope. They vary in size but normally they are about 200 A in diameter. They are said to stain readily with pyronine.

While mitochondria and microsomes occur in all cells, *chloroplasts* are formed only in some. In higher plants chloroplasts are disk-shaped bodies about 5–10 μ in diameter and 3–4 μ in depth. They are always green since their characteristic feature is that they carry chlorophyll. They are normally found only in cells in which active photosynthesis proceeds.

The inactive inclusions which incorporate terminal products of metabolism are the chromoplasts, starch grains, aleurone grains, fat droplets, and various so-called ergastic bodies.

The *chromoplasts* are similar in size to the chloroplasts. They are metabolically inactive, and instead of chlorophyll they usually incorporate an orange or a yellow pigment.

Starch grains are oval bodies which vary considerably in size. They may be as long as 10 μ and they incorporate only reserve starch.

Aleurone grains incorporate reserve protein in an insoluble, and sometimes crystalline, form. They vary considerably in shape and size. The size, however, is usually in the longest dimension of the order of 5 μ.

Oil droplets (*fd*) are spherical bodies consisting, as their name implies, of a fatty or oily reserve material. Their size varies from something below the limit of resolution of the light microscope to about 1.5 μ. Oil droplets are frequent and are probably characteristic of all forms of cytoplasm.

Ergastic bodies are crystals of various substances, some of which may be inorganic. Again sizes and shapes vary considerably. In certain cases they are in the form of simple crystals whereas in others they may assume extremely elaborate and complicated configurations. Ergastic bodies, while being often products of the cytoplasm, may also be formed in the vacuole.

The third category, identified here as *proplastids*, involves a heterogeneous group of inclusions whose only common characteristic is that they may develop into other types of inclusions. They are similar in general size and shape to mitochondria, although they do not stain with Janus green B. The status of these proplastids as precursors of other organelles does not preclude the possibility that they may also sustain particular metabolic reactions.

III. Variety of Cellular Structures

The generalized structural characteristics enumerated in Section II do not fully define the nature of a cell. It is also an important characteristic of the system that it can assume a very large variety of structural forms, and this aspect of the plant cell as a biological entity is considered here.

Every cell in the plant is the product of division in another cell and not, as Schleiden oddly maintained, of budding from the surface of the nucleus. Every vegetative cell in which a normal protoplast has been retained is also probably capable of division when the appropriate stimulus is applied. At the same time it is also certainly the case that, in the intact plant, divisions are considerably more frequent in some cells than they are in others. They are, for instance, considerably more frequent in the apical meristems than in mature tissues and more frequent in the cambium than in any other part of the stele.

Whenever frequent division occurs, the structure of the cells is characteristic, although shape and size may vary. In the apical meristems the cells are small, frequently not more than about 10 μ in the longest axis, and they tend to be isodiametric. In the cambium each cell may be 100 μ or more long, and it is in the form of a flat plate, such that in the transverse plane it appears as a narrow rectangle. All meristematic cells have thin walls, and these have little mechanical rigidity. In the apex of the shoot, at least, the walls, far from being rigid, seem to be plastic and almost semifluid. The cavity within the walls is always completely occupied by the protoplast. There is no prominent central vacuole. Cytologists have described small vacuoles which may or may not be occupied by aqueous fluids. The nucleus is always large and occupies a relatively greater proportion of the cell cavity than it does in mature cells. It is probable that mitochondria in the cytoplasm of meristematic cells are less frequent than they are in mature cells and that they tend to have a characteristic cylindrical shape. One report is available indicating that the microsomes in meristematic cells are particularly large (71).

After they are formed in a meristem, cells are displaced and become involved in a developmental process in the course of which differentiation occurs into one of the many types of cells which occupy mature tissues. Since the parenchymatous cell is the most abundant, the most frequent type of development is that which leads to the structure of Fig. 2. In this development there is normally a considerable increase in volume. When the cell is formed from the apical meristem the increase in volume may be a hundredfold and is due primarily to an absorption of water which is accompanied by a differentiation of the central vacuole. The formation and expansion of the vacuole necessarily occasions a displacement of the protoplast to a peripheral position. At the same time there is also a considerable change in the mass of the wall. After nuclear division has occurred, the protoplast of the parent cell is divided by the formation of a semifluid pectin wall (see below). Before expansion begins a more rigid wall is laid down on either side of the pectin barrier. This is the primary wall, and its greater rigidity is due to its being formed principally from cellulose (again see below). The expansion that occurs during the development into the parenchymatous state necessarily implies a corresponding increase in the area of the wall. This depends on an actual growth. The area does not increase by a simple elastic stretch but by a deposition of further cellulose in the primary wall. This is the process that is known as *growth by intussusception*, and it continues until the mature size of the cell has been reached. During this phase the wall system consists of the original pectin barrier, which is now the middle lamella, and the two primary walls belonging to adjacent cells on either side of it (see Fig. 7 below).

Development is not complete when the mature volume has been established. In particular, the wall continues to change. It ceases to grow by intussusception, and increases in thickness by *apposition*. As a result, a further distinctive layer is laid down which is distinguished from the other two as the secondary wall. This third component is also mainly composed of cellulose, and it eventually becomes thicker than the primary wall. The growth of the secondary wall may continue for a considerable time, and it may itself show layering although it always remains distinct from the primary wall. In many cases the growth of the secondary wall is not uniform. In certain positions no deposition of secondary material occurs and in the final state in parenchymatous cells it is traversed by pits. It is a characteristic feature of the development of pits that those in adjacent cells tend to coincide, and in these positions, therefore, the two cells are separated only by the middle lamella and the two primary walls. There is some evidence that the coincident pits are formed where the primary walls are traversed by bundles of plasmodesmata. Pits are usually not randomly distributed, but they are frequently formed at regular intervals and tend therefore to define particular patterns.

The cell shown in Fig. 2 is a mature cell, but it is something of an abstraction. It conforms to the parenchymatous type in having a relatively thin and uniform wall, peripheral cytoplasm, a nucleus, and a central vacuole. All mature cells, however, are not parenchymatous, and the parenchymatous type itself displays considerable variation.

Divergence from the parenchymatous structure may occur with respect to any one or all of the components of the cell. The wall may become considerably modified by irregular thickening and by the addition to it, or deposition in it, of substances other than cellulose. In certain types the wall, while not being modified chemically, is not of uniform thickness. In collenchyma the secondary wall, while being composed predominantly of cellulose, is markedly thickened at the corners (Fig. 3,a). Collenchyma is one of the tissues which endows the organ with mechanical rigidity, and this is said to be a consequence of the peculiar development of the secondary wall. Irregular thickening in a cellulose wall is also a feature of the development of guard cells. These, when mature, are more or less cylindrical and they are more heavily thickened along the surface that abuts on the stomatal pore than they are on that which is adjacent to an epidermal cell. With this arrangement, when turgor increases stretching is greatest on the side furthest from the pore and the whole cell tends to withdraw from the other member of the pair, leaving an open pore between them (see Volume II, Chapter 3). The wall may become modified by the deposition of a distinctive layer of some substance other than cellulose or pectin over the external surface of the cell. This occurs most frequently when the external surface is not attached to another cell. It occurs in the shoot with tissues such as the epidermis which are in immediate contact with the external atmosphere. A cuticle is then formed which is a fatty material with a firm consistency and with limited elasticity. One case is known in which a cuticle-like substance is embedded between cells which are deep in a tissue. This is the Casparian strip between endodermal cells, which, it is said, limits the diffusion of solutes along radial walls.

In many cases the wall is modified by the deposition of a non-cellulose component such as lignin or suberin. These changes may be accompanied by the death of the protoplast.

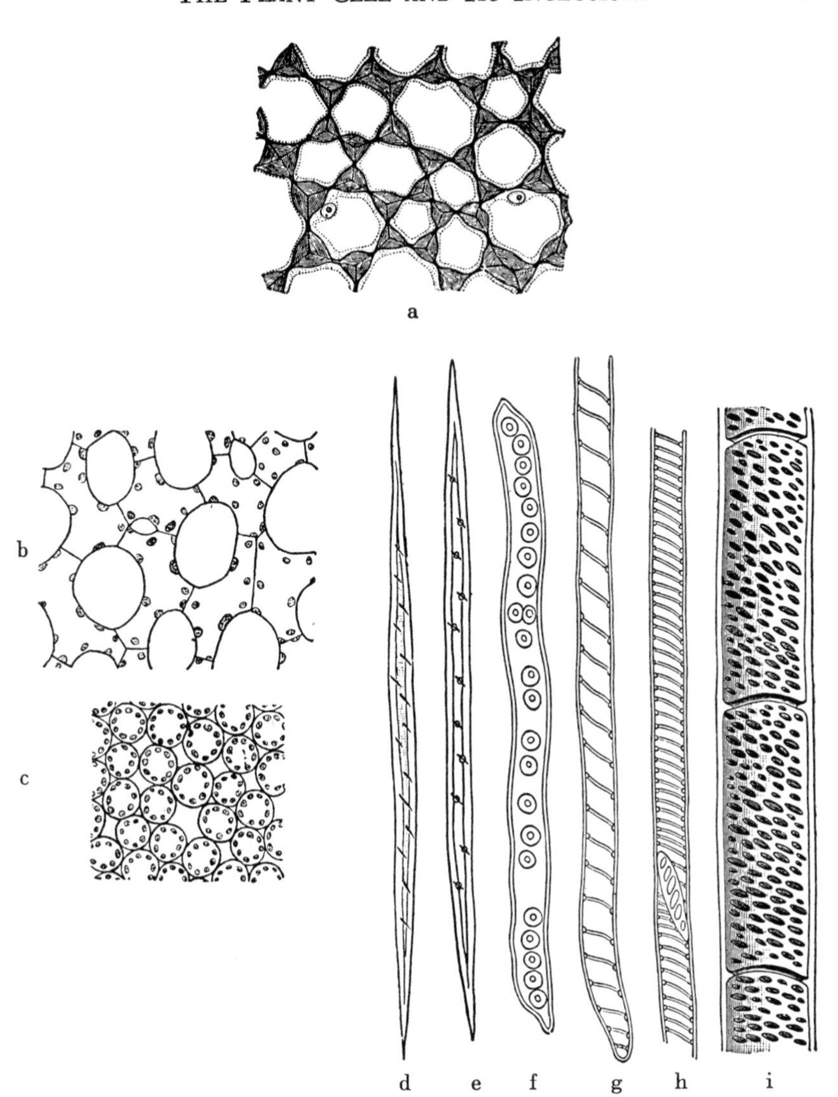

FIG. 3. Different cell types; a, collenchyma; b, spongy parenchyma; c, palisade (surface view); d and e, sclerenchyma fibers; f, tracheid with pits; g and h, vessels with spiral thickenings; i, vessel of secondary xylem with pitted thickening.

Vessels (Fig. 3,g,h,i) are components of the xylem, and they are formed in primary tissues from cylindrical procambial elements which are superimposed in longitudinal ranks. These cells also follow the normal development which culminates in the formation of the secondary wall. The thickening which is consequent on secondary wall formation, however, may be localized in such a way that it leads to the development of intricate and highly characteristic patterns. In normal parenchymatous cells a similar process leads to the development of ranks of pits. Here, pits may also be formed, but in certain immature vessels the thickening leads to the formation of spirals, rings, and sometimes of a combination of the two. While secondary wall formation is proceeding, the transverse walls between successive cells are pierced and remnants of these enter the mature state as flanges within a tubular system. In due course the longitudinal walls become heavily impregnated with lignin and the protoplast is dispersed. The immediate cause of the death of the protoplast is unknown, but as a result of these changes a continuous tubular system is established along which water may flow.

Tracheids (Fig. 3,f) are also components of the xylem, and their development is similar to that of vessels, although the individual cells of the procambial strand do not expand either longitudinally or laterally to the same extent as they do when they are being transformed into vessels. When expansion is complete, the secondary wall is formed and thickens considerably, usually with the development of pits. The transverse wall in the tracheid remains intact and it becomes lignified along with the longitudinal walls. As with the vessel, lignification is accompanied by the destruction of the protoplast. The tracheid system is a superimposed series of tubes which carry part of the transpiration stream. The lignified walls are not impermeable to water, and flow is said to occur longitudinally across the transverse walls and laterally mainly through the pits in the longitudinal walls.

The development of the fiber is in many respects similar to that of the tracheid (Fig. 3,d,e), although there may be very extensive elongation before the mature form is established. In this case the development of the secondary wall is considerably greater than it is in the tracheid. In the final state, it may be pitted, although the development of the wall may be so great as apparently to obliterate the cavity of the cell. In due course, the whole wall system may be lignified and the protoplast dispersed. Within the fiber there is no channel available within which water can flow. The abnormally thick wall system, however, undoubtedly promotes mechanical rigidity.

The development of suberin in walls leads to changes as extensive as those which accompany the deposition of lignin. The characteristic product of suberization is cork. The cells of this tissue are generated from what is usually a superficial meristem in the stem or the root, and when they are formed they have the typical embryonic configuration. Vacuolation occurs leading to the mature size, and this as usual is followed by secondary wall formation. When this is complete the wall system becomes impregnated with suberin. Unlike lignified walls, suberized walls are impermeable to water, and the uniform deposition of the suberin, therefore, leads to the isolation and consequent death of the protoplast. Suberized walls, although not rigid, are not readily disrupted, and cork, therefore, carrying as it does air pockets in the isolated cell cavities, provides a protective mantle over the external surface of the plant.

The divergence from the parenchymatous type with respect to the wall and protoplast is less extreme with the sieve tube and companion cell, the structure of both of which varies widely. For the purpose of this chapter, however, the structure of both may be considered by reference to the comparatively simple situation in *Cucurbita* (Fig. 4). The sieve tube of the primary bundle is again derived from cylindrical superimposed cells in the procambial strand. These cells divide longitudinally to form elements of two kinds, one of which lacks a nucleus when the cells are fully formed and the other retains a complete protoplast when the cells are mature. The enucleated elements become sieve tubes and the nucleated form groups of companion cells. After the longitudinal division which differentiates the sieve and companion cell initials, no further divisions occur in the former. In the latter, on the other hand, several transverse divisions may succeed each other, so that in the mature state the sieve tube may have several superimposed companion cells attached to it along one longitudinal wall. In each of the group of companion cells the walls do not thicken and a prominent central vacuole does not develop. The enucleated sieve-tube initial increases in size, and, as it does so, changes occur in the transverse wall and in the protoplast. The transverse walls between superimposed cells develop well-defined channels through which cytoplasm from the two cells becomes continuous. The transverse wall develops the appearance of a sieve and is accordingly called a sieve plate. Vacuolation occurs in the presumptive sieve tube and the cytoplasm becomes displaced in

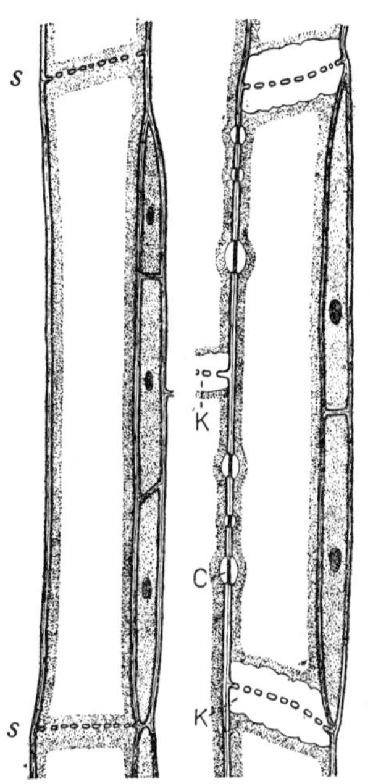

FIG. 4. Sieve tubes with companion cells; *s*, sieve plates (Figs. 3 and 4 from Lehrbuch der Botanik by Fitting, Schumacher, Harden, and Firbas. Fischer, 1947).

the normal succession to a peripheral position. It has been argued that the structure of the sieve tube is particularly adapted to sustain the transport of organic solutions. That it does promote this process there is little doubt, but with the possible exception of the sieve plate it is perhaps difficult to understand how structural features are in this case related to dynamic properties. (For a fuller account of the role of sieve tubes reference may be made to Chapter 5 of Volume II.)

In the companion cell a prominent central vacuole is absent. This feature in mature tissue is characteristic of glandular systems, in the cells of which the wall tends to be thin, the nucleus large and irregular, and the cytoplasm considerably denser and more granular than it is in typical parenchymatous cells. While a central vacuole is usually absent, smaller dispersed vacuoles may, nevertheless, be present, although these may not be occupied by an aqueous fluid. They may contain drops of the medium that is discharged from the gland.

The cellular forms described above are considerably less frequent than the typical parenchymatous type, which contributes about 80% of the total cell complement. It is the dominant cellular type in epidermal tissues, in the cortex, and in the medulla of both the root and the shoot. It is frequently the only type in storage organs since, in these, cells which are not normally parenchymatous may nevertheless acquire this general character. It is the dominant component in the leaf, the epidermal and mesophyll cells being all parenchymatous. Finally, it also occurs sporadically in the xylem and in the phloem. Since it has such an extensive distribution it is inevitable that the type should cover considerable variation with respect to size, shape, and contents.

Size and shape variations within the parenchymatous group are considerable. The greatest dimension of the cell may vary from about 20 μ in vascular parenchyma to about 300 μ in epidermal cells. The most frequent general shape is one that involves an approximately rectangular outline in the longitudinal, and an approximately hexagonal outline in the transverse, plane. The cells of epidermal tissues and of the parenchyma of at least certain leaves, diverge considerably from this pattern. In transverse section epidermal cells are rectangular, and in surface view they may have an irregular outline with wavy walls (in dicotyledons). In mesophyll the palisade cells are highly elongated in the plane at right angles to the surface of the leaf, and in the plane parallel to the surface they are markedly circular in outline (Fig. 3,c). In spongy parenchyma, on the morphological lower surface of the leaf the shapes are very highly irregular. No dominant shape is discernible in any plane and the cells are characterized by apparently random evaginations. The extensions from adjacent cells are in contact, and this involves the complementary aspect of a large intercellular space system (Fig. 3,b).

Parenchymatous cells always carry the essential protoplast components of nuclei, cytoplasm, mitochondria, and microsomes. Frequently they have only these, and this is the position with many epidermal and cortical cells. Sometimes, however, they may carry, in addition, food storage granules, chromoplasts or chloroplasts. In storage tissues the cells may contain starch grains, large fat droplets, or aleurone grains. Fat droplets and starch grains may also occur in normal cortical tissues. Chromoplasts are often present in parenchyma of floral organs, and chloroplasts are absent from mesophyll cells only in exceptional cases. Chloroplasts, however, may also be developed in parenchyma of the stem and of the root.

Finally, whereas in most parenchymatous cells the nucleus is embedded in a peripheral cytoplasm, in some it is found in the center of the vacuole, suspended in that position by fine cytoplasmic strands which stretch across the central cavity.

IV. The Dimensions of the Cellular System

The activity of any system is of course limited by the dimensions within which it is confined, and it is no less true of the cell than it is of the locomotive engine that dynamic properties are intimately related to the size of the whole and to the distribution and size of each component. The subject is indeed an important one and merits extensive attention, especially as dimension may be taken to refer not only to volume, length, and weight, but also to the contents of particular structures and particular chemical components. Unfortunately, only sporadic relevant data are available and the full implications of the size relationships of a parenchymatous cell cannot be fully explored.

The scarcity of primary data is a consequence of the difficulties of measurement. The subject necessarily requires a technique through which quantitative aspects can be specified with some precision. Hitherto, the quantity of a particular component has frequently been defined in terms of that of another. Different aspects of a tissue may be measured and from the array of data different relative quantities may be estimated. Relative quantities, however, do not convey complete information, and they are not satisfactory substitutes for the absolute values that are required. In certain connections absolute values can be determined directly. This is the case with linear dimensions which may be measured with appropriate microscopic equipment. It is also the case where the quantity of a substance in the cell can be measured by a physical technique, such as absorption spectrophotometry. On the other hand, the possibilities of this type of procedure are limited and most measurements for absolute quantities require a different experimental design. The possibilities are considerably greater when determinations can be made on an entire tissue and the results related to the number of cells it contains. This procedure gives a figure for an average cell which is of particular value when the tissue from which it is derived is uniform. The variety of specifications that can be assembled with it is considerably greater than that which can be provided with any other. The application of this technique has been limited by difficulties involved in the determination of the number of cells, but recently a simple and rapid method for determining numbers of cells based on methods previously in use for more anatomical purposes has been elaborated, and it is probable that in the future this will facilitate the determination of particular absolute quantities (11, 12).

The importance of determining numbers of primary units and of specifying their quantitative characteristics may be stressed by drawing attention to the results that this tradition has achieved in other departments of science. In bacteriology it is the common practice to analyze the characteristics of a culture in terms of the numbers of cells it contains, and, partly as a result of this, the conditions required for particular reactions have been analyzed more effectively than they have in other biological disciplines. The moral, however, is most emphatically pointed by the physical sciences. In these, the primary units are enumerated and, therefore, specified with outstanding precision. Contemporary physics is in a sense devoted to numbers and characteristics of ultimate units, and contemporary chemistry to numbers and characteristics of molecular units. The successes of these sciences have undoubtedly been largely due to the application of this pattern of interpretation. In chemistry, for instance, the great importance of the gas laws must be attributed to the fact that they incorporate a precise statement of molecular numbers. It has been suggested that the cell in biology occupies the same status as the molecule does in chemistry. In a formal sense this is patently true, but in a practical, empirical sense it certainly is not. The cell has not been used as a counter of interpretation in biology as the molcule has in chemistry. When it is so used, biology may then attain to some of the precision of the physical sciences; but this, be it noted, will require more comprehensive consideration of characteristics and, therefore, numbers of the basic units.

The size of the plant cell varies. The smallest may be just visible with the low power of the light microscope and the largest may be a centimeter or more in length. The largest cells are usually atypical in being coenocytic. Some algae are composed of cells which are certainly several millimeters long and which are normal in every other respect. Some algae, such as species of *Valonia* (see also Chapter 4 of Volume II), on the other hand may be composed of one or more vesicles which tend to be spherical and to vary from a few millimeters to several centimeters in diameter. These, while they have a central sap cavity, a wall, and peripheral cytoplasm, are not uninucleate. Each cell carries many nuclei embedded in the cytoplasm. In the higher plant the cells tend to be much smaller, although again sizes vary. In the cortex of the stem, the length of the cell may vary from 50 to 300 μ and the breadth from 60 to 100 μ. Volumes vary with the linear dimensions. An average cell volume has been determined for the population in a mature region of the root. This value has been obtained by dividing the volume of a segment by the number of cells it contains, and it is approximately 2.0×10^{-7} cm^3. This volume corresponds to that of a cylinder which is about 100 μ in length and about 50 μ in diameter, and these dimensions are used in estimations that are referred to below.

The average volume of the parenchymatous cell is about a thousand times greater than that of a bacterium, but may be similar to that of an animal cell. These comparisons, while they are frequently made, may be in certain connections extremely misleading. Of the total volume of a plant cell, 5% may be represented by the wall and less than 5% by the protoplast. Thus, the vacuole often represents at least 90% of the total volume. A central vacuole is not present in a bacterial or an animal cell and, while in these the total volume is occupied by the metabolic system, only a small fraction is due to the cytoplasm in the plant cell.

The dry weight of the plant cell varies as much as the volume, but an average weight has been determined in a mature zone of the root, and this is approximately 6.0×10^{-9} gm. It is significant that if the volume is considered to represent water, then the fresh weight is approximately a hundred times greater than the dry weight. This reflects the high proportion of the volume that is occupied by the vacuole, and the consequently high water content of the whole. The average dry weight is considerably greater than that of the bacterial cell and probably greater than that of many animal cells. But again, the comparison is misleading. Plant cells are not peculiar in having a wall. They are peculiar in the extent to which the wall is developed and, whereas in animal and bacterial cells the wall only contributes a small proportion of the total weight, in plants cells it makes a very much larger contribution. In some plant cells about 90% of the dry weight may be due to the wall. Thus, while the dry weight may often be a measure of metabolic components, in some systems in the plant it is primarily a measure of cell wall development.

The significance of over-all dry weight and volume in different types of cells is a matter of some physiological importance. Metabolic rates are frequently referred to fresh weight (which is intimately related to volume) or to dry weight, and comparisons are frequently made between different systems on the basis of one or other of these standards of reference. With such comparisons the rates given with plant cells are frequently found to be lower than those given by other cell types, but it is evident that the comparison does not show that the rates are intrinsically lower. A different result would certainly be obtained by using the mass of the protoplast as the standard of reference. A low value is given when the rate is defined in terms of fresh weight, since in the plant cell this is determined primarily by the vacuole which is metabolically inert, and a low value is again given when it is defined in terms of dry weight since this is largely determined by the wall, which is not a part of the protoplast.

Clearly, as a metabolic system the cell is more adequately defined in terms of protein, and the content of this per cell is a particularly important figure. The average content has been determined in mature regions of the root, and it is approximately 2×10^{-9} gm. However this value is considered, it is a surprisingly low one. Its significance in absolute terms may be gauged by transforming it into an equivalent number of molecules. If the average molecular weight for protein is taken as one million, the average content represents about 10^8 protein molecules per cell. This figure is small compared with the Avogadro number of 6×10^{23}, which is the number of molecules per gram mole, and therefore in a molar solution, of any solute.

The comparison of protein content relative to surface area is instructive. Relative to this aspect of over-all mass, the size of the protoplast is again surprisingly small. The cytoplasm does not form a uniform layer immediately within the wall. In cylindrical cells, it tends to accumulate at the ends. Nevertheless on the average it is probable that the thickness of the cytoplasm is of the order of 1.0 μ. This measurement, however, is not a satisfactory indication of the degree of dispersion of the structural components of the protoplast, since water probably represents at least 95% of the total. From the average protein content and from an estimate of the volume of the protoplast based on the surface area of the cell, a value may be calculated for the concentration of protein. Such a calculation shows that only about 3% of the cytoplasm is protein and shows that, even within the narrow limit of a layer 1.0 μ thick, the solid components are widely dispersed. The same conclusion is indicated perhaps even more vividly by an estimate of the number of protein layers that are scattered across the width of the protoplast. This estimate shows the number of protein molecules that are likely to be crossed by a line stretched transversely across the cyptoplasm. It may be derived from the total protein per cell, although a more satisfactory value would be one that is based on ground-phase protein only. Unfortunately, data are not available from which this quantity could be determined, but the value based on total protein, including as it does all the protein in nuclei and cytoplasmic inclusions, is not likely to be an underestimate, and this is important in view of the value that is actually obtained. The average protein content, if spread into a monolayer, would occupy about 400,000 μ^2. The average surface area of the cell is about 20,000 μ^2. Thus, the cell contains sufficient protein to provide for about twenty successive monolayers within the wall. This figure does not, of course, define the precise situation. It only indicates the general position. Nevertheless, for reasons given above, it is clear that the number is not likely to be substantially greater than this and may be less. The number is surprisingly small and certainly indicates that the structural components of the protoplast are very highly dispersed and very thinly spread over the inner surface of the wall (11, 13, 26).

The proportion of the protoplast that is in each structural component is difficult to determine. If the diameter of the nucleus is taken as 10 μ, its volume would represent about 2% of that of the cytoplasm. Direct determinations of the protein content of the nucleus are not available, but data have been assembled on the deoxyribonucleic acid (DNA) content and an average figure may be taken as 4×10^{-11} gm. If the DNA is taken to represent about 20% of the total insoluble nitrogen of the nucleus, then this would suggest a protein content of about 2×10^{-10} gm, which suggests that the protein content of the nucleus represents about 10% of the total protein content of the mature cell. All the protein of the cell is probably in the cytoplasm and the nucleus, and a comparison of the volume and protein proportions therefore suggest that the nucleus is considerably denser than the cytoplasm in which it is embedded. Determinations of number, volume, or protein content of mitochondria per cell are not available, and the proportion of the total mass of the cytoplasm that is incorporated in these bodies therefore cannot be estimated.

A further peculiar feature of the cellular system is suggested by the figure for the number of protein molecules per cell which in many cells may be 10^8. The average number does not of course refer to any one molecular species. Protein is not a single entity in the same sense as sodium chloride is such. It represents a category of substances, and within this category the number of molecules of any one species is likely to be considerably less than one hundred million. It is not improbable that a single species may contribute one-hundredth of the total, and the number of molecules of this in the cell will then be of the order of 10^6, or one million. Further, if the numbers of certain protein molecules are of this order, then the numbers of molecules of certain other compounds may well be similar. It may be emphasized that the question here is one of the general order of numbers, and the figures quoted are intended as an indication of this.

The significance of molecular numbers of the order of 10^6 may be approached by considering first the pressure exerted by a gas on the walls of a vessel. The molecules of the gas are in thermal agitation and the pressure exerted on the walls of the vessel is a consequence of this state. The larger the number of impacts on the walls of the vessel the greater will be the pressure. Now the number of impacts will depend on the number of molecules and on the temperature. If the temperature remains constant, the pressure exerted within the vessel as a whole will also remain constant. Further, over all areas on the surface of the vessel the pressure will be the same. At this point an important qualification may be noted. The pressure over different areas at the surface will be constant only if the areas are large. The pressure is constant when the distribution of molecules is uniform, and such it may be taken to be when the volume or area involved is large. Each molecule, however, is in constant agitation, and the random dispersal will not give an absolutely uniform distribution. Over very small volumes the molecular density is likely to vary. Thus, if each pressure determination is made over a sufficiently small area, the pressure will not be found to be constant from one area to the next. The random distribution of course ensures that a low density at one point is compensated by a high density at another; therefore, over sufficiently large areas the pressure will be constant. The important point to notice is that when the distances are sufficiently small there are likely to be considerable differences between one interval and the next.

Similarly with the rate of reaction between two substances in solution. So long as the concentrations of the reactants do not change, the rate of the reaction will remain constant. For the system as a whole the rate will remain constant from one moment to the next, and it will be the same in each part of the system so long as the part is sufficiently large. If sufficiently small segments are considered, however, the concentrations of the reactants are not likely to be constant, and the rates of the reaction are therefore not likely to be the same in the small segment from moment to moment and at any one moment the rates are likely to be different between different segments.

Normally rates of reactions are analyzed in terms of molecular numbers of the order of 6.0×10^{23}; this being the number of molecules in one liter of a molar solution. Numbers of the order of 10^6 are considerably smaller than this; how much smaller may be gauged from the volume that 10^6 molecules would occupy in a molar solution. This volume is 10^{-3} μ^3 or 10^{-15} ml. Clearly 10^6 molecules may be of the order within which erratic distributions occur. This probability is of course increased when the volume within which the small number of molecules is confined is large. The lower the concentration the greater the probability of nonuniform distribution. The volume of the cytoplasm in a mature vacuolated cell is approximately 2×10^4 μ^3, and 10^6 molecules in this volume would represent a concentration of about 1×10^{-7} M.

Thus, although the actual numbers of molecules in the cell seem large, they may in fact be small in comparison with those numbers of molecules to which the kinetic theory applies and also their overall concentration is relatively low. The effect of both these conditions is likely to be to promote nonuniform distributions and therefore nonuniform rates of reaction. It is probable that the rates of reaction vary at one time from one cell to the next and with respect to any one cell from moment to moment. This aspect of cellular dynamics is probably obscured by the fact that observations are normally made on tissues. With these the position is comparable to that in the large molecular aggregate. Since the fluctuations are erratic, retardations in one group are compensated by accelerations in another and the whole mass therefore shows a constant rate.

Clearly, both structural features and absolute size of the metabolic system probably tend to promote irregular and fluctuating conditions. The effects of both may, of course, be mitigated by the operation of transport mechanisms such as that of cytoplasmic streaming. This process, however, is not universal, and when it occurs it is usually restricted to a limited region of the cell.

V. The Shape of the Cell

Shape may have considerable significance for the economy of the cell when a vacuole has not been developed. In this state the relationship of surface to volume becomes of decisive importance, and this depends intimately on shape. When surface area is low relative to volume, a high proportion of the cytoplasm is remote from the surface and is separated from it by a long diffusion path. This is the case when the shape is spherical, and with this configuration the supply of oxygen and metabolites to the center of the cell may be limited by the distance of these from the surface. When surface area is high relative to volume, as it is with a cylinder, then relatively more of the cytoplasm is close to the surface and the activity of the whole is less likely to be limited by the distance that solutes must traverse from the environment to the reaction sites.

This consideration is irrelevant when the vacuolated cell is involved, for here, whatever the shape, the cytoplasm is in a peripheral position and is therefore immediately accessible to the environment. With the vacuolated cell, it is indeed not clear what the significance of shape may be for the activity of the cell itself. It is argued, however, and with some vehemence, that shape is, nevertheless, of profound significance since it is an expression of the stresses to which the cell is exposed during development, and it is in deference to this view (84) that the subject is given some prominence here.

That shape may be determined at least partly by tissue stresses is, of course, highly probable, but the investigation of the nature of these, and of their probable effects, is a matter of extreme difficulty. The determinants cannot be measured directly, and much of the discussion must be based not so much on immediate observation as on a consideration of the characteristics of analogous situations. Not the least of the uncertainties that the topic presents is the precise status that must be accorded to the mechanical factor. It is clear that it cannot be the only one. Intrinsic cytoplasmic factors, which are independent of all other cells must also be involved. It is frequently implied, although not explicitly stated, that both sets of conditions probably operate throughout the development of the cell but that mechanical tissue determinants tend to dominate the situation in the earlier, and intrinsic factors in the later, phases. This interpretation corresponds with the known facts regarding the physical state of the cell at different stages of development and is accordingly assumed to be the case in the rest of this discussion.

The simplest form that a cell could assume is that of a sphere, and, although the spherical form is only rarely realized, the properties of a system of spheres in close packing are of some importance for the interpretation of the origin at least of primitive shapes. With close packing, when the spheres are uniform each is in contact with twelve others and a section in any one plane will show six points of contact. The relevance of this pattern to the development of shape is shown by the stellate pith parenchyma of *Juncus* (Fig. 5a). In a transverse section the cells of this tissue are star-shaped and each carries six arms from a central core, the whole structure being comparable to the spokes of a wheel that are attached to a central hub. The cells are unusual only with respect to shape; they are equipped with a normal peripheral cytoplasm and a vacuole which is continuous from the core into the lateral arms. Six arms are also seen when the section is taken

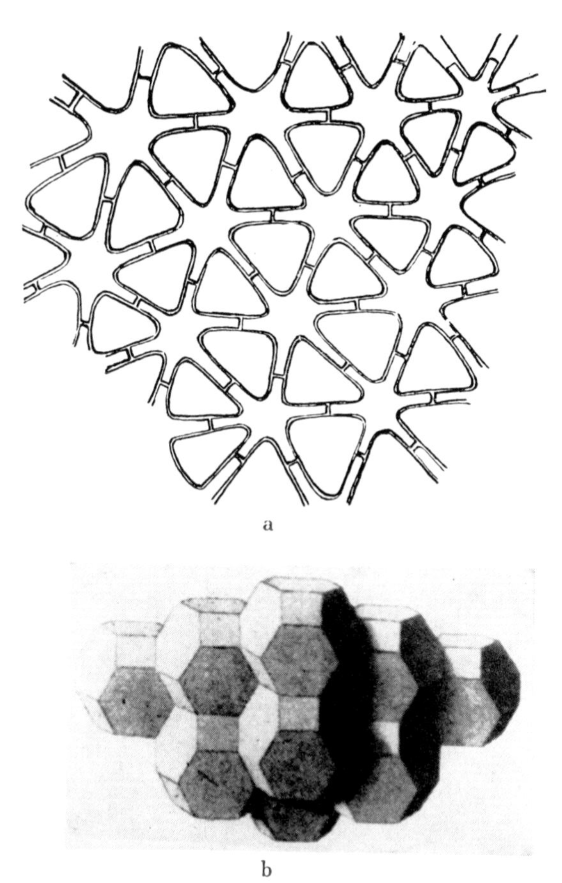

FIG. 5. a. Stellate parenchyma of *Juncus*. b. Model of tetrakaidekahedrons. From Thompson (84).

in the longitudinal plane. Clearly in the solid the cell has the form of a central core carrying twelve lateral uniformly distributed arms. Each arm is in contact with, and attached to, another arm from an adjacent cell, and the whole tissue, therefore, constitutes an aerenchyma with large intercellular spaces. The whole structure suggests strongly that it may be derived at least formally from a system of closely packed uniform spheres where the twelve points of contact on each sphere are also points of attachment. If the change is imagined of the free surfaces of each sphere withdrawing toward the center, then the structure of the stellate parenchyma will be developed. By virtue of the withdrawal inward of the free surfaces, a cell will be left with twelve uniformly dispersed lateral evaginations.

It is probable that the most significant mechanical condition influencing shape is that of compression in the meristem. Each cell tends to swell as a result of the hydrostatic pressure generated within it, and each cell is, therefore, exposed to the pressure exerted by all the other cells around it. With respect to any one cell the situation is similar to that established in a group of inert cells when a uniform pressure is applied externally. In the meristematic state the cell is gelatinous and readily deformed and may be expected to assume an ideal shape which may later be modified but which will, nevertheless, probably influence the final shape.

The precise form into which the recently formed cell might tend to be compressed immediately after formation has been a subject of prolonged controversy. Since compression is not the only determinant, the shape cannot be established, at least not in all cases, by direct inspection and it has had to be inferred from abstract considerations. Whatever it is, it must, of course, fulfill the conditions for maximum stability which are met when the space is most economically filled with the least wall area.

The position may be considered again in terms of an initial state of a system of uniform spheres with close packing. To this a uniform compression similar to that to which meristematic cells are presumably exposed may be applied. At the twelve points of contact of each sphere the surface will begin to flatten, and this will continue until each sphere has been transformed into a polyhedron involving twelve uniform facets, each of which is a quadrilateral. This figure is a rhombic dodecahedron and may also be produced experimentally by allowing closely packed spherical seeds to swell in a confined space or by compressing a mass of clay pellets. Meristematic cells are not strictly spherical, but their general state is at least consistent with the view that they might be constrained into this form, and certain observations are compatible with this interpretation. Twelve-sided figures are relatively frequent, particularly in pith parenchyma, and if the dodecahedron were a characteristic of the meristematic state, then this would explain the hexagonal outline that parenchymatous cells so often display in section.

On the other hand, it is now clear that the dodecahedron does not provide for the greatest occupation of space with the least exposure of wall surface. Any system of partitioning will tend to the fulfillment of this condition of minimal wall surface, and on this ground it is improbable that the primitive ideal figure is, in fact, a twelve-sided polyhedron. This conclusion is the product of mathematical analysis and of observations on the properties of soap films (soap bubbles figure largely in this esoteric discussion). It is now claimed, and with apparently universal assent, that the figure that provides the necessary conditions is the tetrakaidekahedron. This is a fourteen-sided figure, and "it is bounded by three pairs of equal and opposite quadrilateral faces and four pairs of equal and opposite hexagonal faces, neither the quadrilaterals nor the hexagons being necessarily plane" (84). Since this is the most economical figure and since embryonic cells may be at least envisaged as semiliquid drops, then all the cells in the plant formed in meristems might be expected to be derived from it. The formation of the fourteen-sided figure may present what is possibly an unimportant difficulty. Whereas with close packing the dodecahedron can be derived without lateral slip, the tetrakaidekahedron can be formed only when this is possible. The fourteen-sided figure, for instance, can be formed from clay pellets when these are wet. When they are dry and they cannot slide across one another, then only twelve-sided figures are formed. On the other hand, extensive observations have shown that a large number of cells in the plant do, in fact, conform to the fourteen-sided configuration. In elder pith it has been found that, while the number of facets per cell varies considerably, nevertheless, the average number is 13.96, which is clearly a close enough approximation to 14 to indicate that all the cells tend to a fourteen-sided pattern. It has also been shown that cells that are elongating may still retain this pattern, although the ideal shape has been transformed. In the course of elongation an expansion occurs in six parallel facets of the polyhedron, giving a consistent distortion of the ideal shape.

It may be repeated that whatever the relative importance of mechanical tissue stress may be, it is clear that it cannot be the only factor determining shape. During expansion other forces undoubtedly mold the system, and the nature of at least one of these is mentioned below. [For further discussion of cell shape, see Thompson (84).]

VI. Cells in Tissues

The cells with which this chapter is concerned do not normally exist as separate units. They are always components of a tissue, and this circumstance involves particular conditions which must influence their activity.

Cells of the higher plant never display the freedom that some animal cells can exercise. They are almost invariably anchored to neighbors, and they do not migrate from one part of a tissue to another as animal cells may. It is even doubtful whether cells can slide across one another. The view has been held that the adjustments in shape and position in a tissue that occur during development would be impossible without sliding growth, but careful histological examination has shown that normally this is highly improbable. The adjustments are apparently the result of either compensating divisions or of compensating expansions. One case has been recorded in which it seems that a form of sliding growth must occur. Secondary phloem fibers, although they are formed from the cambium, are frequently considerably longer in the mature state than the cells from which they were formed. This suggests that the development of the embryonic fiber cell must be accompanied by a form of intrusion growth in which the fiber reaches its final position by intruding between other cells and separating them.

The anchoring of parenchymatous cells to each other is a function of the middle lamella which, being composed of a firm binding substance, acts in much the same way as the cement layer between superimposed bricks. The binding is surprisingly firm. An estimate of it may be obtained by measuring the breaking strain in a graft before vascular continuity has been established. The initial phase in the formation of the graft union involves over each surface the formation of callus pads which subsequently become attached to each other through what is probably a pectin layer. At this stage the two members in the union may be pulled apart and the break always occurs along the line of junction between the opposite callus tissues. Thus, when the minimal strain necessary to effect a break is measured, this shows the firmness with which the junction between the two groups of cells is established. The breaking strain in a normal tissue is certainly not likely to be less, and will probably be considerably greater, than that given by a graft. Values recorded from grafts are of the general order of 200 gm per square millimeter, which may be compared with the breaking strain for lead which is about 1.0 kg per square millimeter. Clearly, each individual cell is firmly bound and is certainly not likely to be dislodged by stresses developed in the tissue as a whole (10a).

Although the protoplasts of adjacent cells are separated by intervening walls, they are, nevertheless, probably connected through plasmodesmata (Fig. 6a,b). As mentioned above, until recently the existence of these structures was questioned by several observers, but evidence from electron microscope photographs has confirmed their presence in normal cell walls, and it can no longer be doubted that they are integral features of cellular structure. They appear as thin strands 0.2–0.5 μ thick which cross the wall system from one cell into the next and which stain with normal cytoplasmic dyes, such as hematoxylin. Below it is shown that the surface of the protoplast constitutes a distinct membrane, the plasmalemma, and it is at least possible that each plasmodesma strand is an extension from one surface membrane which becomes continuous with the next. In certain tissues the strands occur in groups. Certain electron microscope photographs have shown areas in the primary wall which enclose large numbers of pores, and it is probable that each one of the pores accommodates one of a group of strands. In certain other tissues the plasmodesmata may be randomly distributed.

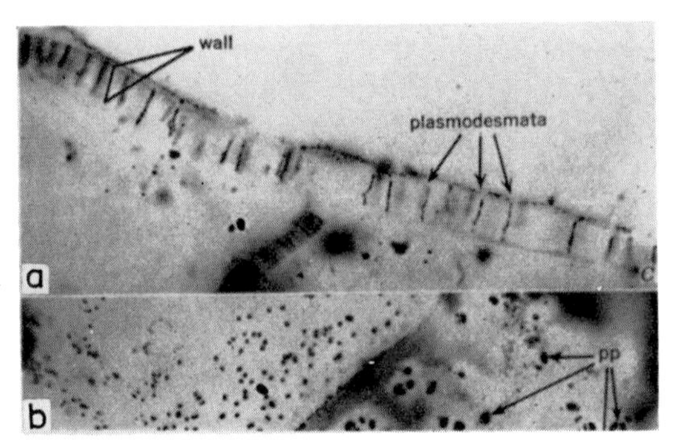

FIG. 6. a. Transverse section across wall of potato (*Solanum tuberosum*) showing plasmodesmata in the wall. b. Surface view of wall showing pits (*pp*) occupied by plasmodesmata. Photographs by A. D. Crafts reproduced in "Plant Anatomy" by Esau.

Although the occurrence of plasmodesmata is now well established, their origin and significance are still matters of some doubt. It is possible, and indeed probable, that they have at least two different origins. Some of the strands may be developed from spindle fibers which have persisted after division has been completed and which have not been interrupted by the formation of the wall. All, however, cannot be formed in this way, since they may be scattered over the whole surface of the mature wall and over every wall. It has been suggested that some have a secondary origin and that they are developed after the primary wall has been formed. It has been claimed that plasmodesmata may be observed between cells with different genetic constitutions in a chimera (48). In this case the strands connect cells which are not derived from each other, and they must, therefore, be formed across initially intact walls. Observations have been recorded which suggest that these secondary plasmodesmata are formed by the wall being pierced by coincident cytoplasmic pegs on the two sides. The subject of the origin of plasmodesmata, however, still awaits intensive investigation.

The importance of the connections is equally obscure. It has been suggested that it is significant that they are particularly prominent in structures such as the pulvinus of *Mimosa pudica* (the sensitive plant), through which stimuli are propagated with unusual rapidity, the inference being that they may be channels along which something in the nature of a nervous impulse is transmitted. Such may be the case, but it must be emphasized that the evidence for this category of phenomena in plant systems is distinctly tenuous and it is relevant that plasmodesmata are richly developed also in markedly unresponsive tissues, such as endosperms. Again it must be allowed that the subject requires further clarification.

The cell which is embedded in a tissue depends on supplies of oxygen and metabolites to the same extent as one that is isolated, but the routes along which the necessary substances reach the two must be different. The requirements of an isolated cell of, say, an alga are met quite simply from an external aqueous medium. With the tissue cell the position is more complicated. Oxygen reaches it from the intercellular space system, and metabolites, at least partly, from other cells.

Immediately after being formed, cells are in contact with other cells over their whole surfaces. This state may persist into the early developmental phase, but in the later, the primary walls tend to separate at the extremities leaving gaps between them. In the mature system these gaps are connected and they form a continuous *intercellular space system* which occupies in many parenchymas about 10% of the tissue volume (Fig. 2). In spongy mesophyll it represents about 30%. The intercellular system terminates externally in stomata or lenticels, and when these are open oxygen diffuses inward and is distributed throughout the tissue. Cells, even those which are deep in the tissue, absorb oxygen from the intercellular channels and return carbon dioxide to them. This diffuses back to the stomata or lenticels and escapes thence into the atmosphere. The intercellular space system cannot in all cases be developed in the manner outlined above. Where aerenchyma are concerned, other mechanisms must be involved, one of which has been described in Section V. These special processes lead to the development of a tissue with a very much higher volume proportion of intercellular space than of cellular material. They are characteristic of plants that are restricted to hydrophytic habitats, and they are said to provide a wide diffusion path which ensures a vigorous gaseous exchange between the atmosphere and cells that may be remote from it.

The solutes that are required by a cell in a tissue often reach it from others cells. It is only in special circumstances that solute absorption occurs from interstitial fluid in the intercellular spaces, and the composition of that interstitial fluid presents special problems which receive some attention in Chapter 4 of Volume II. Even in tissue slices the intercellular system may not be wholly occupied by the external fluid medium in which they are immersed and in intact organs this is not necessarily the case, even when they are immersed in an aqueous fluid, as the roots are when they are in a water culture. It is generally assumed that solutes are transmitted to another cell across the protoplast. The solutes before they reach a cell deep in the tissue traverse the protoplasts of the intervening cells. On the other hand, the possibility has been mooted that the distribution of at least some solutes occurs along the system of interconnected walls. While there is no evidence that this is an important route, it may be noted that the walls are, of course, fully saturated with water and there seems to be no barrier in the system which could prevent solute diffusion (see Volume II, Chapter 4 for further discussion of this problem).

Some at least of the solutes that are absorbed by one cell must be provided from the protoplast of a neighboring cell. At this point it may not be inappropriate to point out one of the oddities of contemporary knowledge. Much is known regarding the absorption of solutes into cells and this topic is considered at length in later chapters. Little, however, is known as to the mechanism by which solutes are released from the cell. Once released they can be absorbed by the next cell in the series, but precisely how and in what conditions this release occurs is still a matter for inspired speculation. The difficulty arises with respect to both inorganic and organic substances. It is a matter of common experience that when a tissue has been accumulating an inorganic salt it does not release this salt readily under aerobic conditions, and reserve materials, such as sucrose, cannot be leached from tissues into water.

The intact autotrophic plant absorbs from the environment inorganic salts and carbon dioxide. It is probable that each cell in the plant also requires these substances, and it is probable that the salts reach tissue cells from other cells and the carbon dioxide, from the intercellular spaces. It is clear that some cells must have additional requirements. It cannot be doubted that cellular differentiation is a metabolic, as well as a cytological, phenomenon. It is probable that the morphological differences that have been described in another connection are accompanied by corresponding metabolic differences, and that different compounds may be synthesized in different cells. This raises the possibility that synthetic activities complement each other and that the products of one cell may be the requirements of another. This is certainly the case with respect to sugar since this is synthesized only in cells with green chloroplasts and is required by all active cells in the plant. Experience with tissue cultures suggests that it may be the case with respect to other compounds as well. In culture, all nongreen tissues require for growth a supply of necessary factors, such as vitamins and hormones, which in normal circumstances may again by synthesized in the leaves and from these distributed to other cells (80, 89). The dependence of certain cells on others for metabolites may extend further than this. With a suitable medium a tissue culture may now be established from a single cell,[1] and this indicates that except with respect to certain compounds supplied in the medium all the syntheses necessary for growth can proceed in a single cell. It does not, however, show that the single parent cell sustains all synthetic reactions at as high a rate as some proceed in other cells. It is possible that a cell which synthesizes a compound may nevertheless still absorb some of that compound from other cells which synthesize it more rapidly. There is some indication that this may indeed be the case and that in certain connections amino acids and nucleotides, for instance, may be consumed in cells in which they are not synthesized. This subject is considered again in a later volume.

VII. The Cell Wall

When the cell is not attached to another cell the wall system involves a thin primary wall on the external surface and a thicker

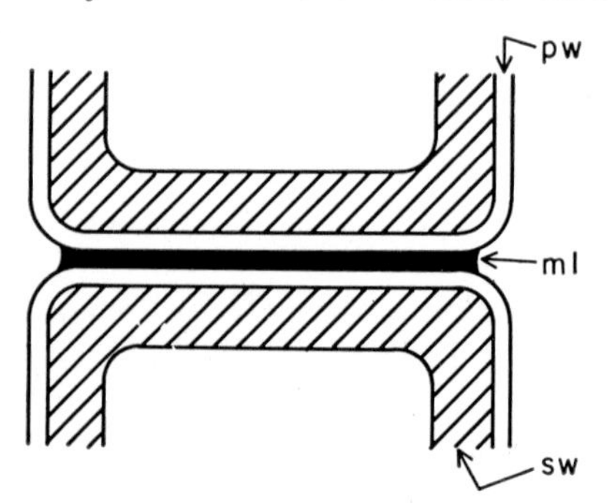

Fig. 7. Succession of wall layers between one protoplast and the next; *sw*, secondary wall; *ml*, middle lamella; *pw*, primary wall.

[1] Muir, W. H. *et al.* (1958). *Amer. Jour. Bot.* **45:** 589–597; Steward, F. C. *et al.* (1958). *Amer. Jour. Bot.* **45:** 693–708; Braun, A. C. (1959). *Proc. Nat. Acad. Sci.* (*U.S.*) **45:** 932–938.

secondary wall between this and the cytoplasm. Where two cells are in contact the position is more complicated and is shown by the diagram of Fig. 7, which gives the succession of layers when the wall system is traversed from one cell into the next. The two cells are separated by a middle lamella (*ml*). On either side there are layers of the primary wall (*pw*) and internal to each of these, the secondary wall (*sw*), each of which commonly has three layers. In each secondary wall the middle layer is the thickest, the inner and outer layers being considerably thinner. Below, the middle lamella is treated first and, subsequently, the primary and secondary walls are described together.

A. MIDDLE LAMELLA

This is a layer about 0.5 μ thick which does not show crystalline properties. Its formation begins during telophase, at the end of mitosis, when drops of a semiliquid substance appear on the equator of the spindle. In time these coalesce to form a continuous plate across the cell. At a later stage primary wall formation begins within the semiliquid barrier. The development of the middle lamella must, however, continue after this stage has been reached, and it is probable that as the two cells grow they secrete the appropriate substances into the space between the two primary walls. In the mature cellular system the middle lamella is a firm cohesive structure, but as the system grows older it may become less firm and the binding between the cells less secure. This change is particularly pronounced in storage organs such as fruits, in which the senescent phase is marked by a dissolution of the middle lamella with a consequent separation of the cells.

The middle lamella always stains with ruthenium red, and this reaction is reputed to be diagnostic for various derivatives of pectic acid, which chemical analysis has shown are probably the only constituents in this layer. Pectic acid, like most other major constituents of the wall system is a polymerized carbohydrate, in which the unit of structure is galacturonic acid (α-D-pyranose form), which is shown in formula (II).

CH_2OH; HO, O, H; H; OH, H; H, OH; H, OH

(I)

COOH; HO, O, H; H; OH, H; H, OH; H, OH

(II)

Galacturonic acid is derived from galactose (α-D-galacto-pyranose) formula (I) by an oxidation at C-6. Polymerization occurs through the formation of 1,4-α-glycosidic linkages as shown in formula (III).

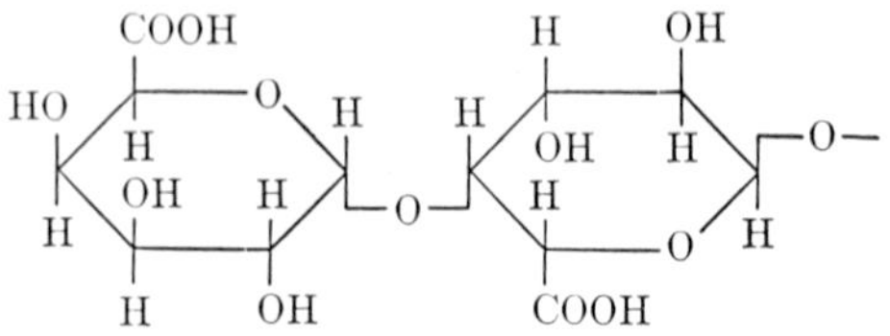

(III)

After extraction the polymer has an average molecular weight of about 200,000, which corresponds to about 1000 hexose residues per unit chain length. The chains are unbranched and they do not aggregate into crystalline units, but are randomly distributed.

Pectic acid reacts readily with calcium and magnesium ions, and it is in the form of the salts of these metals that it is present in the middle lamella. The divalent cations each react with two carboxyl groups from different molecules, and these bind the chains together, the firm cohesive properties of the middle lamella being undoubtedly due to this effect. It has been shown that certain tissues may be induced to develop with only very low levels of calcium, but with these conditions the constituent cells tend to separate, as a consequence probably of a loosening when calcium is not available to bind the separate pectic acid chains.

B. Primary and Secondary Walls

The principal constituent of these is cellulose, but they may also incorporate one or more of the following. (1) pectins, (2) noncellulosic polysaccharides, (3) hemicelluloses, (4) lignin, (5) fats and waxes. These additional substances are considered first.

1. Pectins

This group of substances comprises pectin and protopectin, both of which are simple methyl esters of pectic acid. The two substances differ with respect to solubility in water. The first is readily soluble, and this property is probably a consequence of a short chain length, the molecule being composed of only 10 to 15 hexose residues. The second, protopectin, is insoluble, and this corresponds to a much greater chain length of some thousands of hexose residues. Both, on treatment with weak alkali, are demethylated and yield pectic acid, which is similar in its properties to the acid that is obtained from the middle lamella.

The pectins are abundant in the primary and probably also in the secondary wall. They are readily extracted in water, and particularly protopectin, when dehydrated, gives a firm jelly. This property is exploited commercially in the preparation of jams, in which the sugar content may be as high as 70%. In the presence of this concentration of sugar the pectin is dehydrated and the whole mass sets to a jelly. It is of some interest in relation to the properties of gels as a whole that when this has occurred the concentration of the pectin may be as low as 1%.

2. Noncellulosic Polysaccharides

These are predominantly polymers of mannose, galactose, xylose, and arabinose, and they are distinguished as mannans, galactans, xylans, and arabans, respectively. Structurally this is not a homogeneous group. All of them when hydrolyzed yield the hexose or the pentose. Occasionally more than one sugar may be released by hydrolysis, but usually the molecule contains only the monosaccharide in the pyranose or occasionally in the furanose form and the units are joined through various linkages. The chain length may be relatively short, involving something less than 100 residues. In some the chain is branched and with some the molecules are associated in micelles as in cellulose, but usually they are amorphous and isotropic. The structure of the galactan unit is shown in formula (IV).

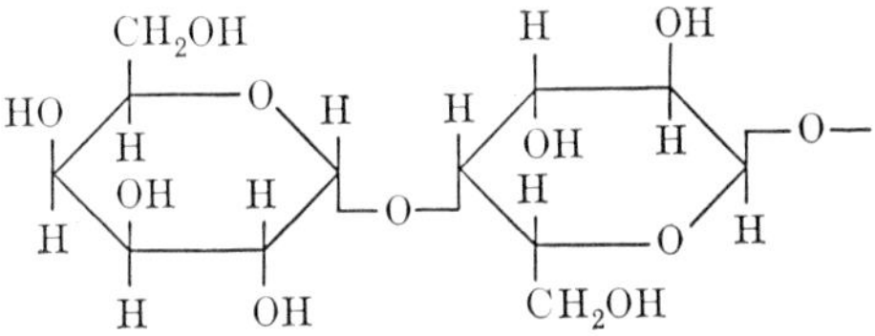

(IV)

3. Hemicelluloses

These are mixed polysaccharides containing uronic acid and hexose or pentose units. Common forms of this group contain either galacturonic acid, galactose, and arabinose (β-L-arabopyranose) formula (V), or glucuronic acid, glucose (α-D-glucopyranose), and xylose (α-D-

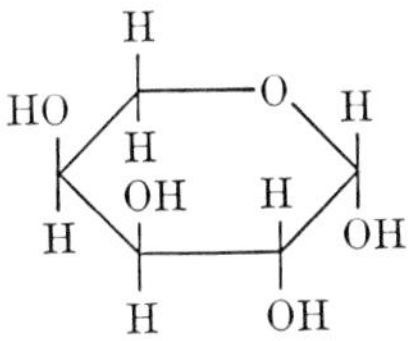

(V)

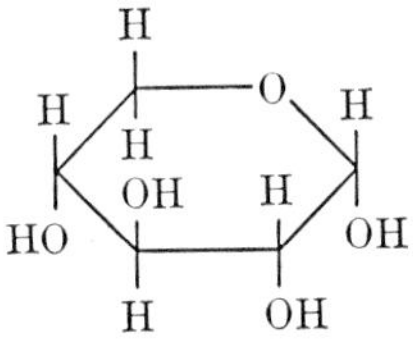

(VI)

xylopyranose) formula (VI). (Glucuronic acid is a derivative of glucose, to which it has the same relation as galacturonic acid has to galactose.) The carboxyl group of the uronic acid may form a methyl ester, and normally the hexose or the pentose predominates. They tend to have a relatively low molecular weight with a short chain length. The chain is unbranched, and the molecules do not associate into crystalline aggregates.

4. *Lignin*

This is not one of the constituents of the wall of actively metabolizing parenchymatous cells. On the other hand, when present it is in the same position as other secondary constituents and it is the most important component of the walls of certain cells which have already been described. Lignin is the main constituent of woody tissues, and it is the substance which endows these with their characteristic properties of hardness and mechanical rigidity. The chemistry of lignin is still not fully understood, but one fact about it is beyond dispute. It is peculiar in being a polymer in which the unit structure is a phenolic compound. Hydrolysis, by whatever method, always yields aromatic, highly unsaturated compounds, and it is to this that the sharp absorption peaks in the ultraviolet must be attributed. It has been suggested that the polymer is formed predominantly from units similar to isoeugenol formula (VII). The evidence indicates, however, that isoeugenol can-

$$(CH_3O)(HO)C_6H_3-CH=CH-CH_3$$

(VII)

not be the only constituent. Other aromatic nuclei are probably involved and the molecule may contain certain aliphatic compounds.

5. *Fats and Waxes*

These do not occur within the wall and do not, therefore, have the same status as the constituents described above. When they are present they tend to be on the outer surfaces of the cell where it is exposed to the atmosphere or is not in contact with another cell. The most prominent of these fatty layers are the cuticles, which are probably mixtures of esters of fatty acids with long-chain alcohols, free fatty acids, free alcohols, long-chain hydrocarbons, and high molecular weight ketones. (The structure of fats is described in connection with the cytoplasm.) The alcohols are monohydric compounds involving 24–

36 carbons. The hydrocarbons also incorporate about this number of carbon atoms. Cuticles normally stain red with Sudan III and Scharlach R, and these reactions are attributed to the free fats they contain.

Cuticles are normally present on the outer surfaces of epidermal tissues, and in these positions since their components are strongly hydrophobic they tend to restrain the loss of water from the surface of the tissue. At the same time the cuticle may exaggerate a condition that is normal to every cell.

6. *Cellulose*

The primary and secondary walls stain with iodine after treatment with sulfuric acid, and this reaction, which is diagnostic for cellulose, indicates that this substance, if not always the main, is certainly an abundant, constituent. Analysis shows that in primary walls cellulose may represent as little as 20% of the dry weight and in secondary walls of actively metabolizing cells it may contribute as much as 60%. In certain exceptional cells cellulose may represent up to 90% of the dry weight. This is the case with cotton (*Gossypium*) and ramie (*Boehmeria nivea*) fibers, and because of the relatively low content of other substances these have been used extensively in studies on the structure of cellulose.

Even when the percentage of cellulose is relatively low, it is probable that this substance determines the physical properties of the wall and, consequently, many of the mechanical properties of the whole plant. The wall, while it is not a completely rigid structure, is nevertheless, not readily deformed. It is flexible and has a limited elasticity. On the other hand, when internal hydrostatic pressures are released it does not crumple and when it becomes flaccid it does not lose structural form. It has a high tensile strength, and this property is exploited in its use as a textile fiber in cotton fabrics.

Cellulose is a long-chain polysaccharide which is insoluble in water but soluble in Schweitzer's reagent, which is cupric hydroxide dissolved in concentrated ammonium hydroxide. It is hydrolyzed by concentrated acids, and this treatment yields only β-D-glucose. With milder treatment and more controlled hydrolysis, cellobiose is obtained. The polymer is a straight-chain compound and the successive glucose units are connected through 1,4-β-linkages. This is also the linkage between the two hexose units in cellobiose, and the whole chain may therefore be considered as being constructed of successive cellobiose units, themselves joined through 1,4-β-linkages. The structure of cellobiose in the cellulose chain is shown in formula (VIII).

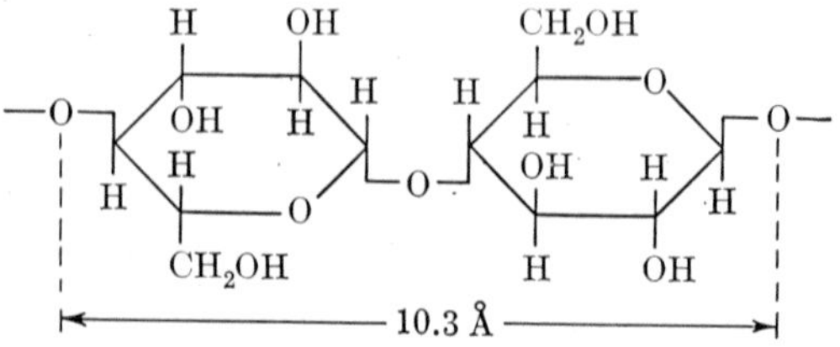

10.3 Å

(VIII)

In certain regions of the wall, cellulose is aggregated into well-defined crystalline zones. This is shown most effectively by the diffraction pattern given when a beam of X-rays is allowed to traverse the wall and then fall on a photographic plate. This diffraction pattern has been intensively studied, and from it much of the structure of the crystalline zones of the wall has been determined. The crystallographic unit cell for cellulose has the dimensions of $10.3 \times 8.3 \times 7.9$ A (Fig. 8,a). 10.3 A is the distance between the oxygen atoms in the glycosidic bonds at the two extremities of the cellobiose unit. Thus the unit cell of cellulose may be considered as a rhombohedron having a cellobiose molecule at each corner, the corners being 8.3 A apart in one direction and 7.9 A apart in the other. Since the unit cell is repeated laterally in both axes in the transverse plane, each cellobiose unit is at the corner of four cells, and without further elaboration this simple arrangement provides for one cellobiose or two glucose units per cell. Density measurements, however, indicate that the unit cell carries not two, but four, glucose units and it has, therefore, been proposed that in addition to the four cellobiose units, one at each corner, a fifth traverses the center of the cell parallel to the other four but out of phase with them. In crystalline zones the unit is, of course, repeated longitudinally and the cellobiose units at the corners are, therefore, segments from long chains, which are held together laterally by hydrogen bonding between adjacent hydroxyl groups. From the intensity and form of the spots in the diffraction pattern an estimate may be made of the number of reflection planes in the longitudinal and in the transverse directions, the number in the first giving a measure of the length, and in the second of the width, of the crystalline aggregate. In ramie the length is about 600 A. The value for the width suggests that the aggregate is a relatively large one and that the wall is composed of successive bundles of fibers. The wall displays form birefringence, and on the basis of this evidence a similar concept for the structure of the wall was elaborated in the nineteenth century by Nägeli, who gave the name of micelle to the individual aggregates. This term has persisted and will be used in this text hereafter. Various observations and notably the

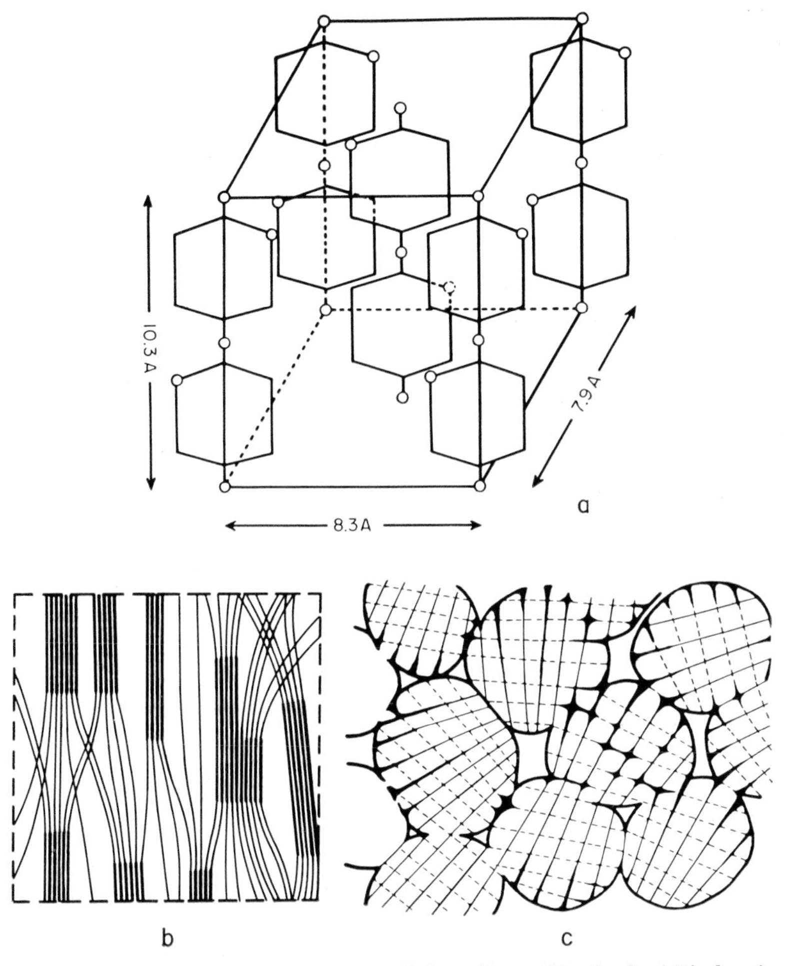

FIG. 8. a. Unit crystallographic cell in cellulose. From "Textbook of Biochemistry" by Gortner. b. Diagram showing relation between micellar and nonmicellar regions. Note that chains that form part of a crystalline region may traverse an amorphous gap and become incorporated in another micelle. c. Diagram of transverse section across a secondary wall to show organization of micelles into fibrils. The spaces between the micelles within the fibrils are about 10 A, and between the fibrils about 100 A. b and c are from Frey-Wyssling (28).

form birefringence of the wall and the fact that swelling with water does not alter the X-ray diffraction pattern, have further emphasized that the micellar pattern does not occupy the whole of the wall. The form birefringence indicates that two phases are involved with different indexes of refraction, and the swelling effect indicates that water, although it becomes incorporated into the wall, does not penetrate into the crystalline regions. Clearly micelles alternate with intermicellar zones in which an ordered molecular pattern is not developed. The width of the average intermicellar space has been measured by a variety of techniques and probably most successfully by measuring the sizes of deposited crystals, and it is of the order of 100 A.

The concept of the micelle has been developed through several forms since it was first formulated. Until comparatively recently it was held that the micelles were in the form of regular independent blocks with an intermicellar cement between them. This, it is now clear, is not the case. The length of the micelle as determined from X-ray diffraction date indicates an average of 120 glucose units in the cellulose chain. But this does not correspond with estimates made with other techniques. When the cellulose is in solution the molecular weight may be determined by the techniques used with macromolecular substances. Of these, the most reliable is probably that of ultracentrifugation, and determinations with this method have given values ranging from 500,000 for cotton to about 2,000,000 for ramie (88, cf. p. 83). The first corresponds to about 3000 glucose residues per unit chain length and the second to about 11,500. Clearly ultracentrifugal methods suggest a considerably greater chain length than the X-ray diffraction technique. The disparity is due to the first being a measure for the whole molecule and to the second for that part of the molecule which is in the micelle. The disparity, in fact, indicates that only part of the molecule contributes to the structure of the micelle. It is evident that the wall must be pictured as being composed of more or less random chains which at certain points aggregate into crystalline micelles (Fig. 8,b). It is probable that a single molecule may contribute to more than one micelle and that it traverses an intermicellar space in stretching between one aggregate and the next (28).

In the primary wall the micelles are not organized into larger units, but they may be so ordered in the secondary wall. Bundles of micelles tend to be formed and to constitute microfibrils. In these, the micelles retain their structure and identity but the intermicellar spaces between them tend to be smaller than the corresponding spaces between the fibrils (Fig, 8,c). It has been shown that as a result of stresses set up in the wall, cracks may develop between them and these are visible as fine striations which define the course of the fibrils (81).

The intermicellar space may be infiltrated with water, but most of it is occupied by subsidiary wall constituents. When they are present the pectins, polyuronides, noncellulosic polysaccharides, or hemicelluloses form an amorphous matrix which separates the micelles, but in which random cellulose chains may be embedded. The intermicellar spaces in the primary wall are large and they, therefore, accommodate a relatively high proportion of matrix noncellulosic compounds. The intermicellar spaces in the secondary wall, on the other hand, are smaller, and the proportion of cellulose in the wall is, therefore, correspondingly higher. Lignin is restricted to the secondary wall, and when it is present it is also in the intermicellar spaces.

From X-ray and birefringence data the direction of the micelles in the wall may be determined. The direction of these is never normal to the plane of the surface but always parallel to it. The direction with respect to the long axis of the cell, however, varies considerably. In primary walls the fibers tend to be aligned in the transverse plane. They tend to form a system which in effect forms a ring in the circumference of the cell. In certain cases the fibers are inclined at an angle of 10° to the horizontal and form a very flat spiral. Even this, however, conforms to the tubular structure which is characteristic of primary walls. It may be emphasized that the directions given for the micelles are statistical averages. This is particularly the case in the primary wall. The fibers are certainly not all aligned in the same direction. They are usually very randomly distributed and the direction that may be assigned to them is only an average for the group (Fig. 9,b).

The tubular structure is of some interest in relation to cell shape. Cells with this structure tend to be cylindrical, and it is probable that in this case the form is being determined by the molecular architecture of the wall. It is clearly not the consequence of tissue stresses and is undoubtedly being molded by the cytoplasmic conditions which regulate wall pattern.

In the primary wall tubular structure persists into the mature state. While it is already developed in the young cell, it is not apparently disturbed by expansion in the surface. Where the tubular structure is accompanied by a slight inclination to the horizontal, a change in the steepness of the spiral might be expected with growth in much the same way as the pitch of the spiral is changed when a spring is extended. This is not observed, and it indicates that growth must be sustained by the intussusception of additional micelles between those already present, the secondary micelles being deposited with the same general alignment as the older.

In the secondary wall the position is more complicated. In this, the tubular structure does not occur, but the chains may be disposed longitudinally as in ramie, giving what is called the fiber structure, or they may traverse the wall in a spiral, the steepness of which varies. The secondary wall commonly shows three layers. When lignification occurs the identity of the three layers persists and the arrangement of

FIG. 9. a. Electron micrograph showing wall structure in *Valonia ventricosa*. Surface view of secondary wall showing three sets of superimposed strands, each intersecting the next at an angle of 120°. Magnification: ×25,000. From Steward and Mühlethaler (81).

the micelles in them may be determined after removal of the lignin. In each layer the fibers traverse a spiral course from base to apex, but whereas in the conifer tracheid, in the inner and outer layers the micelles are inclined at an angle of 50° to the horizontal, in the middle layer they are only inclined 10°, giving a chain direction which is almost parallel to the long axis (69).

FIG. 9. b. Electron micrograph showing wall structure in *Valonia ventricosa*. Primary wall showing micelles apparently randomly dispersed. Magnification: ×20,000. From Steward and Mühlethaler (81).

Most of the results that have been described above were obtained with techniques of X-ray diffraction and polarization optics. Recently, however, wall structure has also been examined with electron microscopy. This technique was used by Steward and Muhlethaler (81) in the investigation of wall structure in *Valonia ventricosa*, in which the condition appears to be particularly complicated. In this species the so-called cell is a large vesicle which may be well over a centimeter in length and which is oval in shape. The wall is thick and may be composed of hundreds of layers which separate after mild treatment

Fig. 9. c. Electron micrograph showing wall structure in *Valonia ventricosa*. Cross section of secondary wall showing repetition of orientation with every fourth layer. Magnification: ×17,000. From Steward and Mühlethaler (81).

with acid or alkali. In each layer the normal structure is observed of micelles with intermicellar regions between them, the micelles being organized into larger fibrillar structures. The whole system, however, involves a succession of layers, each with a dominant micellar orientation. Three dominant spiral arrangements are present, and each intersects the next at an angle of 120°. Thus every fourth layer repeats the micellar orientation of the first and the whole wall involves groups of three layers, in each of which the same succession is repeated (Fig. 9,a). With this arrangement an oblique section would show a zig-zag pattern along the section, and this is shown in Fig. 9,c.

Remarkable as this structure may be, it is perhaps not as remarkable as the mechanism by which it is molded. Each successive wall is laid down by the surface of the protoplast, which presumably carries some configuration which determines that of the wall. But when one layer has been formed there must be an abrupt change which sustains an entirely different pattern. Not only so, but when the reversal occurs back to the first state it involves a reversal to exactly the same position, since the direction in corresponding layers remains exactly the same.

For further details of the composition of the wall the relevant chapters in Bonner (5) may be consulted.

VIII. Chemical Components of the Protoplast

The gross composition of the protoplast is readily determined, and one representative analysis for a myxomycete is shown in Table I (50).

TABLE I
REPRESENTATIVE ANALYSIS FOR A MYXOMYCETE

Substances	Percentage of dry matter
Soluble:	
1. Monosaccharides	14.2
2. Soluble nitrogenous compounds	24.3
3. Proteins	2.2
4. Inorganic substances	4.4
Insoluble:	
1. Nucleoprotein	32.3
2. Free nucleic acid	2.5
3. Lipoprotein	4.8
4. Neutral fats	6.8
5. Phosphatides	1.3
Miscellaneous	9.0

For the structural organization of the cytoplasm the soluble compounds are of little interest, since these are likely to be in free solution circulating within a structural framework. The insoluble compounds are certainly of greater importance, and it is significant that the most abundant are (a) proteins, (b) fats and lipids, and (c) nucleic acids. The chemical characteristics of each of these groups of compounds is important for the elucidation of protoplasmic structure, and these characteristics are considered below.

A. Proteins

The proteins are of decisive importance in the economy of the cell, and a separate chapter is accordingly devoted to them. In this context only certain general characteristics are described.

The proteins are polymeric substances in which the fundamental units are α-amino acids, the general structure of which is shown in formula (IX).

$$
\begin{array}{c}
\mathrm{H} \\
| \\
\mathrm{R{-}C{-}COOH} \\
| \\
\mathrm{NH_2}
\end{array}
$$

(IX)

In each amino acid the alpha carbon carries an amino and a carboxyl group. Since these substances carry both basic and acidic groups they are amphoteric substances. The number of amino acids known to contribute to the structure of proteins is 24, and the differences between them are due to differences in the part of the molecule represented by R in formula (IX). The simplest is glycine in which R is a hydrogen atom. Some are aromatic substances, but most are aliphatic compounds. Two, aspartic and glutamic acids, incorporate a second carboxyl group, and two others, arginine and lysine, a second amino group. In cysteine the β-carbon, which is terminal, carries an SH thiol group, and in leucine the γ-carbon, which is again terminal, carries two methyl groups. In serine the β-terminal carbon carries a hydroxyl group. The dicarboxylic acids may react with ammonia to produce amides ($\mathrm{—CO.NH_2}$).

The amino acids are linked in proteins through peptide bonds which are formed as shown in formula (X) by combination of an α-carboxyl group with an α-amino group with the elimination of one molecule of water to give —CO.NH—, i.e., the peptide bond.

$$
\begin{array}{l}
\qquad\qquad\qquad\qquad\qquad\qquad\qquad\qquad\mathrm{H} \\
\qquad\qquad\qquad\qquad\qquad\qquad\qquad\qquad| \\
\qquad\qquad\qquad\quad\mathrm{H}\qquad\qquad\mathrm{R_2{-}C{-}COOH} \\
\qquad\qquad\qquad\quad|\qquad\qquad\qquad\quad| \\
\quad\mathrm{H}\qquad\quad\mathrm{R_1{-}C{-}CO\,\boxed{OH\ \ H}NH} \\
\quad|\qquad\qquad\qquad\;\;| \\
\mathrm{R_3{-}C{-}CO\,\boxed{OH\ \ H}NH} \\
\quad| \\
\quad\mathrm{NH_2}
\end{array}
$$

(X)

The structure of protein may be written as in formula (XI).

$$\begin{array}{ccccccccc}
 & & \mathrm{H} & & \mathrm{H} & & \mathrm{H} & & \\
 & & | & & | & & | & & \\
\mathrm{R_3} & — & \mathrm{C} & —\mathrm{CO.NH}— & \mathrm{C} & —\mathrm{CO.NH}— & \mathrm{C} & —\mathrm{CONH} & \cdots \\
 & & | & & | & & | & & \\
 & & \mathrm{NH_2} & & \mathrm{R_1} & & \mathrm{R_2} & &
\end{array}$$

(XI)

Or alternatively as in formula (XII).

$$\begin{array}{ccccccccccccccccccc}
 & & & & \mathrm{H} & & \mathrm{O} & & & & \mathrm{R_1} & & & & \mathrm{H} & & \mathrm{H} & & \mathrm{O} \\
 & & & & | & & \| & & & & | & & & & | & & | & & \| \\
\mathrm{H} & — & \mathrm{N} & — & \mathrm{C} & — & \mathrm{C} & — & \mathrm{N} & — & \mathrm{C} & — & \mathrm{C} & — & \mathrm{N} & — & \mathrm{C} & — & \mathrm{C}— \cdots \\
 & & | & & | & & & & | & & | & & \| & & & & | & & \\
 & & \mathrm{H} & & \mathrm{R_3} & & & & \mathrm{H} & & \mathrm{H} & & \mathrm{O} & & & & \mathrm{R_2} & &
\end{array}$$

(XII)

The structure shown in formula (XII) emphasizes that the successive peptide linkages lead to the formation of a backbone chain which consists of a repeating sequence of $—\overset{\overset{\displaystyle \mathrm{O}}{\|}}{\mathrm{C}}—\mathrm{N}—\mathrm{C}—$. One carbon in the sequence carries a side chain which is indicated by R, and the nature of this varies with the structure of the amino acid from which it is derived. The amino acid composition of different proteins differs and the sequence of amino acids in the chain is also known to vary. The sequence has been established only in one relatively simple proteinlike substance, insulin, but the significance of this is still not clear (73).

The number of amino acid units in the molecule, and therefore its molecular weight vary, enormously. While ribonuclease has a molecular weight of 12,000, it has been claimed that some cytoplasmic proteins may have a molecular weight of 100,000,000.

It is clear that the variation in the nature of the side chain provides for the possibility of considerable variations in the properties of the whole molecule. Some fibrous proteins which may be present in cytoplasm may remain as single relatively straight unbranched chains. The differences in the characteristics of the R groups, however, lead to considerable departures from the pattern. While the lengths of the side chains differ, their terminal groups also vary. These may be carboxyl, amino, hydroxyl, methyl, or thiol (SH) groups. With this assemblage, radicals may link with others in different chains. It is clear that different points may be drawn together through general van der Waals' forces, through hydrogen bonding, or through the formation of covalent and ionic bonds. The covalent or ionic bonds that may be formed are: (a) amide linkages between a free carboxyl and a free amino group

(—CO.NH—); (b) salt bridges (H-bonding) involving an imino and a carbonyl group; (c) ester linkages between free hydroxyl and carboxyl groups (—CO.O—); (d) two thiol groups that may be oxidized to produce an —S—S— disulfide bond.

Through any one or more of these, chains may react laterally to form a lattice, or bonding within the chain may lead to folding, in which case albumins or globulins may be produced, which may be as long as fibrous proteins but which are considerably wider since they involve large numbers of chains held randomly together. The state of the albumin or the globulin is, however, an unstable one. Comparatively mild treatment may induce loosening of the structure with a consequent unfolding. When this occurs the proteins are said to be denatured, and they then tend to precipitate. This characteristic reaction has made the study of cytoplasmic proteins a matter of considerable difficulty.

Many of the characteristics of proteins are associated with the amphoteric nature of the molecule. Each protein carries free amino and free carboxyl groups in side chains. The proportion of each of these, however, varies and the reaction to the hydrogen ion concentration of the solution will, therefore, also vary. In crude terms, as the acidity of the medium increases the ionization of the basic groups is enhanced and that of acidic groups depressed. Thus, as the hydrogen ion concentration is changed progressively, the dissociation of one set will tend to increase while that of the other decreases, and in the course of the progressive change a point will be traversed at which the numbers of oppositely charged groups will be the same. The hydrogen ion concentration at which this state is reached, the isoelectric point, will vary with the relative numbers of acidic carboxyl and basic amino groups. Thus, the isoelectric point will vary with the type of protein involved. Other properties inevitably change with the degree of ionization, and at the isoelectric point the degree of hydration is least and the probability of precipitation greatest.

Cytoplasm contains a large variety of proteins, but it has been shown that their isoelectric points usually lie within a range of pH 4 to 6 (64).

The reactions of proteins with inorganic ions are of considerable importance. Different carboxyl groups may be linked together through divalent cations, such as calcium. Also the general properties of protein gels may be affected by alkaline cations and certain anions. These may induce the gel to swell, and the degree of swelling varies with the ionic radius and, therefore, with the diameter of the hydration shell. The proteins may remain independent, and this is the case with simple proteins. The complex variety of terminal groups on the side chains, however, provides the condition for binding with other molecular species. Largely through van der Waals' forces and hydrogen bonding, conjugated proteins are produced. In these the polypeptide is associated with carbohydrates in mucoproteins, with lipids in lipoproteins, and with nucleic acids in nucleoproteins. Enzymes are proteins, some of which are conjugated, but the nonprotein moiety, which is either a prosthetic group or a coenzyme, varies.

B. FATS AND LIPIDS

Various fatty acids may be esterified by an alcohol to form a wax. In these a single molecule of the acid is involved with a single molecule of the alcohol. In the fats the alcohol is replaced by glycerol, and in this case the three fatty acid molecules form ester linkages with the hydroxyl groups of the glycerol.

```
          O
          ‖
CH2O.C.R1
|
|         O
|         ‖
CHO.C.R2
|
|         O
|         ‖
CH2O.C.R3
```

$$
\begin{array}{l}
CH_2O.\overset{\displaystyle O}{\overset{\|}{C}}.R_1 \\
| \\
CHO.\overset{\displaystyle O}{\overset{\|}{C}}.R_2 \\
| \\
CH_2O.\overset{\displaystyle O}{\overset{\|}{C}}.R_3
\end{array}
$$

(XIII)

The fatty acids are a large group and they are of two types, the saturated ($C_nH_{2n}O_2$) and the unsaturated acids which contain one or more ethylenic or acetylenic bonds. They are both long-chain compounds having a methyl group at one end and a carboxyl at the other The unsaturated acids differ from the saturated in having an ethylenic linkage at some point in the chain. In the triglyceride formula (XIII) the groups R_1, R_2, and R_3 are commonly different. Thus in a common fat, R_1 is stearic acid, $CH_3(CH_2)_{16}$—; R_2 is oleic acid, $CH_3(CH_2)_7CH$:$CH(CH_2)_7$—; and R_3 is palmitic acid, $CH_3(CH_2)_{14}$—.

While the fatty acids are polar compounds, the fats are not. The fats do not carry hydrophilic groups and they cannot therefore be associated with hydrophilic compounds.

The phospholipids are a vitally important group of compounds which are related to the fats. They are derived from phosphatidic acid formula (XIV), which is formed by the esterification of one of the alcohol groups of glycerol not with a fatty acid but with phosphoric acid.

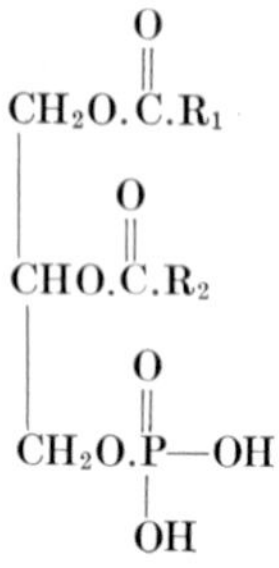

$$
\begin{array}{l}
CH_2O.\overset{\displaystyle O}{\overset{\|}{C}}.R_1 \\
| \\
CHO.\overset{\displaystyle O}{\overset{\|}{C}}.R_2 \\
| \\
CH_2O.\overset{\displaystyle O}{\overset{\|}{P}}\text{—}OH \\
\qquad\quad\ \ | \\
\qquad\quad OH
\end{array}
$$

(XIV)

In the phospholipid, the phosphoric acid of the phosphatidic acid is further combined with a nitrogenous base. In lecithin (formula XV) the base is choline.

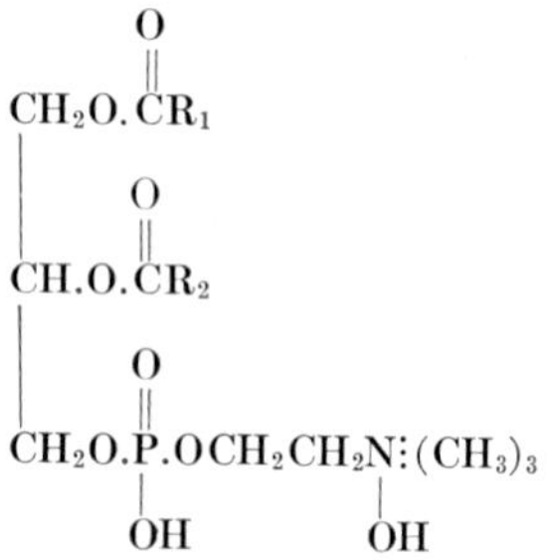

$$
\begin{array}{l}
CH_2O.\overset{\displaystyle O}{\overset{\|}{C}}R_1 \\
| \\
CH.O.\overset{\displaystyle O}{\overset{\|}{C}}R_2 \\
| \\
CH_2O.\overset{\displaystyle O}{\overset{\|}{P}}.OCH_2CH_2N{:}(CH_3)_3 \\
\qquad\quad\ \ | \qquad\qquad\quad | \\
\qquad\quad OH \qquad\quad\ \ OH
\end{array}
$$

(XV)

Lecithin may be taken as a type of what is probably a large group of compounds. In both phosphatidic acid and the phospholipid only one of the hydroxyl groups of the glycerol is esterified by phosphoric acid. The other two (R_1 and R_2) are combined with fatty acids as in normal fats.

The lecithin molecule is polar and it carries a hydrophilic group attached to the phosphoric acid, while the other two side chains have the typical structure of esterified fatty acids and are hydrophobic.

The structure shown in formula XV is that of α-lecithin. β-lecithin, which may also occur, is esterified with the phosphoric acid in the intermediate hydroxyl group. This compound may be compared in shape to a tuning fork, the handle of which carries the hydrophilic group, and the prongs of which carry the hydrophobic radicals. The α-compound may be similarly envisaged, at least in crude terms, although here the hydrophilic group will not, of course, be in exactly the same position relative to the hydrophobic groups.

The fatty acids are polar compounds which may be spread in monolayers at a surface between water and an organic solvent and between water and air. At a water-benzene interface the carboxyl groups of oleic acid, for instance, are attracted to the water and the methyl groups at the other end of the chain, to the benzene. At an air-water interface in a compressed film the carboxyl groups are still immersed in the water while the methyl groups project into the air, and the film is relatively stable since the individual chains are held together laterally by attraction between the hydrocarbon residues.

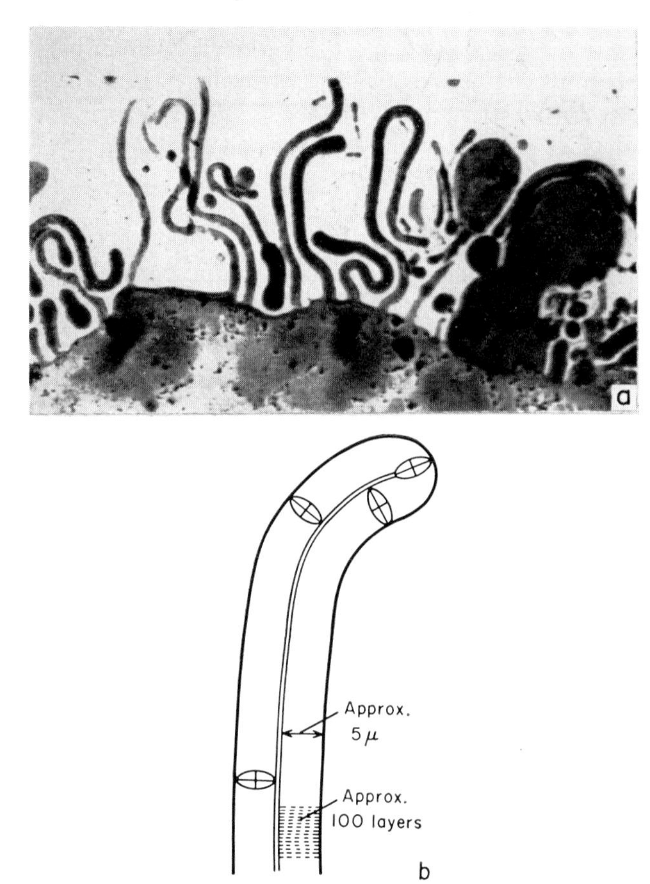

FIG. 10. a. Myelin figures from *Allium cepa* cell protoplasts. From Gicklhorn (33). b. Structure of myelin figure from lecithin. From Frey-Wyssling (28).

A phenomenon similar to that of the formation of oriented monolayers is shown by phospholipids in the development of myelin figures, which are also formed by the alkali salts of the fatty acids. Myelin figures show certain features which are of considerable importance in other connections. When lecithin is exposed to water, it may form a complex system of intertwining cylindrical extensions. These are semifluid and birefringent. They are formed by the lecithin molecules becoming aligned transversely to the lengths of the extensions and in layers, in which the hydrophobic chains are associated together and the hydrophilic ends are associated with phases of water (Fig. 10b). The birefringence is a consequence of the regular alignment of the lipoid in what is tantamount to a crystalline pattern.

Myelin figures may be obtained from plant cells. They are developed for instance in the vacuolar sap of *Allium cepa* epidermis cells after treatment with ammonia or potassium hydroxide. (Fig. 10a). The long tubular strands extend from the surface of the protoplast as a result of the reaction of the alkali with the fats and lipoids of the protoplast (33).

C. Nucleic Acids

These are high polymers in which the fundamental unit is not a single molecular type but is a complex entity—a nucleotide which consists of three distinct compounds (a) an organic base, (b) a sugar, and (c) a phosphoric acid residue. The bases and the sugars in the nucleotide vary.

The bases in nucleic acids as a whole are the purines, adenine (formula XVI) and guanine (formula XVII); and the pyrimidines, cytosine (formula XVIII), 5-methyl cytosine (formula XIX), uracil (formula XX), and thymine (formula XXI).

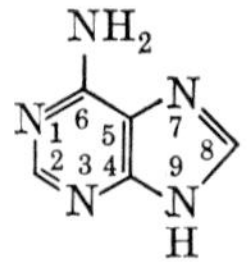

NH_2 N N N N H (XVI) — OH N N H_2N N N (XVII) — NH_2 N HO N (XVIII)

NH_2 CH_3 N HO N (XIX) — OH N HO N (XX) — OH CH_3 N HO N (XXI)

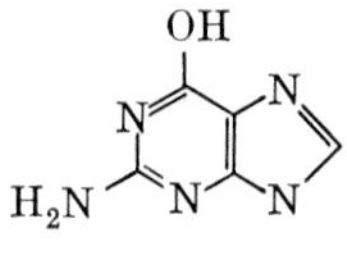

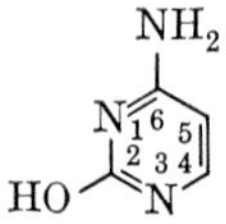

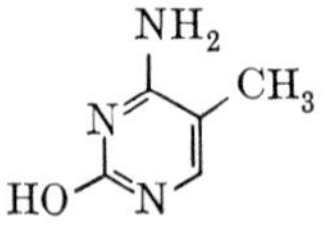

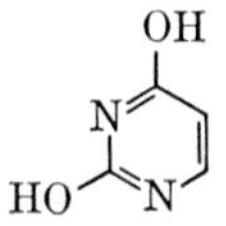

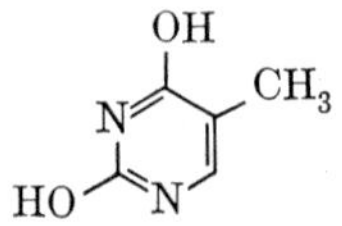

It may be noted that bases having a hydroxyl group at position 6 tautomerize and the form shown above is in equilibrium with the alternative structure, thus:

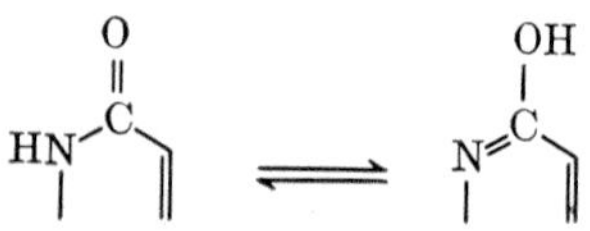

$$\mathrm{HN{-}C({=}O){-}} \rightleftharpoons \mathrm{N{=}C(OH){-}}$$

Also where a hydroxyl group is shown at position 2 this state is in equilibrium with tautomeric form, thus:

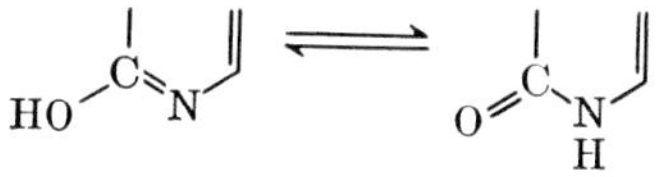

HO—C=N— ⇌ O=C—NH—

The effect of the tautomerism in the first case is to provide a keto group in position 6 and in the second to provide the configuration at position 3 through which a glycosidic linkage can be formed (see below).

The sugars in nucleic acids are ribose (α-D-ribofuranose) (formula XXII) and deoxyribose (2-deoxy-α-D-ribofuranose) (formula XXIII).

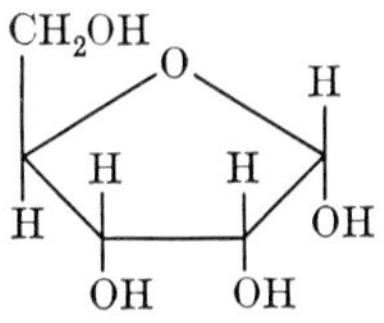

CH_2OH O H H H H OH OH OH

(XXII)

CH_2OH O H H H H OH OH H

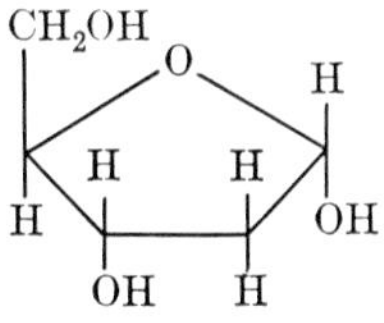

(XXIII)

As indicated above the three components of the polymer are organized into a series of nucleotides. A glycosidic linkage is established between the sugar and the base, the linkage being between position 1 on the sugar and position 9 (formula XXIV, adenosine-3-phosphate) on a purine or position 3 on a pyrimidine (formula XXV, cytidine-3-phosphate).

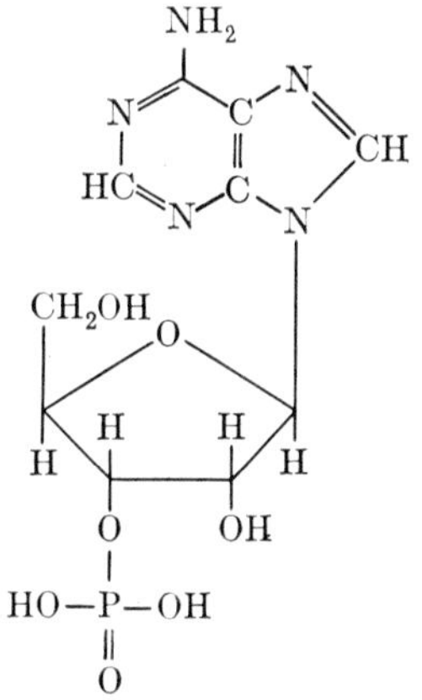

NH_2 N C N CH HC N C N CH_2OH O H H H H O OH HO—P—OH O

(XXIV)

NH_2 N CH HO·C N CH CH_2OH O H H H H O OH HO—P—OH O

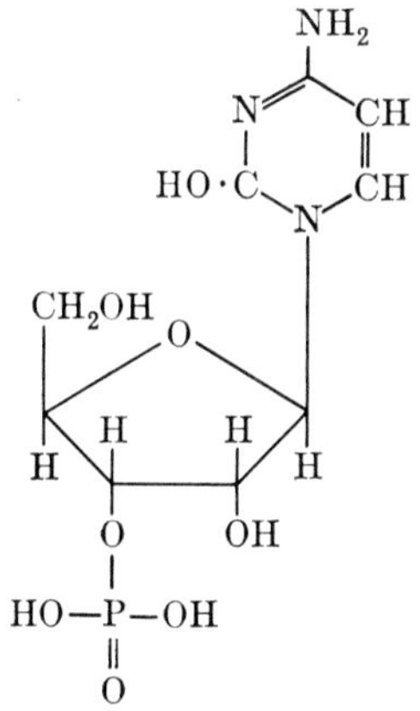

(XXV)

In the polymer the nucleotides are linked through the phosphoric acid groups, each of which is attached to the sugar residue of the next nucleotide, and the structure of the polymer may be represented as shown in (XXVa).

The internucleotide linkage is to position 5 on the sugar, and the structure of the polymer may also be shown as in (XXVb).

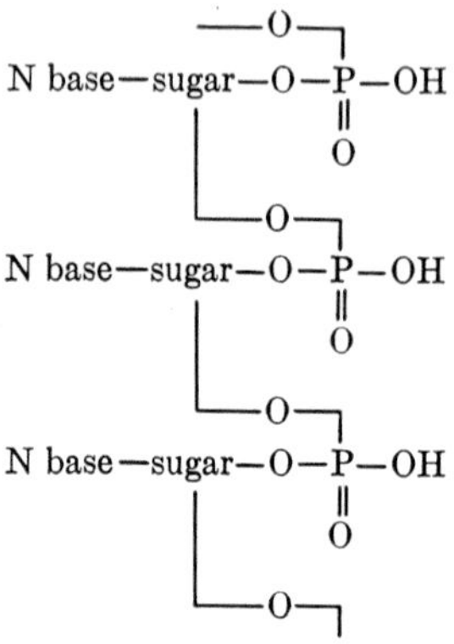

```
                 —O—┐
N base—sugar—O—P—OH
        |       ‖
        |       O
        └——O—┐
N base—sugar—O—P—OH
        |       ‖
        |       O
        └——O—┐
N base—sugar—O—P—OH
        |       ‖
        |       O
        └——O—┐
```

(XXVa)

```
                 \
           ortho phosphoric acid
                      \
          Ribose
N base— [C(1)      C(3)      C(5)]
                    \
           ortho phosphoric acid
                      \
          Ribose
N base— [C(1)      C(3)      C(5)]
                    \
           ortho phosphoric acid
                      \
          Ribose
N base— [C(1)      C(3)      C(5)]
                    \
           ortho phosphoric acid
                      \
```

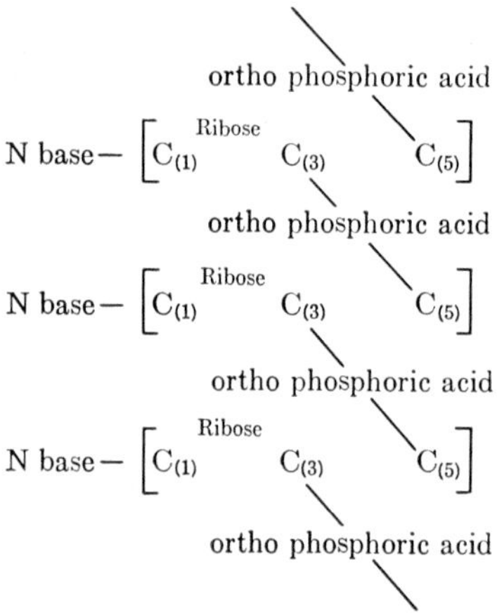

(XXVb)

It is evident that the structure involves one acidic group, being free on each phosphoric acid residue, and this endows the whole molecule with markedly acidic properties. It is by virtue of this that nucleic acids combine readily with basic substances, and notably with the basic groups of proteins.

Two separate nucleic acids have been identified, ribonucleic acid and deoxyribonucleic acid; the first is commonly referred to as RNA and the second, as DNA. The two types of compounds differ with respect to base and sugar composition. RNA incorporates adenine, guanine, cytosine, uracil, and ribose. DNA, on the other hand, contains adenine, guanine, cytosine, 5-methylcytosine, thymine, and deoxyribose. The differences in composition are associated with different staining reactions. RNA stains with pyronine and DNA with methyl green. DNA also gives the Schiff reaction in the Feulgen procedure.

In any one RNA or DNA the constituent bases are not present in the same proportion. Each base does not provide 25% of the whole. Below analyses are given of the base composition of the total RNA and total DNA extracted from pea (*Pisum sativum*) roots (37).

TABLE II
BASE COMPOSITION OF NUCLEIC ACIDS FROM THE TERMINAL CENTIMETER OF SEEDLING PEA (*Pisum sativum*) ROOTS

Bases	Mols (%)	Ratios[a]
RNA: Guanine (G)	29.0	Pu:Py = 1.205
Cytosine (C)	22.1	
Uracil (U)	23.3	(G + U):(C + A) = 1.097
Adenine (A)	25.6	
DNA: Guanine	20.3	Pu:Py = 1.076
Cytosine	14.8	
5-Methylcytosine	5.1	(G + T):(A + C) = 0.943
Adenine	31.5	
Thymine (T)	28.2	

[a] Pu = purine; Py = pyrimidine.

Within any one species the total extractable RNA or DNA does not vary markedly in base composition. This is in contrast to the position with proteins, the amino acid compositions of which are likely to differ according as to whether they are extracted from, say, roots or leaves. The constancy within a species is particularly rigid with DNA.

In contrast as between species, the base composition of the nucleic acid, and particularly of DNA, varies very considerably. With respect to DNA, however, whatever the variation, certain constant analytical features are always found. It has been shown that in a statistical sense all forms of DNA, whatever their origin, show the following characteristics: (a) The purine to pyrimidine ratio is always unity. (b) The adenine to thymine ratio is always unity. (c) The guanine to cytosine ratio is always unity. (d) The ratio of 6-amino to 6-keto bases is always unity. This in effect means that the ratio of guanine and thymine to adenine and cytosine is unity. (Cytosine is interpreted in terms of this substance + 5-methylcytosine.)

Constant features similar to those found in DNA have not been recorded with RNA, although there is some indication that even in RNA the ratio of 6-amino to 6-keto bases is also unity.

Both groups of compounds are highly polymerized substances. After extraction, RNA usually has a lower molecular weight than DNA. RNA is the more labile of the two, and it is possible that its apparently

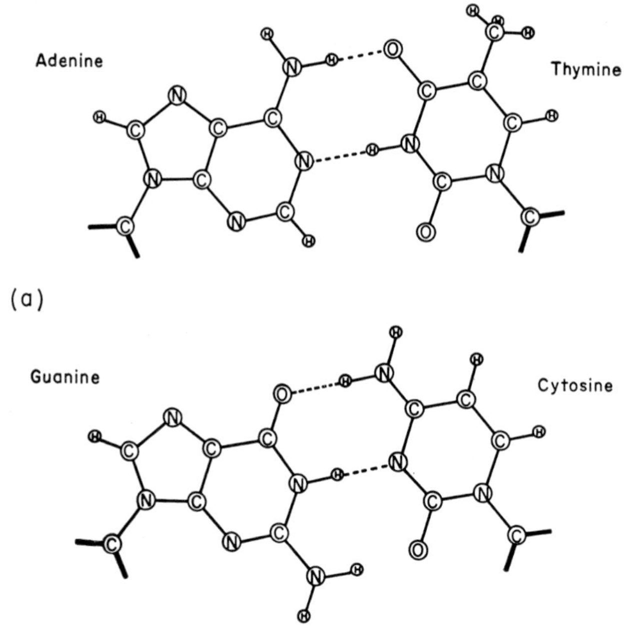

Adenine Thymine

(a)

Guanine Cytosine

Fig. 11. a. Postulated hydrogen bonding between bases in DNA complex, according to the Watson-Crick formulation.

lower molecular weight is a consequence of degradation during extraction. DNA after isolation tends to have a molecular weight which varies between one million and five million. The high lability of RNA has made the study of its molecular structure a matter of some difficulty. The greater stability of DNA has made it a more convenient material for investigation, and consequently more is known of its molecular architecture.

DNA after extraction may be obtained in a paracrystalline form which gives a sharp, but very complicated, X-ray diffraction diagram. Complicated as it is, however, the diffraction diagram has provided the basis for the elucidation of the structure of the molecule. Basically the molecule is a straight chain polynucleotide, and it involves the important feature that the backbone chain is formed from alternate sugar and phosphate residues. The bases are not components of the chain; they are carried laterally from the axial sugar residues. This feature is evident from the structural diagrams given above. The current model of the structure of DNA indicates that the polynucleotide is in the form of a helix and that helices tend to be associated in pairs in a highly characteristic configuration. The two helices are wound in the same way about a common axis, although the two chains run in opposite directions (Fig. 11,b). The pitch of each spiral is 34 A and the diameter 20 A. The two helices are held together rigidly, and the nature of the attachment between the two is one of the most important features of the whole structure. The evidence indicates that the chains are held together by hydrogen bonding between opposite bases on the two spirals. In Fig. 11,b the bars between the two spirals represent pairs of associated bases. As a result of the mode of attachment, the center of the compound structure is occupied by the associated bases and the alternate sugar and phosphate groups are on the external exposed ridges of the system. Further it may be noted that the association of the two helices, with the spiral pitch required, involves two sets of grooves, one relatively narrow and shallow, and the other relatively wide and deep.

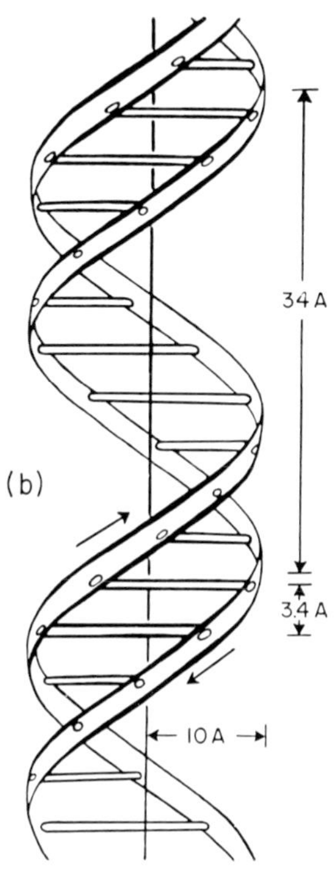

FIG. 11. b. Double spiral structure in DNA complex, after Watson and Crick, from Jordan (49).

It is suggested that hydrogen bonding is between 6-amino and 6-keto groups (Fig. 11,a) and that geometrical considerations require bonding to occur only between a purine and a pyrimidine. This second requirement would necessarily involve a molar equivalence between purine and pyrimidine. Secondly, if bonding is between 6-keto and 6-amino groups, then the ratio between them must be unity. Also if adenine, which carries an amino group in the 6-position must link with a pyrimidine carrying a keto group, then it can link only with thymine; and similarly guanine can link only with cytosine. With these restrictive conditions the ratio between adenine and thymine, and that between guanine and cytosine, must be unity. It is significant that the ratio required by the model built up from X-ray data have (as shown above) been found experimentally.

It is an important feature of the model that it does not require that the number of adenine-thymine and guanine-cytosine pairs should be the same. The constant features of the DNA system will be given by any combination of these pairs, and it is undoubtedly variations in the proportions of the two pairs that give the differences in base composition between extracts from different species. Deoxy acids from different species tend to fall into two groups, the "GC" type, in which guanine and cytosine predominate, and the "AT" type, in which adenine and thymine are the most abundant. The associations within each type might be expected from the observed regularities. For instance if the ratio between adenine and thymine is unity, then with high adenine there must be high thymine content.

As mentioned above, the base composition of DNA from the same species is remarkably constant. Whatever the organ or whatever the age of the tissue, the base composition of the DNA remains the same. This was, and probably still is, held to be a fact of considerable importance. At the same time it is significant that the DNA that is extracted from any tissue is not a single molecular species. Chargaff (17) has shown that by using as solvents a series of sodium chloride solutions increasing in concentration from 0.2 to 1.0 *M*, the DNA from calf thymus can be separated into a series of fractions, each with a distinctive and different base composition. Each fraction shows all the analytical characteristics of DNA enumerated above, but the relative abundance of each pyrimidine with its associated purine nevertheless varies.

Differences in base composition do not exhaust the possibilities of variability. Even when the bases present are the same, the molecules may nevertheless be different. The nucleotides are arranged in a serial order, and even with the same composition the sequence may clearly vary considerably.

It is probable that in the cell nucleic acid is always present as the prosthetic group of a conjugated protein, the combination being due to linkage between the free acidic groups of the nucleic acid and the basic groups in the side chains of the protein.

For an excellent short account of the nucleic acids, Overend and Peacocke (63) may be consulted.

IX. Distribution of Compounds in the Cell

While the gross composition of the protoplast is of interest for the purpose of analyzing the dynamic properties of the system, the distribution of particular compounds within the cell is possibly of greater significance. For the analysis of activity it is clearly as important to determine the distribution of, say, phospholipids in the different components of the protoplast as it is to establish the total quantity of phospholipid in the cell.

The determination of the quantitative distribution of particular compounds presents considerable technical difficulties and appropriate techniques have only recently been developed. In principle two different procedures may be used. The first involves maceration of the tissue, followed by separation of the different organelles by centrifugation of a homogenate. The second involves the determination of the quantity of a particular substance in the intact cell by the application of certain chemical techniques on a cytological scale.

The maceration and centrifugation procedure is described in greater detail below. Here it may be noted that the maceration is designed to break the wall system and to release the protoplast into a fluid in which different particulates are allegedly not disrupted. In the centrifugation stages differences in size and density of the particles are exploited. With a controlled speed of rotation the longer and denser particles are deposited first and the smallest and least dense last. Thus in principle different fractions may be separated from a homogenate, each of which may be taken to represent a particular category of organelles. Also a residue is available after centrifugation which may be derived from the continuous phase of the cytoplasm. Finally, conventional procedures may be applied to each of the isolated fractions, and the distribution within the cell of particular chemical constituents thus determined (44).

The alternative approach of determining localization in an intact cellular system is more complicated and burdened with more subtle difficulties. In a sense it is the more attractive, and potentially it may ultimately yield the more valuable information. So far, however, the results of applying cytochemical techniques have not been generally impressive, although there have been one or two spectacular successes.

The simplest form of the cytochemical procedure is that in which a beam of light is passed, either with or without staining, through a cell and absorption in particular wavelengths determined. The apparatus necessary for this technique is extremely elaborate. Since it may involve passing a beam through a limited area of a cell, it necessarily involves incorporating a microscopic system into a spectrophotometric assembly. Further, the intensity of the transmitted beam may be low and the charge in intensity at particular wavelengths slight, thus an elaborate recording system is required. The major difficulty with cytochemical spectrophotometry, however, arises from diffraction in the specimen. The incident light does not of course pass through a homogeneous system, and scatter may be substantial. Unfortunately a correction for this is difficult to apply since with different specimens the degree of heterogeneity and the thickness may vary.

The technique may be applied either with or without staining. It may be used without staining when the distribution is being examined of a compound which has a sharp absorption maximum either in the visible or the ultraviolet regions. It has been used for the determination of the intracellular distribution of nucleic acids which have an absorption peak at about 260 μ; of chlorophylls which have a peak at about 420 μ; and of reduced cytochrome C with a peak at 55 μ.

Many cellular substances give colored products when treated with particular reagents, and in principle it is possible to determine the quantity of the colored product by measuring the absorption after passing a monochromatic beam through a particular part of the specimen. Clearly this technique can be used safely only when the reaction is highly specific. When, in fact, it can be assumed that with a particular reagent the color is given only by a particular substance or a particular group of substances. This ideal state is only occasionally realized. Moreover, the necessary condition that the color obtained should not be interfered with by other substances is even more rarely found. Nevertheless, the quantitative estimation of colored compounds has been used with notable success in some connections.

When staining is not involved, the observations can be made on living cells, in which case fixation is not a necessary preliminary step of the procedure. When staining is involved, however, some form of fixation is clearly essential. With staining the cell almost certainly has to be killed and, unless rigid and effective fixation is used, some components might be displaced and others lost from the tissue altogether. The necessity for fixation introduces another difficulty. No chemical fixatives are known which will anchor all components of the cell. A fixative has to be chosen which is appropriate for the determination that is being undertaken, but even then it is extremely difficult to exclude all possibility of diffusion and consequent displacement from an original site.

Some of the difficulties of the cytochemical approach are mitigated when the substance whose distribution is being studied can also be removed from the cell without disturbing other components. In that case, the determination with the substance in position may be compared with another carried out after it has been removed. This provides an extremely valuable control and may be used when a pure enzyme is available which acts selectively on a particular substrate. Recently several enzymes have become available in a pure, crystalline state, and some have been used in cytochemical tests. The most popular of these have been ribonuclease and deoxyribonuclease. These are hydrolytic enzymes which act on the corresponding nucleic acids. They act on the backbone chain and degrade the polymer to single nucleotides or to fragments containing a limited number of nucleotides. In either case the fragment is dislodged from the tissue and dispersed into the suspending medium. All of the nucleic acid is not hydrolyzed. Both RNA and DNA carry "cores" which are resistant to the enzymes. The core, however, is a small proportion of the total complement and is sufficiently small to be disregarded, especially in view of the high errors inevitably associated with all cytochemical methods.

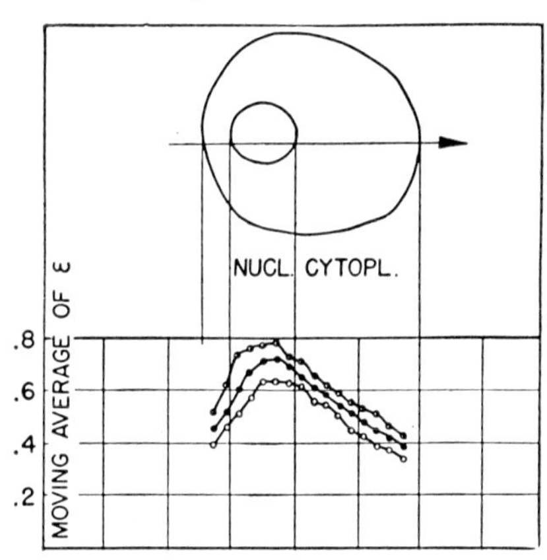

FIG. 12. Ultraviolet light absorption in different parts of the cell. From Caspersson (14). (E on ordinate = extinction coefficient.)

The greatest successes of the cytochemical method have been obtained with the nucleic acids and in spite of all the difficulties with the cytochemical procedure the experience with the nucleic acids suggests that ultimately similar results may be obtained with other substances. Caspersson (14) has used the technique of ultraviolet absorption for the determination of nucleic acids with notable success (Fig. 12). Several workers, notably Swift (83), have determined DNA cytochemically after Feulgen staining.

Since the Feulgen reaction has been so extensively exploited, its characteristics as a model for other cytochemical work are worth noting. In the standard procedure the tissue is fixed in acetic alcohol and then treated for 15 minutes with 1.0 *N* HCl at 60°C. This treatment with plant tissue has the incidental effect of converting a calcium pectate into pectic acid and thus loosening the binding between adjacent cells. The most significant effect of the acid treatment is on the DNA. It apparently hydrolyzes the glycosidic linkage between purine and the deoxy sugar. It does not affect the pyrimidine-sugar linkage, but tends to give for the whole molecule the apurinic acid structure (17). While breaking the purine-sugar linkage, the acid treatment also converts the subsequent free sugar into an aldehyde. The particular substance being, it is said, ω-hydroxy levulinic aldehyde, which, since it is presumably still attached to phosphate radicals on either side, remains in position on the protein. After washing, the tissue is transferred to the Schiff's reagent, which is a sulfonated fuchsin solution. The reagent colors the DNA a characteristic red, the intensity of which may be measured by spectrophotometric techniques. The Feulgen reaction has been used extensively in quantitative studies, and there is now little doubt of its validity. It is evident, however, that the value of the method depends on the following three circumstances; the reagent evidently reacts only with the DNA, the color developed (in the conditions of the cytological procedure) is not influenced by interfering substances, and the nucleic acid itself is highly localized. At the same time it is clear that the effective use of the method requires rigid sandardization with respect to fixation, acid treatment, and staining with the Feulgen reagent (51).

In the above discussion of cytochemical methods, their use has been considered in terms of the determination of the distribution of particular constituents in the cell. In certain circumstances it may be valuable to have data for the whole cell. Average values are readily obtained, but occasionally information may be necessary on the values for individual cells. Such data can be obtained with the cytochemical techniques described for localization of particular components, and the difficulties in this case are not as formidable as those indicated earlier. In particular, diffusion artifacts may be disregarded when whole-cell values are being determined.

Cytochemical data for localization within the cell, when they have been obtained, may raise a further difficulty. When values are available, the problem remains of the terms in which they should be stated. With whole tissue the amount of any particular substance may be expressed in terms of fresh or dry weight. Until recently a corresponding standard has not been available for cytochemical determinations. The introduction of the interference microscope, however, has mitigated this difficulty. By the use of this instrument it may in certain circumstances be possible to determine the dry matter in a particular organelle. This technique, which depends on the measurement of the phase change that occurs when light encounters a density change in the medium, is clearly one of considerable importance in a variety of connections. It is, however, in particular of considerable promise for the general development of cytochemistry (3).

X. Mesoplasm

The cytoplasm in mature vacuolated plant cells, is confined within a layer about 1.0 μ thick and can be observed only with difficulty. Frequently its characteristics cannot be determined directly, and these often have to be inferred by analogy from those of other protoplasmic systems which are more accessible. This introduces an element of uncertainty into the discussion, especially as in some of its gross features the cytoplasm of the mature plant cell is patently different from that of other organisms. Nevertheless, from this embarrassment there is at present no escape and reference to other systems when indications of the position in plant cells are required cannot be avoided.

The next three sections are devoted to a discussion of the structure of the protoplast. The position in the continuous phase of the cytoplasm is considered first, and this is treated in two sections dealing respectively with the mesoplasm and with the two boundary membranes. Since the vacuole is an integral feature of the protoplast a short discussion of this structure is provided before the detailed treatment of the cytoplasmic inclusions begins.

The material of this section is confined to the structure of the mesoplasm, and the interpretation that is presented is derived from the results of two different groups of investigations. The first group involves physical observations which have continued over at least the last fifty years, and the second involves electron microscope studies that have been developed during about the last ten years.

The mesoplasm is that part of the continuous phase of the cytoplasm which is between the two boundary membranes. It is extremely difficult if not impossible to make determinations on the physical properties of this phase in a system which does not include the surface membranes. Observations on the whole cytoplasm, however, are likely to show primarily the position in the mesoplasm, since the proportion of the whole which is in the boundary layers is relatively small. Accordingly physical conditions in the mesoplasm are frequently inferred below from the results of experiments based on the whole protoplast.

No determinations of the composition of the ground phase of the cytoplasm have been published. Cytochemical tests, however, show that a great deal of it is composed of protein and that it contains phospholipids; certain observations indicate that it incorporates RNA. General considerations suggest that it contains soluble carbohydrates and inorganic ions. In addition it may of course incorporate some or all of the metabolic products of the cell, but the substances mentioned are probably those that contribute most to the dry matter of the system.

The continuous phase of the cytoplasm when it can be examined in bulk is a gray hyaline mass with fluid properties. It is optically empty although small particles (often fat droplets) embedded in it may show the rapid oscillation characteristic of Brownian movement. This phenomenon, which is due to the random impact of molecules in solution, is characteristic of many colloidal suspensions, and this and a slight viscous consistency were the basis for the colloidal theory of cytoplasmic structure. In its original form this theory provided for a sol structure with droplets of hydrated protein and other substances as the disperse phase suspended in a solution of sugars and inorganic salts representing the continuous phase. Many hydrophilic sols do indeed have the general consistency of mesoplasm. If it is a sol in the terms suggested, then it is difficult to understand how it maintains its cohesion in water, and this it certainly does. Secondly, it is difficult to reconcile this interpretation with the observation that mechanical deformation impairs general activity.

It has been shown (61) that when the plasmodium of a myxomycete is allowed to flow through a sieve, the organism apparently remains intact. When, on the other hand, it is forced through the sieve under pressure it may not survive. This immediately suggests that the cytoplasm carries structural components which may accomodate themselves to gradual displacement but which may be disrupted by abrupt deformation. It suggests, in fact, that the mesoplasm is not so much a simple colloid as a system which is held together by an organized structural framework. This framework could be a system of interlocking random fibers as in a gel, and this interpretation is consistent with the results of certain studies on viscosity.

The viscosity of cytoplasm is a theme which has been investigated very elaborately over a considerable number of years. It has been measured by a variety of techniques, the most prominent of which are based on the measurement of the rate of fall of a body of known density through unit distance or on the determination of the amplitude of the Brownian movement. With increasing viscosity the rate of fall of a particle and the amplitude of the oscillation both decrease. One series of measurements has shown that when the viscosity of water is taken as 1.0, that of the cytoplasm in the epidermal cells of *Allium cepa* has the value of 2.0 and in the parenchyma cells in the stem of *Vicia faba* it has a value of 24.0.

With regard to the structure of mesoplasm, the studies of the effect of shear stress on viscosity are particularly significant. When a simple solution of say, sugar, is caused to flow through a capillary, the viscosity of the liquid does not change with increasing pressure and in this respect it behaves as a Newtonian fluid. With a suspension of a solution of a fibrous macromolecular substance, however, viscosity may decrease with increasing pressure. Flow through a capillary is accompanied by the development of a shear stress between the liquid and the walls of the vessel, and with increasing pressure the shear also increases. In an undisturbed suspension of fibrous molecules these interlock and so promote a relatively high viscosity. The same effect may be observed with cytoplasm. It has been shown with isolated protoplasts from a number of plants that when they are drawn into a capillary under pressure and Brownian movement subsequently measured, then as the pressure is increased, viscosity decreases. The interpretation for this could be the same as it is with other non-Newtonian fluids. Mesoplasm, it might be suggested, is traversed by long polypeptide chains that are randomly distributed and locked together in much the same way as sticks in an untidy heap. This pattern, it might be suggested further, endows the cytoplasm with viscosity which, limited though it is, nevertheless decreases with increasing pressure during flow through a capillary, since the chains become progressively more independent as they become progressively more aligned. Pfeiffer (65) has shown that during flow through the capillary, cytoplasm becomes birefringent. It is not anisotropic in normal circumstances, and this observation therefore tends to support the view that the decreasing viscosity is due to an alignment of normally random threads (28).

The random thread structure, if it exists, is presumably held together by sporadic attachments between the different chains. At the same time these attachments must be comparatively weak. Cytoplasm is a thixotropic colloid, and in certain connections it displays elastic properties. Many gels, and among them gelatin and clay, may be converted to the sol state by simple shaking. The viscosity of cytoplasm may also be depressed by gentle mechanical disturbance. In these cases, attachments between the suspended particles have been loosened by the agitation, and the attachments must therefore be comparatively weak ones and due to weak van der Waals' forces. Where elastic properties are displayed another order of linking must be involved altogether. The elasticity of the mesoplasm is difficult to estimate, but some it probably has (see below). The boundary membranes are certainly elastic, and in these cases covalent bonding between the chains may well be involved. The bonds may be any one or all of those listed above. It is now well established that in albumin gels, in which the structure is again due to interlocking fibers, cohesion is maintained through disulfide S-S linkages between the chains (46).

The interpretation of cytoplasmic ground-phase structure in terms of a system of randomly interlocked fibers has to meet the objection that the consistency of this phase is certainly not that of a gel. The water content is high (see above) and the viscosity, although higher than that of water, is still comparatively low. The recorded relative viscosities for cytoplasm may, for instance, be compared with that for glycerol, which is 87. On the other hand, it is relevant that many sols with a low viscosity have been shown to have a fiber structure and, however high the viscosity of glycerol may be, it is also relevant that it does not show structural viscosity. Moreover, it is certainly the case that a firm gel-like consistency is readily induced in cytoplasm. Relatively weak agitation may decrease viscosity, but violent shock induces it to set to a firm jelly in which all Brownian movement is arrested.

The long fibers that, from the evidence presented above, constitute the structural framework are almost certainly proteins. These, it may be supposed, are randomly interlocked and leave a considerable intermediate space through which liquid could circulate. The liquid volume is likely to be greater than any other and is probably occupied by a fluid with various organic metabolites and inorganic salts in solution, and possibly with fatty substances in suspension. The fluid may also carry other proteins, but this possibility is discussed more fully elsewhere.

It may be noticed that if the hypothesis of fiber structure were valid then the effect of various environmental conditions, on viscosity, would be due to effects on interchain linkages. It is of course not improbable that changes in metabolic activity that accompany change in temperature, light, and nutrient supply affect linking and particularly weak interchain linking. Even the maintenance of comparatively strong linkages such as those of disulfide bonds may well depend on the state of oxidation.

The interpretation developed above has until recently seemed to be at least plausible. Within the last few years, however, the results of investigations with the electron microscope have become available, and these indicate that the hypothesis of random fiber structure, while not irrelevant, requires at the very least considerable amplification.

In mammalian cells, fixed in osmium tetroxide, the whole cytoplasmic mass is traversed by a system of membranes, which constitutes the endoplasmic reticulum. They traverse the continuous matrix phase of the cytoplasm and frequently carry small granules, probably ribonucleoprotein particles.

A similar system has been seen in nonvacuolated plant cells, particularly after fixation with potassium permanganate.[1] A matrix has been shown to be present, and in a sense the reticulum ramifies throughout the matrix. An endoplasmatic reticulum has been reported in cells in which vacuolation has begun but not yet in fully mature plant cells; it has not, however, been excluded. The investigation of the cytoplasm of mature plant cells is particularly difficult, and convincing electron microscope photographs of mature cytoplasm have not yet been published.

In some respects it is difficult to see how the mesoplasm could have a complex structure. It has been shown above that it accommodates only about fifty protein layers at the most, and it is difficult to see how these could be constituted into an elaborate structural complex. At the same time it is equally difficult to imagine a state in which the mature cell does not inherit some characteristics of the endoplasmic reticulum from the nonvacuolated unit. It seems, indeed, highly probable that at least some features of the system are retained into the fully vacuolated state, and in that event the earlier hypothesis of cytoplasmic structure requires reconsideration.

While the membrane system of the endosplasmic reticulum is well defined, there is no evidence that it is anything but highly labile. The electron microscope observations themselves suggest this, and it is not improbable that the system is highly susceptible to shock, mechanical deformation, nutrient conditions, temperature, and so on. If this is the case then it is clearly possible to reconcile the fiber structure hypothesis with the electron microscope evidence. It is difficult to understand how changes in structural viscosity could be measured if the endoplasmic reticulum is a rigid unyielding structure.

In fact it probably is not present in the experimental conditions in which the physical observations are made. These necessarily involve considerable manipulation, and mechanical deformation of the system. It is possible that the shock involved disperses the reticulum and that the observations are in fact made on a cytoplasm which is characterized by a more or less random fiber structure. In these terms the two sets of observations complement each other. It may be supposed that the matrix contains protein in a state similar to that postulated by the fiber

[1] See Whalley *et al.* (1959). *J. Biophys. Biochem. Cytol.* **5**, 504–506.

structure. It may be further supposed that the membranes of the reticulum incorporate protein (and for this there is some evidence, see below). The protein of the membranes is no doubt in a condensed, closely packed form. On the other hand, if it is readily dispersed it cannot be held together by a strong bonding system; and even though there is a reticulum the protein is probably held in the membranes in much the same sort of way as the fiber structure postulates.

Thus the evidence indicates that the mesoplasm is indeed constituted of randomly dispersed fibers. The electron microscope evidence, however, suggests that these fibers are not dispersed with a uniform density. They tend to be sufficiently densely aggregated in certain zones to give membranes, and less densely in others to give an apparently structureless matrix. It is, of course, highly probable that the greater density (and possibly also the presence of phospholipids) endows the membranes with significant mechanical cohesion.

The interpretation proposed is of significance in several connections, but particularly with respect to the remarkable protoplasmic phenomenon of *cytoplasmic streaming*. This process is readily observed in a variety of cells and its rate is comparatively easily measured. It may be seen in the peripheral cytoplasm or in strands that stretch across the vacuole to a central nucleus. Wherever it occurs, it is emphasized by the movement of particles which may be at the limit of resolution or may be as large as chloroplasts. The rate is measured by observing the time required by particles of approximately the same size to traverse unit distance. It undoubtedly involves movement of the whole cytoplasm and not simply the movement of particles through a stationary fluid phase, and it may involve the bewildering feature of movement in opposite directions within a strand which may be less than 1 μ in diameter.

It is an important feature of the process that the whole cell is not involved. In the leaf parenchyma of *Elodea* (*Anacharis*), for instance, the streaming occurs in a narrow belt, and in the root hair, while cytoplasm tends to stream in and away from the tip, in the tip itself there is an apparently stationary mass.

In streaming, work is clearly being done and energy consumed. It is therefore not surprising to find that it is affected by all conditions that influence metabolic activity. The rate is depressed by anaerobic conditions, depressed by various respiratory inhibitors, accelerated by increasing temperature, and dependent on nutrient supply. However, since all other energy-consuming activities are similarly affected, protoplasmic streaming is not unique in these respects. On the other hand, an important contribution was made to the subject when the effects of high hydrostatic pressures were examined. In this investigation the pressure was applied directly to the surface of water in which the tissue was immersed and simultaneously the rate of streaming was determined. The pressures used were high, ranging from about 1000 to about 7000 pounds per square inch. It may be noted that since the pressure was applied directly to the surface of the liquid, the effects observed could not be due to increases in the quantities of gas in solution in the immersion fluid (55).

When pressures of the order of 1500 pounds per square inch are applied, streaming ceases, and when the pressure is released, the process is restored. The treatment has apparently no permanent injurious effect. Further, while high pressures have little effect on at least two vital processes, they do have marked effects on two other processes in addition to streaming. Ciliary movement and muscle contraction are apparently unaffected, while mitosis and amoeboid movement are immediately arrested. Clearly the treatment does not affect all vital activity and those processes that are affected all have the one feature in common that they involve a reversible gelation. The arrest in mitosis is apparently related to a solation in the cortex of the egg, and that in amoeboid movement to an inhibition of gel formation within the surfaces of the growing pseudopodia. That something similar is involved in streaming is indicated by measurements of viscosity under pressure. In this case the viscosity was estimated by observing the ease with which chloroplasts could be displaced to one end of the cell in a centrifugal field, and it was found that, while the displacement occurs rapidly under high pressure, it is relatively sluggish at atmospheric pressure. Clearly the evidence indicates very persuasively that the cessation in streaming is intimately linked to a general solation which implies a decrease in viscosity (55).

The effect of high pressure is not restricted to organized systems. It has been demonstrated with certain artificial gels whose formation is accompanied by swelling. With these, when pressure is applied solation occurs. The nature of the effect in the inanimate system has not been fully elucidated. In the cellular system it may well be due to breaking of lateral attachments between long polyteptides, which certainly promotes decrease in viscosity with other treatments. Even if this is the case, however, it is not clear how change in viscosity can affect streaming. It has been suggested that in normal circumstances, at a certain point in the cytoplasm, a sol is converted to a gel state, that this involves a change in elasticity, and that therefore as the gel is formed, so a tendency to contract is developed. Inevitably this exerts a traction on the rest of the sol phase (which has some cohesion) which draws it toward the point of gelation. This interpretation has the virtue that it shows how the prevention of gelation restricts the streaming. But, even if true, it leaves much unexplained and is at best inadequate. It may be noted that if the effect of pressure is to release lateral attachment, then, in the terms of the interpretation suggested above, this might involve the dissolution of the endoplasmic reticulum membrane system. The implication of this would be that streaming somehow depends on the integrity of a system of membranes. How the continuity of these could influence the position is not immediately apparent. The membrane system has one property that might make it significant, namely that it is continuous. It is conceivable that traction exerted at one point could draw a good deal of the membrane system, and therefore of the cytoplasm, to that point.

Whatever the interpretation of the pressure effect may be, unquestionably it demonstrates a connection between viscosity and cytoplasmic movement. Moreover, the streaming phenomenon indicates that changes in viscosity may be local. These two facts prompt a speculation with regard to the movements of organelles in cells. The observation has been recorded that mitochondria may move from one point to another in a cell, and this has been attributed to a capacity for autonomous movement (36). On the other hand, mitochondria undoubtedly produce a variety of substances which may well have a local effect on viscosity (and therefore on the endoplasmic reticulum) and this in turn, may promote a slow but definite movement of the whole cytoplasm which carries mitochondria along with it. Such an effect might, for instance, be induced by a local accumulation of adenosine triphosphate (ATP) which is produced in mitochondria and to which much of the streaming in amoeba has been attributed. A capacity of autonomous movement has also been attributed to chloroplasts, since these tend to migrate between transverse and longitudinal walls with change in light intensity. It is significant, however, that cytoplasmic viscosity may change very markedly when the cell is exposed to light. Further, it is possible that the change will not be uniform since it is highly improbable that the whole cell will be uniformly illuminated. Thus, it is possible that a local change in viscosity (and of firmness in cytoplasmic membrances) may occur which will promote a cytoplasmic movement which will carry the chloroplasts along with it. The movement involved here if indeed it occurs, must be considerably slower than that involved in streaming and may on that account escape observation.

XI. Surfaces of the Cytoplasm

The nature of the surface layers of the cytoplasm have been deduced from studies on the conditions that restrain the penetration of solutes into the vacuole, from observations on the physical properties of the surfaces, and from investigations with the electron microscope.

The conditions which control the penetration of solutes into the cell are of decisive importance in the economy of the cellular system, since the maintenance of metabolic activity must depend on an exchange of solutes with the environment. The subject is an extremely large and elaborate one (see Volume II), and it is certainly not the intention to provide a comprehensive treatment of it here. Only those aspects are considered which are of immediate relevance to the elucidation of the structure of the cytoplasm.

The entry of solutes into the cell as a whole does not occur with conditions of free diffusion. Several items of evidence indicate that barriers to free diffusion are present in the cytoplasm which restrain the movement of solutes. The resistance of tissue to a low-frequency alternating current is relatively high, but it tends to decrease as the frequency of the current is increased. This has been interpreted as an effect of the diffusion barriers. As the frequency increases the distance that ions must move diminishes, the restraining effect of barriers to ion movement decreases, and the resistance to the current consequently also decreases. The effect of barriers to diffusion is also shown in the classical experiment on plasmolysis. When a tissue is placed in a hypertonic solution, whether of an electrolyte or of a nonelectrolyte, the protoplast withdraws from the wall and contracts, in certain instances into a spherical mass in which a well-defined protoplast encloses a vacuole with an abnormally restricted volume. The original interpretation given to the phenomenon is still unimpeachable. It indicates (a) that the wall is completely permeable to water and all solutes, (b) that the cytoplasm as a whole constitutes a membrane system across which water moves more readily than solutes, and (c) that consequently when the tissue is placed in a hypertonic solution, water is withdrawn from the vacuole and discharged into the plasmolyzing fluid. A crucial aspect of this experiment may be emphasized. It is important to notice that the contraction of the protoplast is due to the withdrawal of water from the vacuole and may not be accompanied by the withdrawal of water from the cell as a whole. Many cells that do not have a vacuole also contract when they are immersed in hypertonic solutions, but these are undoubtedly covered by a membrane over the external surface across which the osmotic system operates, so that water is withdrawn from the whole cell. The simple plasmolysis situation does not indicate that a semipermeable system is present over the external surface of the protoplast and does not, therefore, indicate that water is withdrawn from the cytoplasm as well as from the vacuole.

The diffusion barrier is certainly not in the wall in the majority of cells. If it were, and the protoplast were fully permeable to solutes, then in a hypertonic solution the cell would continue to shrink until the elastic stretch had been released, but this would not be followed by the withdrawal of the protoplast. In the majority of cells the wall is fully permeable, the plasmolyzing solution comes into immediate contact with the protoplast, and the solute gradient is established across some phase of this component. As the protoplast contracts, the plasmolyzing solution flows through the wall and occupies the space between it and the wall. Also the fluid that is withdrawn from the vacuole is discharged into this space.

The further elaboration of this subject involves the consideration of two related topics, the nature of the barrier system and its probable location. Although these are intimately related, it will be convenient here to treat them separately and concisely, recognizing that the topic is treated more fully elsewhere in this work.

Certain characteristics of the barrier system may be inferred from the results of studies on the rates at which different solutes penetrate into the vacuoles, and it has been shown with nonelectrolytes that two properties of the molecule are of particular importance—lipoid solubility and molecular volume. The greater the solubility of the compound in a nonpolar solvent, the greater, frequently, the rate at which the substance traverses the cytoplasm into the vacuole. The importance of molecular volume is particularly evident with substances that tend to be water-soluble. With these it has been shown that the smaller the molecular volume, the greater is the rate of penetration.

Clearly from these two generalizations it may be inferred that the barrier system incorporates a lipoid[1] phase and that it is probably a mosaic having pores occupied by water through which water-soluble molecules may diffuse (39).

[1] The term "lipoid" has acquired a historical place in the literature of permeability, and when used in this or subsequent chapters in this work it is used in this sense to denote materials which, though of varied chemical character, are all generally soluble in fat solvents, reduce the interfacial tension, accumulate at the interface, and are thus thought to be contributory to the relatively nonaqueous portion of surface membranes, and therefore responsible for permeability properties. The term is not to be confused with the chemically more precise term "lipid," but is convenient in such usages as "the lipoid theory of permeability" or to denote lipoidal solvents.

Further characteristics of the barrier may be inferred from the state found in certain invertebrate eggs. Penetration in these is characterized by the same features as it is in vacuolated plant cells, and the two systems are probably essentially similar with regard to the conditions that determine absorption of nonelectrolytes. The investigation of the barrier in the egg or the red cell is facilitated by the fact that it may be assumed that it is at the surface of the system, and the properties of the membrane may therefore be inferred from those of the surface. A variety of observations have shown that the surface membrane cannot consist simply of lipoid. By measuring the force necessary to deform the cell when it is immersed in an aqueous medium, it has been shown that in these conditions the tension at the surface is considerably less than might be expected if it were composed only of lipoid. Values have been recorded which are less than 1.0 dyne per centimeter, whereas at an oil-water interface they might be expected to be of the order of 9.0 dynes per centimeter (20). The low values suggest that the surface is occupied completely by a hydrophilic substance, and the most probable material that would fulfill this and other conditions is a protein. Observations on tensions at the inner surface of the external membrane have suggested that this also is occupied by protein. The appropriate measurements have been made by observing the effect of centrifuging against the inner surface cytoplasmic oil droplets which are themselves probably encased in protein. With this experimental treatment the oil droplet is readily deformed, again suggesting that the tension at the surfaces of contact is low, and such as might be expected if the protein at the surface of the oil globule is in contact with another protein layer.

Thus the evidence suggests that the inner and outer surfaces of the external membrane in the amphibian egg are occupied by protein. At the same time the evidence from absorption studies indicates that this membrane probably incorporates a layer of lipoid over at least a considerable proportion of its area. The simplest structure which would reconcile these two sets of requirements is a laminated structure having lipoid in the center which is covered internally and externally by sheets of protein. The protein is probably a globulin and the lipoid, a phospholipid. The membrane, it is clear, must have structural coherence, and this implies that the lipoid molecules are attached to the protein and that they cohere laterally. These conditions are not provided by a lipoid layer composed of simple fats, for these are nonpolar and do not carry hydrophilic groups which could become associated with the protein. They may be provided, however, by phospholipids which are hydrophilic at one end and lipophilic at the other. It is suggested that the lipoid molecules are aligned radially in two layers, the hydrophilic groups being attached to the inner and outer protein layers and the lipophilic ends to each other in the mid-phase of the membrane. In this structure the lipoid molecules are likely to cohere laterally through adhesion between the hydrocarbon chains (22).

This structure for the barrier membranes in biological systems was originally suggested by Danielli and Harvey (20) in 1935, and it was originally deduced from physicochemical considerations. Subsequently the occurrence of it has been demonstrated with the electron microscope. The arresting fact may be noted that this membrane has been shown not only at the surface of protoplasm but also at the surfaces of mitochondria, nuclei, and chloroplasts. It has also been shown to occur in the baffles of mitochondria. It is always characterized by a central zone, which is about 50 A thick, formed of two layers of phospholipids and internal and external zones of protein which are each about 40 A thick.

The similarity between the molecular requirements for penetration in the invertebrate egg and the vacuolated plant cell suggests that the diffusion barrier in both is essentially similar. It suggests that, in both, inner and outer surfaces of the barrier are occupied by protein and over much of the area these cover a lipoid layer. In certain areas the lipoid layer is interrupted and the barrier in these zones is traversed by pores through a protein matrix. On the other hand, while it is certain that the barrier is at the surface of the cell in the egg, evidence is not available indicating that this is the case with the plant cell.

The position or positions of the barrier system has until recently been a matter of some doubt. With the plant cell, penetration eventually involves access to the vacuole, and restriction of movement into this could be due to uniform resistance throughout the cytoplasm, to a resistance at the external surface, or to a combination of conditions in both surfaces. The evidence that is adduced in favor of the view that the resistance is uniform across the whole matrix is not convincing. It has been suggested that, since neutral red when it is in the mesoplasm is in a fluorescent nondissociated form such as might be expected if it were dissolved in a lipoid material, the selective permeability associated with a lipoid structure is a property of the cytoplasm as a whole (82). This evidence, however, indicates only that lipoid material is present in the mesoplasm and does not show that it affects diffusion through it. The possibility of a restriction to solute movement in the mesoplasm as a whole may indeed be disregarded. The very low dry-matter content and the very high water content of the mesoplasm make this highly improbable.

On the other hand, there is considerable evidence for a barrier to diffusion due to a well-defined membrane at the inner surface of the protoplast, and some evidence for a barrier again due to a particular membrane at the outer surface of the protoplast.

There is considerable evidence that at least certain solutes penetrate into the cytoplasm considerably more rapidly than they do into the vacuole. It has been shown with radioactive isotopes that there may be an accumulation in the cytoplasm which precedes a corresponding accumulation in the vacuole (7). This could not occur if free diffusion were possible between the mesoplasm and the vacuole. The phenomenon of *Kappenplasmolyse* again indicates that ions which in certain circumstances may not penetrate into the vacuole may, nevertheless, be present in high concentration in the cytoplasm (42).

More direct evidence is also available for the presence of a barrier membrane at the external surface of the vacuole. This membrane, which has been called the tonoplast, may be separated from the rest of the system. Cells are plasmolyzed, and naked protoplasts may be withdrawn after the wall has been cut at one end. With appropriate micromanipulative treatment the mesoplasm and the external surface may be stripped away from these protoplasts, leaving a naked tonoplast enclosing the vacuolar fluid. The same structure is obtained when the protoplast is allowed to remain in contact with a solution of potassium chloride for 24 hours. As a result of this treatment the external membrane and the mesoplasm disperse, leaving what is probably a simple tonoplast. The isolated membranes are similar to the intact cytoplasm system in being semipermeable. They enclose the vacuolar sap, and the whole spherical mass may be induced to swell or shrink when immersed in solutions of appropriate concentration. The membranes are rapidly disintegrated by fat solvents, they fuse readily with oil drops, and they have marked elastic properties. The first two reactions have been taken to indicate that they incorporate lipoids, and the third, that they carry protein. The components of the membrane are, therefore, those of the general type which accounts for the resistance properties of the cytoplasm as a whole (66).

The indirect evidence for a tonoplast, while it shows the presence on the inner surface of a membrane with a high resistance, does not, of course, demonstrate the complete absence of resistance at the external surface. All the effects enumerated only demonstrate a considerably greater resistance to diffusion at the inner than at the outer surface. The possibility still remains of some resistance at the external surface, and for such there is indeed some evidence. Some dyes do not readily penetrate into the vacuole, and of these some do not penetrate rapidly into the mesoplasm. When a tissue is immersed in solutions of aniline blue, acid fuchsin, bromocresol purple, or phenol red, the dye does not extend beyond the external surface, but it has been shown that the dye may be injected either into the vacuole or into the mesoplasm. When it is injected into the vacuole it spreads throughout the sap but does not stain the cytoplasm. When it is injected into the ground phase it spreads laterally from the point of introduction and, while it colors the cytoplasm, it does not penetrate into the vacuole. These observations, while they support the conclusion that a tonoplast is present at the periphery of the vacuole, also indicate that a membrane is present in the external surface which is not permeable to the dye. This membrane has been characterized as the plasmalemma (67).

An independent structure from the external surface similar to the free tonoplast has not been isolated from plant cells. Certain observations, however, suggest that the physical characteristics of the surface may be different from those of the mesoplasm. When a cell from the pulp of *Symphoricarpos albus* fruit is plasmolyzed, a contracted protoplast is established in the normal pattern, but the surface of the protoplast remains attached to the wall by long, fine cytoplasmic strands (18). In the undisturbed cell cytoplasm may envelop some of the micelles of the wall. In the positions in which this occurs the ground phase would be anchored, and when plasmolysis is induced the attachment is not broken, but as the protoplast retreats, threads are drawn out from the surface. The development of the threads, however, indicates a physical coherence in the components of the surface which might not be expected from the highly fluid character of the mesoplasm. Similar evidence is available from studies with micromanipulation. When a needle is thrust into the surface of a plasmolyzed protoplast and then withdrawn it carries with it a fine thread which at first is traversed axially by a more fluid core. With further stretching the core breaks into independent drops which are embedded in the more coherent casing. At this stage, the tip of the needle may be brought back to the protoplast and, as this is approached, the firm casing merges with the original surface. This suggests that the external surface is an elastic structure and considerably more coherent than the mesoplasm. It is evident that the mesoplasm itself involves slight structural coherence, since the core to the thread does not break immediately, but this coherence is considerably less than that of the plasmalemma. High elasticity in the plasmalemma, while it suggests the probability of protein as a main component, with firmer binding between the protein threads than in the mesoplasm, does not exclude the incorporation of phospholipid.

Recently the position with regard to the barrier membranes has been further clarified by electron microscopy. Further evidence for the tonoplast has been assembled (57). This has been identified in a number of photographic records and there is little doubt from these that it involves a central zone due to phospholipid and external and internal protein layers.

The published results of electron microscope studies do not show unequivocally the presence of a plasmalemma on the external surface of the protoplast. It may be noted, however, that it has been shown that in mammalian cells the external boundary membrane is associated with the endoplasmic reticulum and may indeed be considered as an integral feature of it. Thus since an endoplasmic reticulum has been identified in some plant cells, this may imply the presence of a plasmalemma over the external surface. If such is the case, then the position that has been proposed in animal cells may help to clarify the problem, discussed above, of the apparent relative permeability of the plasmalemma. In mammalian cells the external membrane invaginates and may form channels with boundary membranes which become part of the endoplasmic reticulum. The invaginations, however, may also become cut off leaving a vesicle in the cytoplasm, the external membrane being reformed across the mouth of the depression. The vesicle may ultimately disperse into a cytoplasmic matrix. Thus solutes may be carried into the cytoplasm without actually traversing any barrier. A similar mechanism may operate at the external surface of the plant cell. In this case also, vesicles carrying an external solution may be budded off from the plasmalemma internally, and these may disperse, discharging their contents into the mesoplasm. In this event the plasmalemma may not restrain some solutes, although its permeability to these may be relatively low (4).

XII. The Vacuole

The vacuole may be considered as a liquid inclusion of the protoplast, which is separated from the cytoplasm by the tonoplast. Many observers have considered that the vacuole is an organelle of the cell in the same sense as a mitochondrion or a chloroplast is such. According to this view the vacuole arises from a distinctive proplastid in the meristematic cell. If it does develop in this way then there can be no question that it must be considered as one of the structural entities of the protoplast, and not merely as the product of a more or less fortuitous accumulation of fluid in the cytoplasm of the meristematic cell. All other organelles undoubtedly develop from well-defined structural entities in the embryonic state, and the vacuole also may do so. Unfortunately the cytological details involved in the origin of the vacuole are not easily resolved and the question is still being debated. It is significant, however, that one of the most persistent structures of the protoplast is the tonoplast. This fact in itself does not suggest that the tonoplast is a derivative from a casual accumulation of water. It suggests, on the contrary, that the tonoplast has the same structure as the boundary membrane of, say, the chloroplast, which is undoubtedly derived from a distinctive proplastid (35).

In many plant cells in the mature state, the cytoplasm encloses a single central vacuole. During development and expansion, however, several vacuoles may be present, and frequently in the final mature state the single vacuole may be traversed by cytoplasmic strands.

The tonoplast is apparently relatively impermeable to many solutes, and while these may be transported into the vacuole they do not readily diffuse back into the cytoplasm. Thus many compounds may occur in the vacuole at a higher concentration than they are present in the cytoplasm. The vacuolar fluid carries in solution probably all the normal substrate metabolites, such as sugars, inorganic salts, many hydroxy and keto acids, and amino acids. It may also carry certain compounds in suspension. Fat droplets have been observed in the vacuolar fluid.

Occasionally the vacuole also contains in solution flavone or anthocyanin pigments. These are important compounds since they are the main coloring matter of many flowers and they frequently occur in the vacuoles of parenchyma cells in the petals. Flavones in particular may be present in bark and in certain parenchymatous tissues.

The flavones are all derivatives of γ-pyrone (formula XXVI). Flavone itself is a phenylbenzo-γ-pyrone (formula XXVII), and xanthone (formula XXVIII), which is a closely related substance, is dibenzo-γ-pyrone.

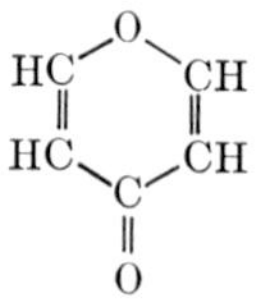

(XXVI) 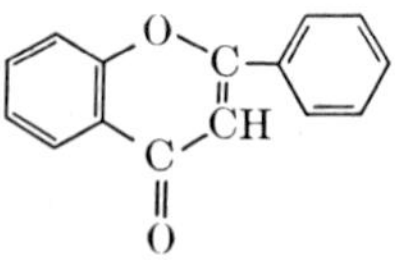 (XXVII) 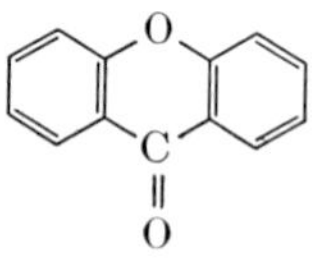 (XXVIII)

Flavonol, from which several pigments are derived, is 3-hydroxyflavone. Hydroxy and methoxy derivatives of flavone, flavonol, and xanthone occur in various species either in the free state or in glycosidic combination with glucose or rhamnose. Quercitin is a derivative of flavonol which is in oak (*Quercus*) bark, *Rhamnus* berries and in a large variety of flowers and leaves. Luteolin is a yellow pigment which for thousands of years has been extracted from various species of *Genista* (dyer's weed); it is a tetrahydroxy-flavone.

The anthocyanins are probably the more important group since they give a wider variety of colors, the flavones and xanthones being mostly yellow.

The anthocyanins may be considered as being derived from 3-hydroxy-2-phenylbenzo-pyrylium (formula XXIX), which is reduced flavonol.

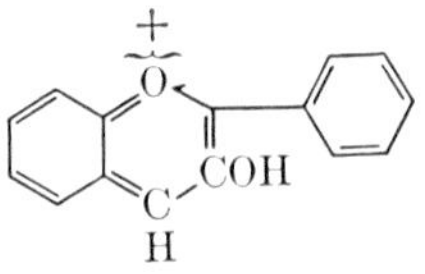

(XXIX)

The reduced flavonols are called anthocyanidins. The anthocyanins are nearly all glycosides of the anthocyanidins. The sugar represented in the molecule varies. It may be glucose, galactose, rhamnose, or a disaccharide. In certain cases diglycosides may occur.

There is a very large variety of anthocyanins. A large group of anthocyanidins, each derived by reduction of a corresponding flavone, and each anthocyanidin may give rise to a group of anthocyanins by different substitutions with hydroxy and methoxy groups. They are present usually in solution in the sap of flowers and they promote the development of a wide variety of colors. In many cases the color varies with the pH of the sap (62).

The anthocyanins are of interest in the history of biology since they were among the first chemical compounds to be studied in relation to genetical inheritance (76).

Another group of pigments, the carotenoids, are considered below. Like most of the flavones and xanthones, these are also yellow or orange pigments. They have, however, an entirely different chemical structure with different solubility properties. They are not water-soluble, and unlike the flavones they are developed in organelles, the chromoplasts which are similar to chloroplasts. They are also normal components of chloroplasts.

XIII. Cytoplasmic Food Reserve Particles

The cytoplasm frequently carries particles which are not metabolically active but which incorporate the products of metabolism. These particles store certain products in an insoluble form and withdraw them from the metabolic system. The variety of these is large, but four in particular are frequent; they are: (a) starch grains, (b) aleurone grains, (c) fat droplets, and (d) crystals.

A. Starch Grains

Starch is formed from glucose, which is polymerized in particular plastids to give ultimately the characteristic starch grain. There is no evidence that starch is ever formed anywhere but in a plastid. It is the most frequent, and probably the most important, reserve material in plants but the grains are formed more abundantly in certain tissues than they are in others. They are particularly abundant in certain storage organs, such as tubers and in endosperms of seeds, and they are least frequent in rapidly growing cells.

On hydrolysis with acid, starch yields only glucose, but on enzymatic hydrolysis with amylase it gives maltose, which is a disaccharide containing two glucose units. Starch is similar to cellulose but differs from it in having the successive glucose units joined through 1,4-α- instead of β-linkages. Starch may also be considered to consist of successive maltose units which are joined through 1,4-α-linkages (formula XXX), the two residues of maltose being themselves joined through a 1,4-α-linkage.

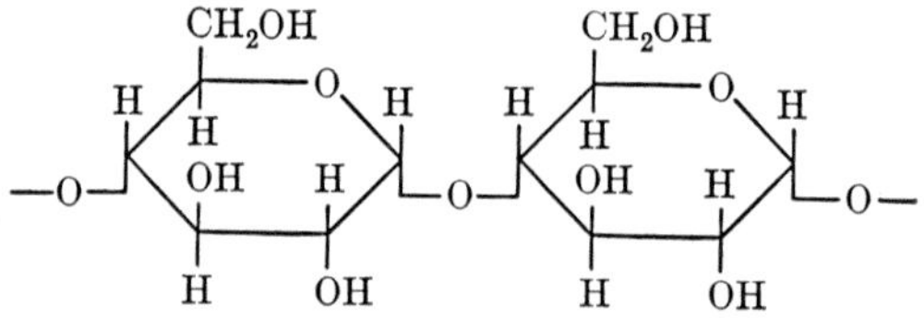

(XXX)

Starch normally occurs in two forms which tend to be present together in the grain. The two types are amylopectin, which is only sparingly soluble in water and gives heavily viscous solutions; and amylose which, while being more soluble in water, gives considerably less viscous solutions. Starch in the cell is normally identified by the blue color which is given with iodine, but the effect of this reagent is different with the two types, the blue color being considerably more intense with amylose than it is with amylopectin. Molecular structure in the two is also different. Amylose is probably an unbranched chain compound in which the molecule involves 300–1000 glucose residues. The amylopectin molecule on the other hand almost certainly involves a branched structure, with each branch carrying 24–30 glucose residues. In the branches the linkage is the normal 1,4 type, but the branching is apparently due to the formation of sporadic 1,6 linkages.

The solubilities of the two starches and the viscosities of their solutions are, of course, consequences of the different molecular structures.

The starch chains are probably not straight but in spirals. It is significant that the enzyme α-amylase degrades starch to dextrin, the molecule of which contains six or twelve glucose units. This has been the basis for the suggestion that the chains are in the form of a spiral with six glucose units in each gyre.

The shapes and sizes of starch grains vary. In potato starch they tend to be oval with a maximum length of 10–20 μ. The grains may be enclosed in a thin protein membrane which is said to be a legacy from

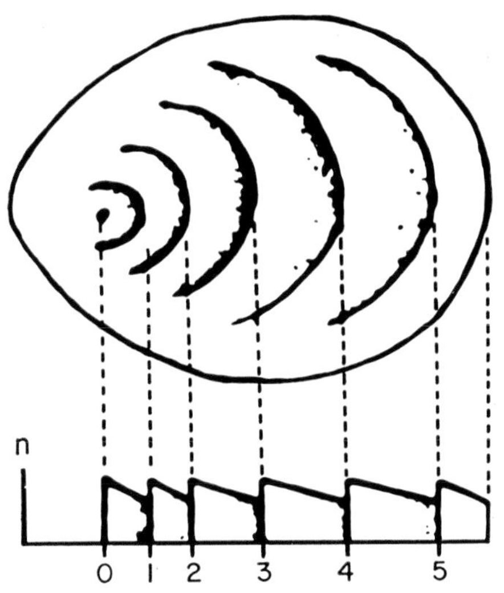

FIG. 13. Structure of starch grain showing hilum (0) and successive zones of changing refractive index (*1, 2, 3, 4, 5*). From Frey-Wyssling (28).

the original proplastid in which the starch was deposited. The intact grain has a stratified structure and consists of concentric layers which converge to a central hilum. The layering is the effect of an alternation of dense, closely packed, and of less dense, more loosely dispersed, materials. Layering is not observed when the grain has been formed in constant conditions. Observation indicates that the dense, highly refractive zones are formed during the day, while the looser zones with the lower refractive index are deposited in the dark (Fig. 13).

B. ALEURONE GRAINS

These are granules of reserve protein, the structure of which varies. They may consist of an irregular amorphous mass of protein, or they may involve a central crystalline zone which is surrounded by amorphous protein. It is said that the crystalline zone also consists of protein. Certain elaborate grains have been described which, in addition to protein in different forms, incorporate various inorganic crystals.

Aleurone grains in angiosperms are characteristic of cells in endosperms and embryos. There is no evidence that they are formed from proplastids, and it is probable that they are the products of a process analogous to crystallization in small vacuoles.

C. Oil Droplets

These are ubiquitous. They are probably present in all cells and they tend to be particularly prominent in rapidly metabolizing tissues. They are spherical bodies probably consisting only of fats and certainly semifluid. They may be 2–3 μ in diameter, or they may be just beyond the limit of microscopic resolution. The smallest fat droplets show Brownian movement particularly well.

D. Crystals

Crystals of various types occur in different positions in a variety of cells. Simple crystals may occur in the cytoplasm or the vacuole. Bundles of crystals ("raphides") are frequently found in leaf vacuoles, and complicated crystal aggregates have been observed in a number of leaves. The crystals, whatever their form, are usually said to be composed either wholly or mainly of calcium oxalate.

XIV. Cytoplasmic Inclusions

Cytoplasm carries a variety of particulate inclusions which are of great importance for the activity of the metabolic system. These are (a) proplastids, (b) mitochondria, (c) microsomes, and (d) in some cells, chloroplasts.

A. Proplastids

This group includes all particles which are neither mitochondria, microsomes, chloroplasts, or any other readily identifiable organelle. The group is certainly not homogeneous, and it contains units which differ with respect to size and shape. A category which is defined only in terms of negative characteristics is certainly not a satisfactory one. The inclusion of it here, however, is an attempt to evade the verbal luxuriance of some contemporary cytology. Many particles of this group have been described in terms of a rich and intricate nomenclature, but the structures are evanescent and the nomenclature elusive, and it seems preferable to collect them all into one class, however imperfect it may be. In this connection, it may be emphasized that while the term proplastid has been used with other meanings in earlier texts, it has not always been used with conspicuous consistency, and the meaning that is attached to it here does not violate any established usage.

The group includes all those particles which have been claimed as precursors for some of the more well-defined organelles. It certainly includes the entities from which some starch grains may arise and, if they exist, those from which chloroplasts and mitochondria develop.

There is reason for thinking that mitochondria and chloroplasts at least may arise from particulate precursors. It has been claimed that chloroplasts may arise from mitochondria, but this is doubtful. It has also been claimed that both may be formed spontaneously from the cytoplasm. This again is doubtful, and indeed there is some evidence that indicates that both are formed from precursors that are transmitted from a parent to a daughter cell and that the development of each represents an elaboration of such a precursor. This evidence comes from genetical studies on mutations that are maternally inherited. Various mutants have been recognized in higher plants which involve abnormalities in the chloroplasts. Some of these are inherited in such a way as to indicate that they are transmitted through the maternal cytoplasm. In some instances there is evidence that chloroplast structure may be the product not only of maternal cytoplasm, but of an interaction between this and a nuclear gene (87). But, however elaborate the situation, the evidence is that a determinant which is genetically independent of any nuclear gene is carried in the cytoplasm of the egg. There is some evidence that determinants for mitochondria may be similarly transmitted. A *Neurospora* mutant has been identified which is without certain components of the cytochrome system, and it has been shown that this abnormality is maternally inherited. Since all components of the cytochrome system are probably carried in the mitochondria the observations indicate the transmission of a mitochondrion precursor through the cytoplasm of the egg (60). An earlier observation of a similar kind is that due to Ephrussi (25) and co-workers on yeast. Transmission through extranuclear regions necessarily implies that at each division the cytoplasmic determinant must itself divide independently of the nucleus, and the products be distributed to daughter cells. Thus genetical evidence indicates strongly that particular determinants are present in the cytoplasm which control the development of both chloroplasts and mitochondria. The nature of the determinant in each case is unknown, but it is at least conceivable that it is particulate and that it may be one of the bodies of the proplastid fraction. Different determinants are, of course, required for chloroplasts and mitochondria, and this would involve a different proplastid for each.

B. MITOCHONDRIA

These are bodies embedded in the matrix which stain with Janus green B. This is a diagnostic reaction and other organelles are said not to absorb the dye. Mitochondria vary considerably in shape and size. They may be cylindrical, spherical, or of indeterminate form. When cylindrical they are rarely more than 3 μ in length, and when spherical they are 0.5–1.5 μ in diameter. Within the same tissue, size and form may change with metabolic state and age. They may shrink markedly when the tissue is starved and they tend to disintegrate as it ages. The cylindrical form during shrinkage may contract to a sphere or it may disperse into smaller fragments. When in the cytoplasm they are apparently highly sensitive to shock, and when this is sufficiently severe they may disperse completely. Since they are so labile, it was at one time held that they could not be structural entities and that they were probably local coacervate aggregates in the colloidal system of the cytoplasm, but this view has not survived the results of recent studies, and it is now beyond doubt that they are well-defined cytological units with characteristic structures.

Mitochondria may be separated from the cytoplasm and collected in a relatively undamaged state. The techniques with which they are isolated are described elsewhere. Preparations of isolated mitochondria may be used for chemical analysis, and the percentage of the dry weight that is due to proteins, lipoids, and RNA respectively has been determined. It is probable that about 40% of the dry weight represents protein; 25%, phospholipid, and 5%, RNA (36).

It is evident that the mitochondria contain little other than these three components. It is significant that while protein is high, lipoid is also high. The chemical analysis indicates that lipoid is probably a major structural constituent and confirms cytological experience that

---

FIG. 14. Electron micrographs showing structure of plant mitochondria, d and e. Cross sections through isolated mitochondria. Note double layers in boundary membrane, and double internal membrane (*X*) Magnification: d, ×94,000; e, ×76,000. From Farrant *et al.* (27).

a, b, and c. Interpretation of structure of (d) and (e). Cristae have much the same structure as the external membrane. In each case, two protein layers [*p* in (c)] each about 40 A (b) are separated by a phospholipid layer [*l* in (c)] which is also about 40 A wide.

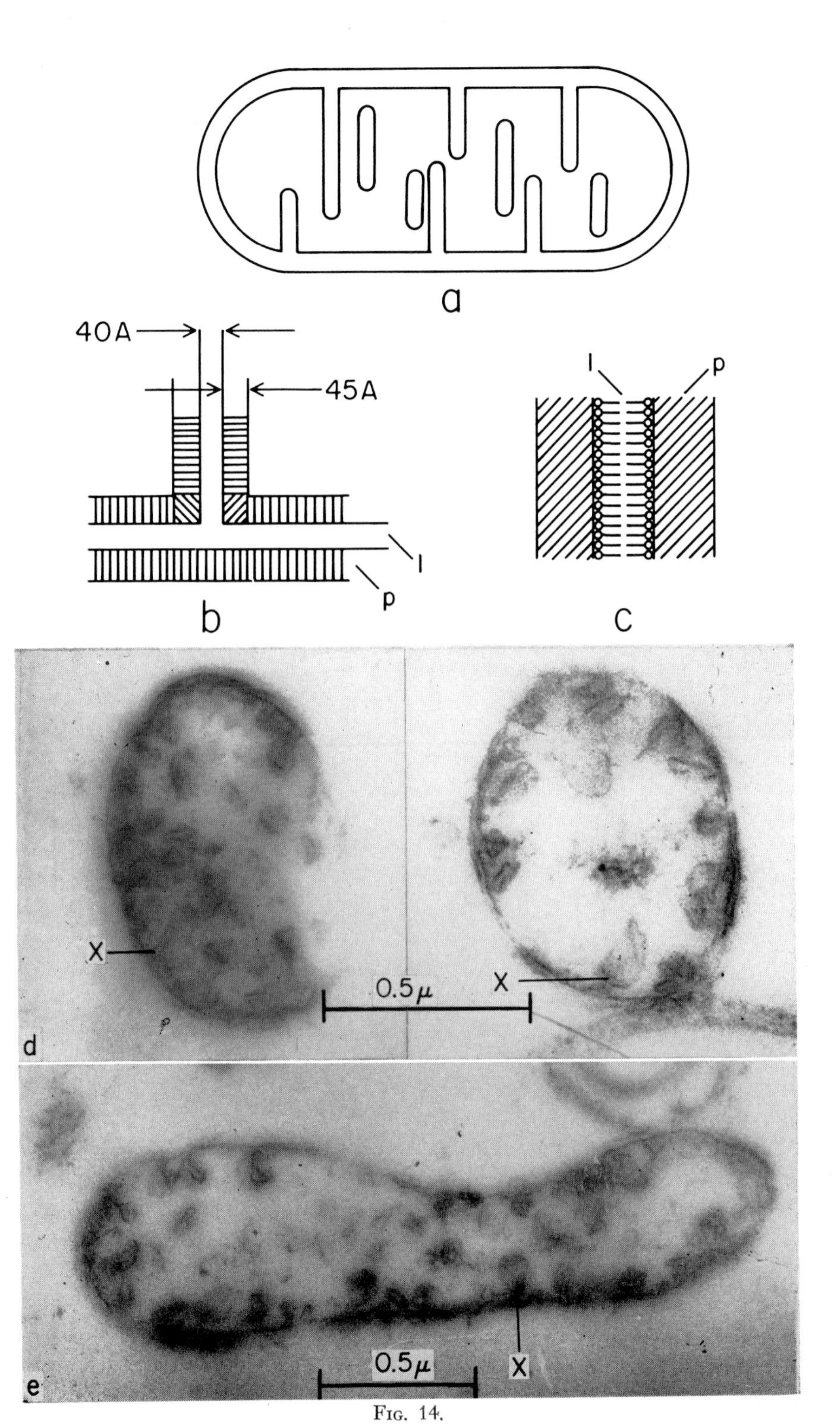

Fig. 14.

mitochondria are only preserved in tissue when a fixative is used that is not also a fat solvent. The content of RNA is evidently low and this is important in the comparison with the state in microsomes.

The structure of mitochondria in tissues and in isolated preparations has been studied intensively during the last ten years. Fine sections not more than 150 A have been prepared and examined in the electron microscope. The structure has been most intensively examined in mammalian tissues in which the mitochondrion has the general form of a cylinder which is enclosed in an outer skin and which has a core partially transversed by a series of baffles ("cristae"). The skin on the outer surface is a membrane which is in two distinct dark layers which are probably composed of protein. Tissues for electron microscope investigations are normally fixed in osmium tetroxide solution, and it is probable that the dark areas represent a complex of protein with the heavy metal. The zone between the two dark layers is clear and is probably occupied by phospholipid. Each of the dark protein layers is about 45 A thick and the clear intermediate zone is about 50 A thick. It is probable that at intervals the inner protein layer folds inward to form a baffle which stretches part of the way across the core (68). Since the baffle is a fold from the inner protein layer it involves two protein layers, again with, in photographs, a clear zone between them. This intermediate area is continuous with the clear zone between the protein layers of the boundary membrane and again is probably occupied with phospholipid. In the cristae the dimensions of the different layers are similar to those of the corresponding layers in the boundary membrane. The structure of the mitochondrial membrane system is clearly very similar to that of the tonoplast and probably involves the same arrangement. The central phospholipid zone probably involves two monomolecular layers aligned at right angles to the surface of the membrane.

The spaces between the cristae are occupied by a densely granular matrix which does not show any well-defined structure. It is probable that this matrix consists of soluble protein. When the mitochondrion is disrupted, about 60% of its normal protein content may be lost, although the general structural continuity of the membrane system is not disturbed. Evidently when the mitochondrion is disrupted, the matrix between the cristae is discharged into the suspending fluid.

The structure of the plant mitochondrion is similar to that described above (27). In higher plants the baffles are replaced by fingerlike intrusions which seem to be less frequent than the cristae of animal mitochondria (Fig. 14, d–e).

The external membrane is an important structural feature for the metabolic activity of the mitochondrion. When tissue is immersed in solutions of different concentrations, the organelle may shrink or swell. The volume change is due to an osmotic withdrawal or absorption of water, and the membrane, which has a structure similar to that of the cytoplasmic diffusion barrier, apparently has similar semipermeable properties. The mitochondrion may also accumulate solutes at least to a limited extent. This has been demonstrated with isolated plant mitochondria which have been suspended in a solution of potassium chloride.

C. MICROSOMES

These are considerably smaller than any other organelles. They are spherical and are about 400–250 A in diameter. Plant microsomes were first observed from photographs of the products of tissue maceration (71). Later they were described from sections again examined in the electron microscope. Later still they were separated as a distinct fraction in the centrifugation procedure. Hodge and associates (41) examined the structure of isolated microsomes and found that they tended to be vesicular bodies, some having a dense content within a boundary layer, while others seemed to be hollow spheres. A similar vesicular structure has been found with microsomes isolated from mammalian tissue. It is not clear, however, whether the vesiculation is a consequence of isolation or whether it is a characteristic of the organelles in the parent tissue. The chemical composition in terms of major components has been determined, and one analysis shows that 40% of the dry weight is protein, 20% phospholipid, and 10% RNA. The characteristic feature of the composition of microsomes is evidently the high content of RNA (52).

It is probable that microsomes are embedded in the membrane system of the endoplasmic reticulum. In mammalian cells the reticulum carries large numbers of small spherical bodies which are electron-dense and appear as sharp black spots in electron micrographs. A similar arrangement has recently been described by Hodge and co-workers (41) in plant cells, and it is probable that in these as well as in animal cells microsomes are an integral feature of the membrane system of the endoplasmic reticulum.

It is of some interest to compare microsomes with the simpler plant viruses. Both are approximately of the same size, and at least some of the virus particles also appear to be spherical in electron micrographs. Further, both are apparently rich in RNA. The two are certainly superficially similar, and the significance of this is discussed below.

D. CHLOROPLASTS

These are the largest organelles of the cytoplasm, and they are characteristically green. They are not invariably present although frequently their formation may be induced in tissues in which they do not normally occur. They are not commonly found in roots for instance, but when these are exposed to light, sporadic chloroplasts may, nevertheless, develop, and this is perhaps not surprising if the particular proplastids from which they originate are indeed present in all cells. In angiosperms they are most abundant in the palisade cells of the mesophyll, in which they tend to be circular or oval in surface view and biconvex in section. The size varies, but they are rarely more than 10 μ wide. There may be as many as 200 per cell, although in the spongy mesophyll they are usually fewer.

Chloroplasts are robust bodies, and they are readily separated from the rest of the tissue. Their composition has been determined with isolated samples, and it has been found that of the total dry matter about 50% is protein, about 35% lipoids, and aboout 7% pigments. It has been shown that the lipoid fraction contains phosphatidic acid and compounds similar to lecithin, the presence of which is indicated by the formation of myelin figures after treatment of the chloroplasts with surface-active substances, such as sodium oleate, or with glycine or urea. It has been claimed that both RNA and DNA are present in the chloroplasts. If the incidence of DNA is confirmed, this is a particularly important observation. The evidence is unequivocal that chloroplasts have a genetic continuity of their own, and if they in fact carry DNA, then this might be the vehicle of their independent continuity.

The pigments of the chloroplast are of fundamental importance since the photolysis of water depends on at least the green compounds. Two groups of pigments are normally present, the chlorophylls and the carotenoids. The chemical structure of chlorophyll is shown in formula (XXXI).

The chlorophyll molecule may for the present purpose be considered in terms of a porphyrin head which is constituted from four pyrrole rings and an extended hydrocarbon tail which represents an alcohol (phytol) attached to one pyrrole through an ester linkage. The center of the porphyrin ring system is occupied by a single magnesium atom (70). In most angiosperms, two chlorophylls, a and b, are found. Formula (XXXI) shows the structure of a. In b, one methyl is replaced by an aldehyde group (shown in parentheses). It is important to notice that the structure involves hydrophilic properties in the porphyrin head and lipophilic properties in the hydrocarbon tail.

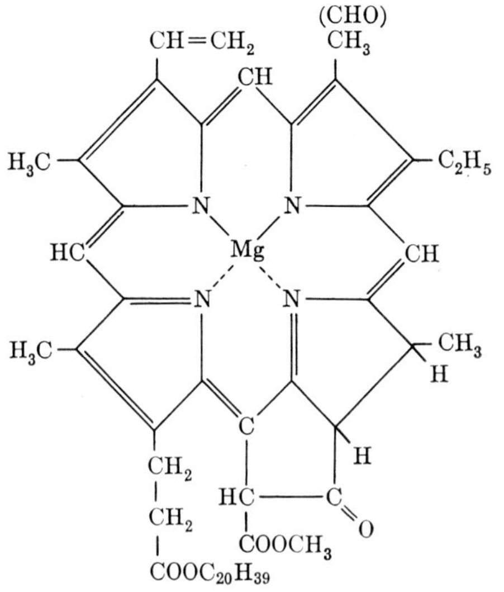

(CHO)
$CH=CH_2$ CH_3
CH
H_3C C_2H_5
N N
HC Mg CH
N N
H_3C CH_3
H
C
CH_2 H
HC C
CH_2 O
$COOCH_3$
$COOC_{20}H_{39}$

(XXXI)

Several carotenoids have been identified in chloroplasts, but they are all similar to β-carotene, the structure of which is shown in formula

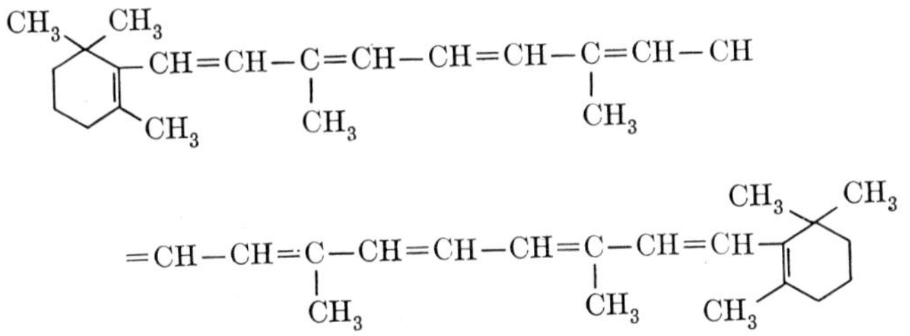

CH_3 CH_3
$-CH=CH-C=CH-CH=CH-C=CH-CH$
CH_3 CH_3 CH_3

CH_3 CH_3
$=CH-CH=C-CH=CH-CH=C-CH=CH-$
CH_3 CH_3 CH_3

(XXXII)

(XXXII). β-Carotene consists of two six-membered rings with a hydrocarbon chain stretched between them. The hydrocarbon chain is a conjugated double-bond system which may be considered as being composed of successive isoprenelike units. Both ring systems are lipophilic, and the whole molecule is therefore hydrophobic.

The chloroplasts from metabolically active leaves may contain starch grains. It is probable that these are formed at various centers during active photosynthesis. During illumination they increase in size and they may after prolonged exposure to light almost obliterate the original outline of the chloroplast. In darkness, after a period of illumination, the starch grains shrink and may finally disperse. Evidently during the dark phase the starch is degraded to sugars which are translocated to other parts of the plant.

The structural details discernible at the conventional magnifications of the light microscope are limited but, nevertheless, important. A surface membrane can frequently be seen, especially when cells from a starved leaf or from a leaf that has been kept in the dark are examined. The membrane appears as a thin, grayish boundary, and it gives positive reactions with cytochemical tests for protein. Within the membrane certain chloroplasts appear to be uniformly green, whereas others appear to have a granular texture. The significance of the granulation was uncertain until comparatively recently. It was argued that since some plastids are characterized by a uniform structure, the granular appearance of others may be the manifestation of a post-mortem change. Recent observations have resolved the doubt, and it is now clear that heterogeneity may be a characteristic feature of the living state. Chloroplasts showing this feature are composed of two phases: a continuous substratum, the stroma, and a system of dark, dense granules, the grana. At the same time it is also certain that all chloroplasts do not involve this structure. While it is certainly present in some chloroplasts, it is equally certainly absent from others. The two types may be present in the same plant, or one type only may be characteristic of a particular species. There is certainly no reason to believe that one type is a moribund form of the other, or that either is photosynthetically less active than the other (40).

The grana structure is based on elementary bodies which in the mesophyll chloroplasts of maize (*Zea mays*) in one plane appears as dispersed rectangular bodies and in another as circular disks each with a diameter of about 0.4 μ. The stroma occupies the space between the grana, and, as shown below, it may be traversed by threads which connect one granum with the next (70).

The investigation of the submicroscopic structure of the chloroplast has occurred in two phases. In the first, certain structural aspects were deduced from observations on the properties of chlorophyll and on the optical properties of whole chloroplasts; in the second, structural details have been examined with the electron microscope. The results of the second phase have extended and amplified those of the first. The results of the first, however, are still of considerable importance, not only for historical reasons but because they incorporate some information which has not yet been obtained by the more recent technique.

Chlorophyll, when it is present in the leaf, fluoresces and it has a maximum absorption in the red. The same properties may also be observed when the chlorophyll has been extracted, and the state in which the pigment shows one or other of the leaf characteristics may be taken as an indication of the state in which it is present in the chloroplast. There is little doubt that chlorophyll in the leaf is in some form of combination with protein. Aqueous extracts prepared by fine grinding of chloroplasts yields a pigmented suspension, the particles of which have the properties of proteins. This and other observations suggest that chlorophyll is an integral component of a chromoprotein complex, similar to that of hemoglobin. In aqueous colloidal solution, the chlorophyll has the same absorption spectrum as it has in the intact leaf, but in this state it gives no fluorescence.

On the other hand, the pigment is readily soluble in various fats, and in true solution in these it fluoresces strongly, but with absorption maxima that are shifted toward the shorter wavelengths. Thus, the evidence indicates that, in the leaf, the absorption characteristics are a consequence of association with protein, and the fluorescence, of association with lipids that are known to be in the chloroplast. Two interpretations for this are possible. Either that in the intact chloroplast, part of the chlorophyll is associated with protein and a separate and independent fraction is associated with lipid, or that part of the molecule is anchored to protein and another part of the same molecule is in a complex with lipids. The first interpretation may be disregarded since it is incompatible with two further important observations. When chlorophyll is dissolved in lipid the fluorescence spectrum is not identical with that of the leaf, the peaks being shifted toward shorter wavelengths; and when a leaf is plunged into hot water, fluorescence at first disappears but then reappears again after some minutes. These properties are certainly more consistent with the second interpretation than with the first.

Chlorophyll, while having a hydrophilic head has a lipophilic tail, and in the chloroplast it could, therefore, be aligned between aqueous protein and nonaqueous lipid layers. The model shown (Fig. 15,a) incorporates this possibility and accounts for the optical properties of the pigment. In this system the hydrophilic porphyrin head is associated with protein and the lipophilic tail with the hydrocarbon chains of a phospholipid. The hydrophilic group of the lipid is attached to a corresponding structure in another lipid layer which is in turn associated with another layer of chlorophyll. In this model carotene molecules are aligned parallel to the hydrocarbon chains of the phospholipid, held in this position by cohesion between adjacent hydrocarbon groups. In the model the association of the porphyrin with the protein provides for the absorption spectrum of chlorophyll and the association of the phytol tail with the lipid, for fluorescence and for the characteristics of the fluorescence spectrum. When the chloroplast is exposed to boiling water the immediate denaturation of the protein envelopes, it may be supposed, the chlorophyll, and this quenches the fluorescence; subsequently the pigment returns in solution to a molten lipid phase and fluorescence is consequently restored (28).

This model, providing as it does for successive layers of lipid and protein, carries the implication that the chloroplast is constructed of successive sheets of protein and lipid in much the same way as a "multidecker" sandwich is composed of successive sheets of bread and meat slices. If this is the structure, then the chloroplast might be expected to show form birefringence. It has been known for many years that in fact it does, and this may be taken as further evidence in favor of the postulated structure.

The structure that has been elaborated from optical data refers to the chloroplast as a whole. From the relevant evidence a discrimination cannot be made between grana and stroma, or between the states of chloroplasts with, and of those without, grana. Where a grana structure is observed, the optical properties could be due to the grana with the stroma representing a structureless aqueous phase consisting of a solution of protein. This and other aspects have, however, been clarified through electron microscope studies.

Electron microscope photographs show that a membrane is always present on the external surface and that it consists of two layers which absorb the osmium and of an intermediate layer which does not. Clearly this represents the usual structure of two protein layers with a phospholipid layer between them. The studies that have been made on the contents of the chloroplast confirm in many respects the structure postulated in the model, although they also show that it requires some amplification. Full agreement has still not been reached regarding the ultrastructure of the chloroplast. The results and conclusions of different investigations differ in important respects. The description given here is based on the results of Hodge and associates (40), since these seem to be most decisive (Fig. 15,b). The observations of these

Fig. 15. Structure of chloroplast. a. Model of Hubert as modified by Frey-Wyssling (28). Protein sheets alternate with bifoliar layers consisting of chlorophyll (T) phospholipid (└┬┘) and carotenoids (|°). b. Structure of chloroplast according to Hodge *et al.* (40). Note that the grana structure is similar to that postulated by Hubert and Frey-Wyssling, although in this reconstruction the chlorophyll molecule is reversed.

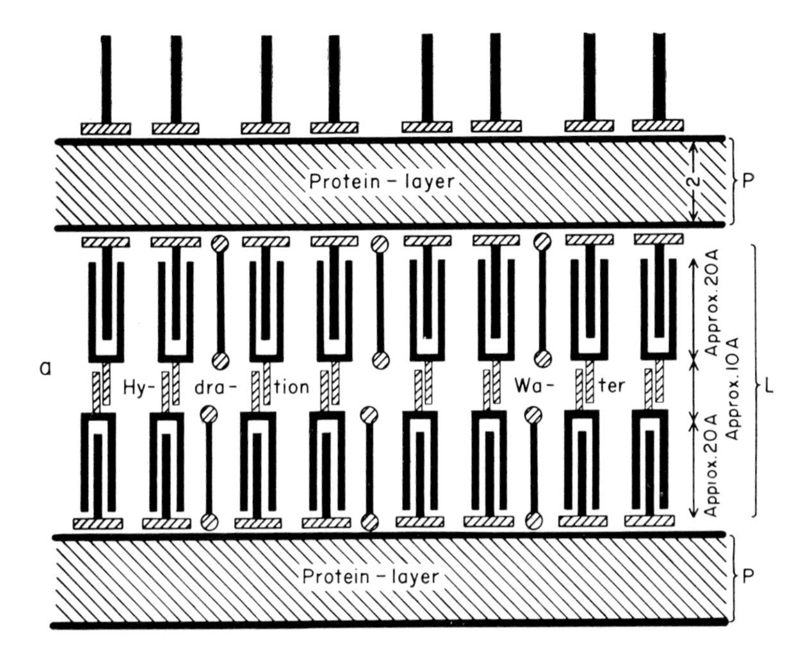

a
Protein – layer
Hy-
dra-
tion
Wa-
ter
Protein – layer
Approx. 20 A
Approx. 10 A
Approx. 20 A
P
L
P

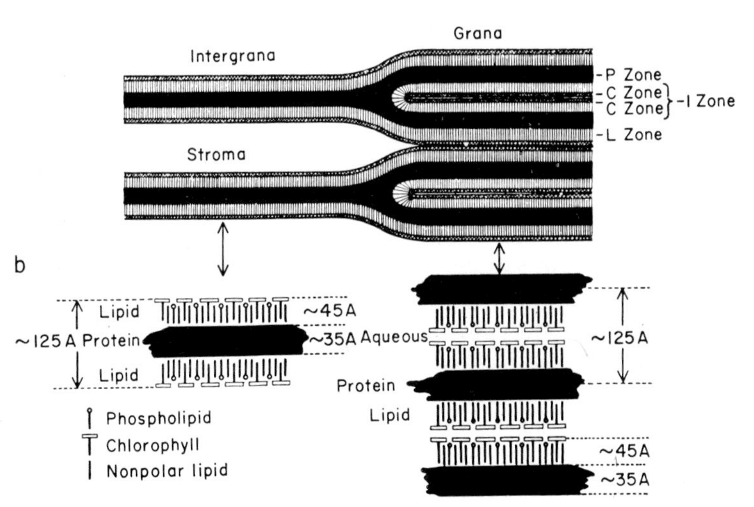

b
Grana
Intergrana
Stroma
-P Zone
-C Zone
-C Zone
-I Zone
-L Zone
Lipid
~125 A Protein
Lipid
~45A
~35A
Aqueous
~125 A
Protein
Lipid
~45A
~35A
Phospholipid
Chlorophyll
Nonpolar lipid

FIG. 15.

investigators were made with maize chloroplasts, and they examined the structure in parenchyma sheath chloroplasts, which do not show the grana structure, and mesophyll chloroplasts, which have well-developed grana. In the parenchyma sheath chloroplasts, membranes traverse the whole length of the body from one edge to the other. The membranes are the chlorophyll carriers and each has a characteristic structure. In section each membrane involves a central dense zone (*P*) which is about 35 A thick, with on either side of this a lighter less dense layer which is about 45 A thick (*L*). On the extreme outer limit of the light zone there is a thin darker layer again (*C*). Since with osmium fixed material the dense layers are usually considered as being protein and the lighterzones as being phospholipid, in this structure the central *P* zone is considered to be protein, and the lateral *L* zones to be phospholipid. If this is the case, however, then the hydrophilic head would have to be on the outside and the lipophilic tail, associated with nonpolar groups on the protein. The chlorophyll is considered to be part of the lipid layer, again with the lipophilic phytol tail associated with the protein and the hydrophilic porphyrin head on the external surface. In this chloroplast, where there is no granum structure, the plates are separated from each other by a stroma matrix.

In the mesophyll, chloroplast plates similar to those of the sheath chloroplast are again observed, and they have exactly the same structure. In the mesophyll chloroplast, the plates connect separate grana. They stretch between one granum body and the next, although still embedded in a structureless stroma (Fig. 16). In a sense each plate becomes embedded in the granum. At the point where they enter the granum, the plates may bifurcate and the two branches enter the granum in close juxtaposition. The granum is not formed solely from bifurcating intergranum lamellae, but these are nevertheless an important ingredient. The two lamellae from the intergranum plate become closely attached to other lamellae, and throughout the granum no stroma or matrix of any kind is present. Each lamella in the granum has exactly the same structure as the intergranum plate, and since this is limited by two thin *C* zones (see Fig. 15,b), the granum is constituted from successive lamellae which are in contact over their *C* zones. The two give a broader band than the individual *C* zones and the composite band becomes an *I* zone. Thus the whole granum involves wide, dense *P* bands alternating with lighter *L* zones which are separated from each other by darker *I* zones. This structure is clearly very similar to the structure postulated in the earlier model. The dark *P* bands may be taken to be protein alternating with a complex of two

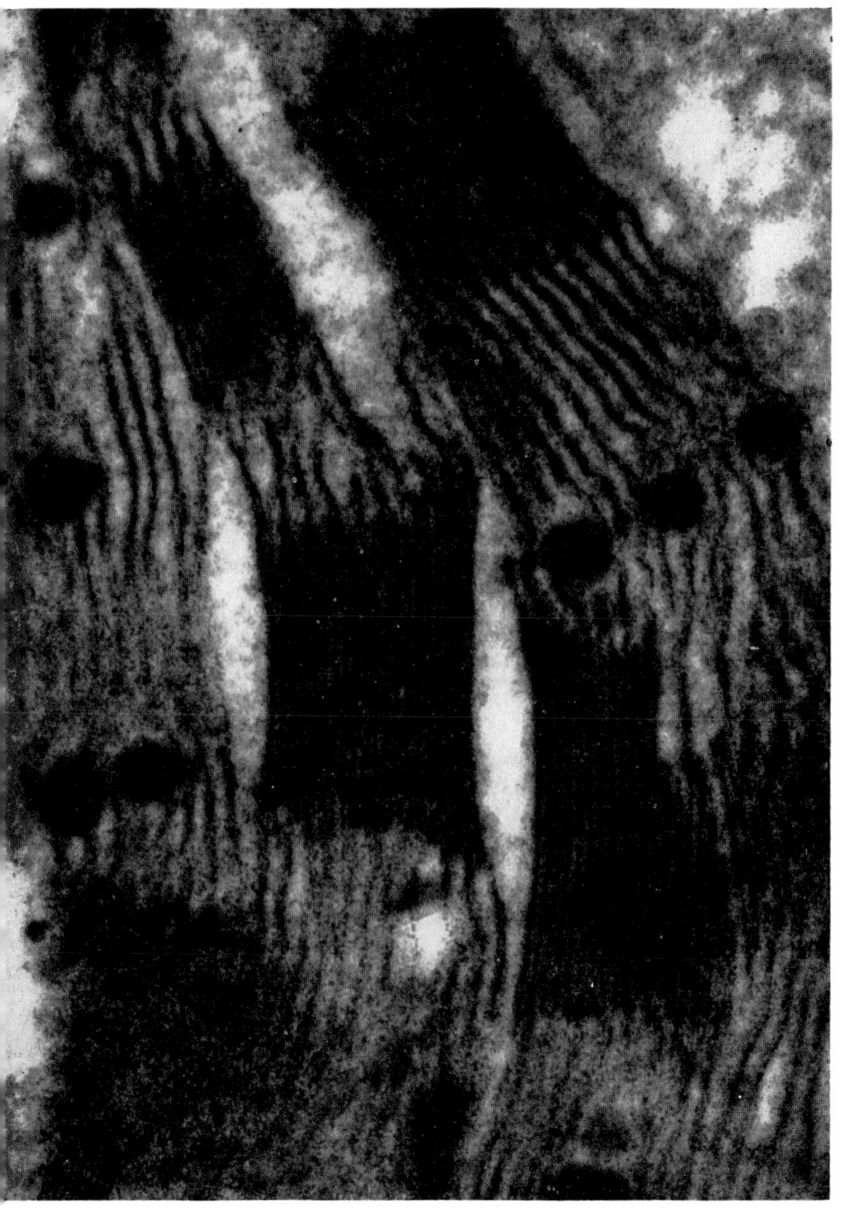

FIG. 16. Electron micrograph of section through chloroplast, showing grana and intergrana regions. From Hodge *et al.* (40). Magnification: ×143,000. (For more detail on the photochemical apparatus, see Brookhaven Symposium No. 11, 1959.)

L zones and two *C* zones, which together may be taken to represent a bifoliar structure involving phospholipid. It is suggested that in the granum the lipid configuration is the same as it is in the intergranum lamellae, in which the lipophilic tail of the phospholipid is associated with the protein and the hydrophilic head is associated with the same group in the succeeding layer. In this structure again the phytol tail of the chlorophyll is anchored in the protein and the porphyrin head of the chlorophyll is associated with another head in the next lipid layer. To this extent the structure is different from that of the model in which the arrangement of lipid and chlorophyll molecules is reversed (Fig. 15,b).

Clearly the electron microscope data show that the two types of chloroplasts are not fundamentally different. The structure of the chloroplast without grana is similar to that of the intergranum regions of the body with grana. In both, lamellae are present which are regularly spaced throughout a matrix. The chloroplast with grana is peculiar only to the extent that at intervals the intergranum lamellae become closely compacted with the elimination of the matrix.

Finally it may be noted that the chloroplast membrane is likely to have as great an effect on the activity of this organelle as the corresponding structure has on that of the mitochondrion. It is evident that like all membranes of the same structure that of the chloroplast is not freely permeable to solutes. The chloroplasts can be caused to swell or shrink by placing them in solutions of the appropriate tonicity. When immersed in a hypotonic solution, they swell with the development of cavities in the center. If the swelling is sufficiently extensive, the whole chloroplast may become disrupted.

XV. The Nucleus

Normally each cell contains a single nucleus. In certain unusual tissues (of the higher plant) the cell may contain more than one. In galls, proliferating callus, and pathological tissues, occasional cells may be multinucleate. The uninucleate, however, is the typical condition, and the single nucleus is embedded either in the peripheral cytoplasm or in the center of the vacuole, where it is suspended by fine cytoplasmic strands which extend from the peripheral cytoplasm. When the nucleus is central it tends to be spherical and when it is peripheral it tends to be flattened and approximately biconvex. In the peripheral position it is probably being compressed by the tonoplast, which is stretched across it.

The size of the nucleus varies. When spherical, the diameter is of the order of 6–7 μ and when flattened the width is about 10–12 μ. It is probable that the volume of the nucleus increases as the cell ages. Several investigators have urged that there is an intimate connection between the volume of the nucleus and that of the cytoplasm and have insisted that the nuclear cytoplasmic ratio is a value of some significance. Since volume of cytoplasm is not only difficult to determine but also certainly subject to fluctuation, this may be doubted. An evaluation of the connection in terms of dry weight or nitrogen content would certainly be more informative. Unfortunately, relevant determinations for the nucleus have not been made, and it is possible only to make a general estimate of the order of protein nitrogen content for plant nuclei as a whole. The protein content of a mature nucleus is probably of the order of 2×10^{-10} gm. This may be compared with the corresponding value for the whole cell, which is about 6×10^{-9} gm. Thus, the nucleus probably carries one-tenth to one-twentieth of the total protein of the cell.

Although the nucleus is frequently the most prominent single inclusion of the protoplast, considerably less is known about it chemically and metabolically than about mitochondria, microsomes, and chloroplasts, and for this there are two reasons. The nucleus, although large, does not comprise as great a proportion of the cell as the other components, and, secondly, it is considerably more difficult with plant tissues to isolate a nuclear, than it is a mitochondrial or a chloroplast, fraction. The nucleus seems to be considerably more fragile and seems to succumb more rapidly to the robust treatments that have to be applied to plant tissues to release the cellular inclusions. Nuclei have been isolated repeatedly and successfully from a variety of vertebrate tissues. So far they have been isolated only from plant tissues in which the wall system is poorly developed, from the embryos of cereal grains, and from root tips (10, 79). Nuclei have also been separated from coconut milk, i.e., the liquid endosperm of the coconut, but since this is scarcely a tissue in the conventional sense, the value of such preparations is open to some doubt. It is highly probable that the nuclei from this source are moribund and are not comparable with those from actively metabolizing tissues.

Since the cytological characteristics of plant and animal nuclei are similar, the chemical composition of the second may be taken as at least an indication of the position in the first. A variety of determinations suggest that of the total dry weight of nuclei about 70% is due to protein, about 3% is due to lipids, about 10% to DNA, and 2%–3% to RNA (24).

The protein of the nucleus is unusual, and this may reflect a peculiar composition of the chromosomes. The earliest studies on nuclear proteins were made with salmon sperm, and these suggested that the dominant protein in this is one having a low molecular weight and having about 80% of its amino acid complement represented by arginine. Later, other nuclei were found to contain similar basic proteins, although in these the proportion of arginine was found to be less and the proportion of other basic amino acids, such as lysine and histidine, greater. The general conclusion that was drawn from these earlier studies is probably valid also for plant nuclei. On the other hand, later investigations have shown that although the nucleus certainly involves a high proportion of basic proteins it also contains a distinctive fraction which is acidic and which contains not only a large proportion of dicarboxylic acids but also tryptophan,which is present only in trace amounts in the more basic proteins (47).

The basic character of nuclear proteins is important structurally. They carry free basic groups which may combine with the free acidic groups of the nucleic acid and thus stabilize a nucleoprotein complex in the nucleus and, by implication, in the chromosomes.

It is only rarely that a membrane can be seen around the nucleus with the light microscope. The presence of it, however, may be demonstrated by microdissection and by the use of polarization optics, and its structure has been examined in the electron microscope. Microdissection needles invaginate the surface until this is pierced, suggesting an elastic skin which covers a nonelastic core (16). With polarization optics a birefringent zone is frequently seen at the surface. The birefringence is such that it suggests a well-defined layer of the order of 150–200 μ thick composed of protein fibers aligned parallel to the surface. The anisotropic zone is shown not only by nuclei in sections but also by those isolated from tissues, and not only by animal, but also by plant, nuclei (74). Electron microscope studies have shown that the membrane is in many respects unusual (86). It involves a pair of electron-dense boundary layers with a clear strip between them, and this may correspond to the standard pattern of two protein layers with an intermediate phospholipid zone. The whole system, however, at least in certain cases, is traversed by large pores which are about 200 A in diameter. Both the inner and outer layers are pierced and a continuous channel is present which connects the body of the nucleus with the cytoplasm. This structural detail is clearly a matter of some importance since it provides conditions in which *large molecules may escape from the nucleus.* It is significant that metabolic components are more readily dispersed from the nucleus than from any other organelle during isolation. It is a common experience that protein is lost particularly readily.

In many nuclei a large proportion of the cavity within the membrane is occupied by a nuclear fluid, which after acid hydrolysis has been shown in one case to yield a large variety of amino acids (8). The cavity, however, certainly accommodates more than the nuclear sap. At the end of telophase and after the nuclear membrane has been re-formed, the chromosomes of the daughter nucleus disperse. They cannot be identified cytologically during the interphase, but that they are present cannot be doubted since they re-emerge at the following metaphase, each in the same relative position that was occupied at the end of the previous telophase. Although distinctive chromosomes cannot be seen in the interphase nucleus, indirect evidence, cytological appearance, and the results of electron microscope studies nevertheless indicate the presence of structural elements that are no doubt derived from them.

The indirect evidence is derived from observations of physical properties. Although the cavity is occupied by a fluid the viscosity of this is higher than that of water. Further, shock frequently induces gelation throughout the nucleus. This occurs during isolation, and, as a result, after separation from the cytoplasm the nucleus may have the general appearance and consistency of a small sphere of jelly (9). After gelation the system has the same properties as those of any other protein gel, and it is therefore probable that in the living state the cavity is traversed by fine fibrils in a mesh that is bathed by the nuclear sap. It is probable, in fact, that the nucleus has a similar submicroscopic structure to that of the cytoplasm and that the fibrils of the meshwork are joined by much the same sort of unions. A system of fibrils can frequently be seen in the light microscope after fixation and staining, but it has been claimed that the appearance of these is an artifact induced by the method of preparation. Fibers, however, may also be seen without fixation in a phase-contrast system. The refractive indexes of the liquid and solid phases are evidently similar, and with the conventional microscope the fibers are visible only after staining. Clearly they correspond to the structural elements indicated by physical observations, and their cytological characteristics are therefore important. After fixation they are apparently randomly dispersed, forming a reticulum. At frequent intervals the fibers carry small granules which stain deeply with basic dyes, and which are therefore probably composed of DNA.

Electron microscope studies of nuclear structure within the boundary membrane have not yielded extensive results. One investigation has shown that paired threads are present in certain nuclei and that each thread is of the order of 200 A in diameter. The significance of this observation is difficult to evaluate, but it may be that the stainable threads represent bundles of such fibrils since units of this dimension would certainly not be visible in the light microscope.

Each nucleus usually contains one or more nucleoli. These are spherical highly refractive bodies which are each 1–2 μ in diameter. They each involve a boundary membrane which encloses a fluid medium. They absorb basic dyes readily and they probably contain most of the RNA of the nucleus. They contain protein and this is probably different from that of the rest of the nucleus in being more acidic and therefore resembling more closely the protein of the cytoplasm. The number in each nucleus is not constant, although it is usually limited. Frequently, there is only one, although occasionally the number may be five or six. The nucleolus is independent and is not firmly anchored to any part of the reticulum. It may be centrifuged from one part of the nucleus to another, and it can be separated from it readily (47).

XVI. The Metabolic System of the Cell

The structure that has been described above provides the framework within which the metabolic cycle of the cell operates. Structure and activity are intimately linked, and the rest of this chapter is concerned with the nature of this relationship. The treatment of the theme begins with a consideration of certain relevant aspects of metabolism, and it may be emphasized that this is not intended either as an introduction or as a summary for other chapters in which particular phases of metabolism are more fully and more completely discussed.

The metabolism of the cell is a cyclical process which comprises a series of synthetic, and also a series of degradative, reactions. These constitute the anabolic and catabolic phases, respectively. This distinction is a traditional one and is still of some significance. In contemporary terms, however, it is less easily maintained than it was before the highly labile character of the biological system was fully recognized. In classical terms energy that is released in degradative reactions is consumed in the formation of compounds that promote growth and expansion. Within this pattern of interpretation catabolic reactions are limited to processes in which a release of energy occurs and anabolic reactions to processes in which compounds are synthesized which become permanent components of an expanding system. Recent interpretations do not affect the claim that extensive syntheses of complex molecules are a necessary condition for growth. They do, however, invalidate the general assumption that such synthesis is significant only in this connection. Until recently it was generally assumed that when a biological structure had been synthesized it was then a more or less stable entity from which chemical compounds were released only when dissolution occurs. The use of isotopes, however, has shown that biological structures after they have been formed are far from stable. It is now clear that the mature cell is not a system in which the component structures are relatively immobile. On the contrary, it is now beyond doubt that probably every single structural component is subject to continual degradation and reformation. It has been shown that in a tissue in which the protein content is not changing, nevertheless the incorporation of heavy nitrogen introduced with an ammonium ion or of radioactive carbon introduced with carbon dioxide may occur rapidly. Similarly, it has been found that radioactive phosphorus after absorption may become incorporated in an insoluble form in the cell within minutes, and radioactive carbon may become an integral component of the wall, again within minutes. Clearly, the mature cell is not a system of persistent structures, but may be compared with a house in which bricks of the walls are continually being withdrawn and replaced by others (75).

In the cyclical process of metabolism chemical components of structural elements, such as the wall, the cytoplasm, and the nucleus, are continually being released and discharged in a soluble form into a metabolic pool. From this they may escape into other cells or after further degradation into the environment—with consequent wastage. All, of course, are not lost and some are undoubtedly drawn into the metabolic sequence, but the loss of some implies that synthesis which maintains a constant structural state must depend on fragments which are supplied from another source. The process of synthesis, however, also involves another requirement—that of a source of energy. The elaboration of complex from simple molecules necessarily implies a consumption of energy. This, in the normal sequence, is provided from respiration. Thus, for analytical purposes the following phases of the cycle may be recognized: (a) degradation of structural components, (b) respiration, (c) mechanism of energy transfer, and (d) synthesis.

Since the immediate interest here is the relation between structure and activity, each of these phases is considered below with particular reference to the main chemical constituent of all protoplast structures —which is protein.

A. Degradation of Structures

Biological structures, it is evident from the discussion of this chapter, are the products of the aggregation of macromolecules, and the basic process of degradation is therefore one which involves the disruption of these elements. It is a curious feature of current knowledge that little is known about the mechanism of this degradation. The cell is apparently highly charged with hydrolytic enzymes which can disrupt these macromolecular units, but there is some doubt as to whether they are active—at least in hydrolyses—in the intact cell. With regard to protein, the cell incorporates some very active proteolytic enzymes, but there is some evidence that other systems may be involved in the disruption of protein during active metabolism. In one other case there is no doubt about the truth of this concept. Many cells contain large quantities of the enzymes, the diastases, which disrupt starch hydrolytically, but it is nevertheless clear that in active metabolism starch is degraded through a phosphorylase.

B. Respiration

This is also a metabolic process, but since it is a mechanism through which energy is mobilized and a variety of carbon skeletons generated, it is basic to the whole metabolic cycle.

In its simplest form respiration involves the degradation of sugar to carbon dioxide and water with the absorption of oxygen. It occurs in two broad phases. In the first, which may proceed in the absence of oxygen, the six-carbon sugar molecule is degraded into any one of a number of smaller fragments. In the second, all these are drawn into an oxidation cycle in which they are converted to carbon dioxide and water and which proceeds only in the presence of oxygen.

The first phase may take one of two forms. It may involve the degradation of the sugar into two three-carbon fragments in the process of glycolysis which is similar to fermentation. Or it may involve the direct oxidation of the sugar.

Two important features of the whole oxidation mechanism are displayed during glycolysis. The process depends on repeated phosphorylation and it yields adenosine triphosphate (ATP). In the initial phase the sugar molecule is esterified to give fructose diphosphate, in which phosphate is incorporated in ester linkages at positions one and six. After this stage the hexose is split into two three-carbon fragments and further phosphorylation of each fragment occurs. At a late stage in the process pyruvic acid is generated, but before this each phosphate group is transferred to adenosine diphosphate with the formation of adenosine triphosphate, the release of which constitutes a decisively important aspect of respiration.

In glycolysis one mole of sugar is converted to two moles of pyruvic acid. In this process several steps and a corresponding number of enzymes are involved. These enzymes do not require aerobic conditions and whether oxygen is present or absent pyruvic acid continues to be generated. In the presence of oxygen when the acid cycle is operating (see below) the pyruvic acid may be further degraded to two-carbon acetate. In the absence of oxygen the pyruvic acid is converted to alcohol with the intermediate formation of acetaldehyde, as in formula (XXXIII).

$$\begin{array}{lcllcl} CH_3 & & CH_3 & & & CH_3 \\ | & & | & & & | \\ C{=}O & \rightarrow & CH{=}O & + 2H & \rightarrow & CH_2OH \\ | & & \;+ & & & \\ COOH & & CO_2 & & & \end{array}$$

(XXXIII)

The direct oxidation of the sugar, which is in a sense alternative to glycolysis, involves a dehydrogenation of glucose-6-phosphate. In this a ketopentose sugar is formed. The immediate oxidation of the sugar probably involves the formation of a gluconic acid which is decarboxylated to give the pentose, thus:

$$\text{G—6—P} \rightarrow \text{Gluconate—6—P} \rightarrow \text{Pentose} + CO_2$$

The pentose is further metabolized to yield fragments which are drawn into the common oxidation cycle.

In the presence of oxygen the ultimate products of glycolysis and of direct oxidation are degraded in an acid cycle. In this a cyclical process is involved in which a conversion of one acid to the next occurs with the elimination of either hydrogen or carbon dioxide and in which an acid derived from the products of the first phase is regenerated in the course of the cycle.

The acid cycle depends on a particular group of enzymes, the different members of which mediate different stages. Of its products, carbon dioxide escapes into the atmosphere and the hydrogen pairs are ultimately transferred to oxygen with the formation of water through the electron transfer system. The hydrogen pairs are released from the substrate acids with the mediation of particular dehydrogenases, but these in most cases do not transfer the hydrogen immediately to oxygen. They transfer it to other hydrogen carriers which, in turn, may donate them to still other carriers in the chain. In most (if not in all) plant tissues the final carrier is a cytochrome complex from which the hydrogen is transferred to oxygen through a cytochrome oxidase. Diagrammatically the process may be represented as shown in (XXXIV).

Substrate (From acid cycle) — A — BH_2 — Cyt — H_2O

Oxidized substrate — AH_2 — B — Cyt H_2 — $\frac{1}{2}O_2$

(XXXIV)

ATP, which is formed during glycolysis, is also generated, but more abundantly, in the aerobic phase. It is a product of the process of electron transfer. The mechanism of the generation of the pyrophosphate bond is unknown, but that it occurs is well established, and it has been shown that ATP is generated at each step of the transfer. It is important that the quantity formed in the aerobic phase is considerably greater than that generated in the glycolytic phase. Whereas, 2 moles of ATP are formed per mole of sugar in glycolysis, 22 (or more?) moles are formed in the course of transfer through the cytochrome system. The significance of this is considered below.

Another important consequence of the respiratory sequence is due to the development within it of a large variety of compounds. Respiration may indeed be considered as a mechanism through which small fragments are generated. Many of these are ultimately degraded to carbon dioxide and oxygen. Some, however, are withdrawn from the sequence and form the substrates for many indispensable syntheses. In this connection, the products of the acid cycle are of particular importance, since they provide the basis for some of the most important synthetic reactions of the plant. This is the reason why some now regard the importance of the acid cycle as a route of synthesis as comparable to its importance in the release of energy.

C. MECHANISM OF ENERGY TRANSFER

When the sugar molecule is degraded to smaller fragments in respiration, chemical bonds are broken and the energy they incorporate is released. In respiration this energy is not immediately dissipated as heat, but it is in a sense trapped into another chemical compound in which it is stored. A variety of chemical compounds fulfill this function of storage centers. Their action, however, may be considered in terms of adenosine triphosphate which is probably the most frequent and the most important. Appropriate reactions promote the addition of a pyrophosphate bond to adenosine diphosphate. This third phosphate bond carries a high energy value. Also it is labile and the energy it carries is readily transferred and utilized in the formation of other bonds in synthetic reactions (29).

Adenosine triphosphate is therefore the principal device through which energy is mobilized in respiration and transferred to synthetic reactions. The rate at which it is formed is of decisive importance and is likely to affect the whole activity of the system. One factor is known which certainly affects the rate—the degree of aeration. Since only 2 moles are produced in glycolysis and 22 in the aerobic phase per mole of sugar, the relative rates of production in anaerobic and aerobic conditions are likely to be in the ratio of 2:24. Clearly, to this must be attributed the depressing effect of anaerobic conditions on all cellular activity in aerobic organisms. In these conditions sufficient ATP is not being generated to promote the processes that are sustained with vigorous aeration.

D. SYNTHESIS

This treatment, as stated above, is restricted to the synthesis of protein, which is not only the main structural component of the protoplast but is also the vehicle of all the catalytic properties of the cell. It is the peculiar feature of biological systems that the activities on which they depend are promoted by catalysts which are proteins (see Chapter 2). Thus the synthesis of proteins implies the elaboration of structural elements and also the elaboration of the mechanism on which metabolism depends.

Clearly in a biological context the synthesis of proteins carries two aspects, the mechanism involved in the formation of the gross characteristics of the chemical molecule and that involved in the induction of particular catalytic properties. The two aspects are, of course, not independent, and both are evolved in the same process. It is convenient to consider them separately, however, since they raise different issues.

The synthesis of the polypeptide requires the prior synthesis of amino acids, and these, in turn, depend on the provision of carbon skeletons from the acid cycle of respiration, and of reduced forms of nitrogen, probably ammonia. Ammonia may be absorbed by the cell directly from the environment as the ammonium ion, or it may be generated from the reduction of nitrate, which is itself absorbed from the external medium. Normally ammonia does not accumulate but combines either directly or indirectly with one of the products of the acid cycle, three of which are of particular significance in this connection: pyruvic acid, oxalacetic acid, and α-ketoglutaric acid. These are keto acids and they are particularly active in transamination reactions, as in formula (XXXV).

$$\mathrm{NH_2\overset{\overset{R}{|}}{C}HCOOH + O{=}\overset{\overset{R'}{|}}{C}COOH \rightleftharpoons O{=}\overset{\overset{R}{|}}{C}COOH + NH_2\overset{\overset{R'}{|}}{C}HCOOH}$$

(XXXV)

In the transamination sequence, an amino group is transferred to the keto acid after incorporation of ammonia into another carbon skeleton. It is now known, however, that plants contain a much greater array of keto acids than the three mentioned above and these also may function as acceptors of nitrogen (this topic will be treated in later chapters on nitrogen metabolism).

The elaboration of amino acids to protein involves the synthesis of peptide bonds. The mechanism involved is uncertain, but two possibilities have been suggested, a transpeptidation reaction, or a phosphorylation. The first may be characterized as shown in formula (XXXVI).

$$\mathrm{R'CO{-}NH\overset{\displaystyle R^2 \atop |}{C}HCO{-}NHR^3 + NH_2X \rightleftharpoons R'CO{-}NH\overset{\displaystyle R^2 \atop |}{C}HCO{-}NHX + NH_2R^3}$$

(XXXVI)

In this a simple replacement is involved with the formation of another peptide bond, and it is promoted by a proteolytic enzyme.

The transpeptidation reaction does not require ATP, but various other reactions have been suggested which do require it. Evidence has been adduced for the following, as shown in reaction (XXXVII).

$$\mathrm{RCOOH + ATP \rightleftharpoons RCOO\underset{\displaystyle | \atop OH}{\overset{\displaystyle OH \atop |}{P}}{=}O + ADP}$$

$$\mathrm{RCOO\underset{\displaystyle | \atop OH}{\overset{\displaystyle OH \atop |}{P}}{=}O + NH_2R \rightarrow RCO{-}NHR_1 + H_3PO_4}$$

(XXXVII)

In this one amino acid reacts with ATP to produce a phosphorylated compound which then reacts with another amino acid with the formation of a peptide bond. It may be noted that this hypothetical scheme illustrates the sequence through which the energy of the pyrophosphate bond may be utilized in synthesis (29).

The evidence that ATP is involved in the synthesis of the peptide bond is considerable. It may not, however, be involved in a reaction such as that shown. Other possibilities are not excluded, and one of these is mentioned below.

While the protein molecule as such is being elaborated, it is also being endowed with specific properties, and the conditions that determine these are at present even more obscure than those that control the formation of the successive bonds. Recent work, however, has provided some intimation of what the general character of these conditions might be.

A decisive factor in the synthesis of proteins is possibly the participation of nucleic acids. A close connection between proteins and nucleic acids has been suspected since about 1940 (14). Cytochemical observations have repeatedly shown that when protein synthesis is active the nucleic acids are particularly prominent, and bodies such as the nucleus which may be associated with the synthesis of particular enzymatic proteins have been shown to be particularly rich in nucleic acids. These qualititive correlations, however, do not establish a causal connection, and it is only during the last three or four years that decisive evidence for the participation of nucleic acids in protein synthesis has been adduced. Such evidence probably cannot be assembled with intact living cells, and an appropriate cell-free system has only recently been described. This is obtained from active cultures of *Staphylococcus aureus* (30). When organisms from such cultures are disintegrated by the conventional grinding techniques, protein synthesis cannot be demonstrated in the preparation. This may, however, be shown when the cells are disrupted with supersonic treatment. When carefully controlled, this yields fragments which contain the necessary enzymatic systems, and when the nucleic acid that the fragments incorporate has been dispersed, the effect of nucleic acid in the medium can be demonstrated. The fragments are treated with ribonuclease. This removes the nucleic acid without disturbing enzymatic protein. When these particles which have been freed of their own nucleic acids are suspended in a medium containing nucleic acid, two types of synthetic reactions may be demonstrated. In a medium containing a single amino acid the incorporation of this occurs into the protein which is already present, and in a medium in which a complete amino acid mixture is available a net increase of protein has been observed. With both situations ATP is required in addition to the nucleic acid, which indicates that in this system both incorporation and net synthesis involve a phosphorylation. This may involve a reaction of the ATP with amino acids or with the nucleic acids. Both would provide for a transfer of energy to the peptide bond; in addition to the mechanism outlined above, another has been suggested which involves the phosphorylation of the nucleic acids.

Net synthesis of protein in the system with supersonically disrupted cells also yields specific proteins. It has been shown that the proteins that are formed in this *in vitro* system have specific catalytic properties. It has been shown that in the presence of the nucleic acids the net synthesis of protein may involve a considerable increase in a glucozymase, a catalase, and a β-galactosidase. This is clearly an extremely important observation since it indicates that the nucleic acids not only promote the formation of protein, but endow it with specificity.

Specificity in the protein necessarily implies a particular sequential arrangement of amino acids, and this is evidently determined by the pattern of the nucleic acid itself. The nucleic acid acts as a *template*, and evidently the synthesis of successive peptide bonds occurs through a series of phosphorylations that are effective on it. The template, however, also organizes the order in which the amino acids are arranged, and it does so presumably by virtue of the fact that particular parts are involved in the incorporation of particular amino acids in the protein. The nucleic acid may be envisaged as a mold which carries a series of reaction sites. Different amino acids are involved at the different reaction sites, and when they combine they do so in a particular order. Thus, the mold promotes a particular arrangement which determines the specific catalytic properties of the protein.

For net synthesis of protein both RNA and DNA are required. There is some evidence, however, that the immediate template for protein may be the RNA and that the DNA promotes the synthesis of the RNA. This tentative interpretation is based on the observation that, although some synthesis occurs with RNA only, nevertheless the reaction proceeds more rapidly and for a longer time when both acids are present. RNA it may be supposed is as labile as any other constituent of the cell, and during the course of the reaction it tends to be degraded to the component nucelotides. In the presence of DNA this degradation continues but it is accompanied by an immediate resynthesis, and the level of RNA is therefore maintained (31).

It may be noted in this connection that nucleic acids may not be the only substances involved in the determination of the specificity of the protein. It has been known for some decades that with microorganisms the level of some enzymes may be determined by the substrate on which they are cultured. With these it has frequently been shown that a substrate may promote the development of an enzyme or enzyme system which is involved in its metabolism. Thus in the presence of galactose a particular group of enzymes may be enhanced to the extent that the organism can use this sugar metabolically. This is the phenomenon of *enzyme adaptation*, and the enzymes whose level can be affected by the substrate are distinguished as adaptive enzymes. Certain enzymes are apparently substrate-independent, and these are called constitutive enzymes. Two cases of enzyme adaptation have been described with plants. It has been shown that the level of an indolyl acetic acid oxidase varies with the substrate in the tissue (32); and similarly with a glycollic acid oxidase (85). With adaptive enzymes, while it has been shown that the substrate effect is decisive, it has also been shown that the development of the enzyme involves the participation of a template nucleic acid. In Gale's experiments, for instance, the formation of the β-galactosidase, while it required the presence of galactose in the medium, also required the presence of nucleic acid

(30). In spite of extensive speculation, it is not at the moment clear how substrate and nucleic acid interact.

XVII. Distribution of Enzyme Systems

The variety of metabolic reactions that proceed within a cell are very large, and it is inconceivable that they could all proceed simultaneously within a homogenous system. Some separation and segregation there clearly must be. If different reactions did not proceed in spatially isolated zones, distinctive reaction sequences could not occur, since different reactions would inevitably interfere with each other. This has been recognized since the metabolism of cells was first examined, but it is only during the last ten years that techniques have become available through which the subject could be investigated.

A. Technique

Two procedures have been developed which are of particular importance: the cytochemical localization of enzymes and the identification of particular reactions in fractions isolated from a homogenate.

The first is illustrated by the Gomori procedure for the localization of alkaline phosphatase. In this, tissue is incubated with a solution containing a phosphate ester and a calcium salt. When it comes in contact with the enzyme, the ester is hydrolyzed and releases a phosphate group which reacts with calcium to form insoluble calcium phosphate. It is assumed that the release of the phosphate and the formation of the calcium phosphate occurs at the site of the enzyme. Thus if the localization of the calcium salt can be determined this should show the site of the enzyme. The phosphate, however, although insoluble, is colorless, and the complete technique requires further steps to convert the precipitate to a visible compound. After incubation the tissue is treated with cobalt nitrate and then with ammonium sulfide. The first step ensures the formation of cobalt phosphate, which is insoluble but still colorless, and the second, of cobalt sulfide, which, while being insoluble, is black. Other techniques have been developed with other enzymes but most involve the same characteristic feature of the formation of an insoluble compound at the site of the reaction (34).

Valuable information has been obtained with this method. It is open, however, to certain objections and has been regarded with some scepticism by many investigators. In particular, it is not always certain that all the reactants are present at the primary reaction site, and the product may therefore move some distance before the insoluble substance is formed. If this happens, then the distribution of the precipitate may not be an accurate index of the localization of the enzyme (19).

The second method, which is essentially the technique described above for the separation of different organelles, has been extensively developed and exploited in recent years. It involves (as already described) the maceration of the tissue in such a way that all the organelles are dispersed without being disintegrated, followed by a separation of the different particulate fractions by centrifugation. When separation has been achieved, for studying the distribution of enzymes, the different fractions are suspended in different media and changes in these are determined (44).

The conditions of maceration are critical, and in particular the composition of the medium in which disruption is promoted is important. Many of the cell organelles are enclosed in selectively semipermeable membranes and they incorporate substances in solution which have a comparatively high osmotic pressure. The preservation of the particle, therefore, requires that it shall be released into a medium which is isotonic with the internal solution. If it is exposed to water or a hypotonic solution it will absorb water and burst, and if it is placed in contact with a hypertonic solution it will shrink and may consequently become internally disorganized. It is also necessary that it should be dispersed into a medium with an appropriate hydrogen ion concentration and with an appropriate ionic composition. The acidity and ionic composition are both likely to affect the organization of the particle and the activity of the enzymes it holds.

The separation of the different components of the homogenate is induced by centrifugation, which exploits differences in density and size of the component particles. When a particular centrifugal force is applied to all the particles in a suspension, those which are largest and densest will tend to be deposited first, and those which are smallest and least dense, last. Similarly within a given time the first category are deposited with a low, and the second with a high, centrifugal force. In the normal procedure the suspension is exposed to a series of treatments of increasing centrifugal force, and, as this is increased, so the size and density of the particular fraction which is isolated decreases. The technique may be elaborated by inducing a separation through a series of fluids of increasing density. If large particles are allowed to settle under gravity in a stationary tube in which a series of fluids of increasing density have been superimposed, then they will fall until they reach a layer which is of the same density as themselves. A similar effect is observed when particles are induced to traverse a gradient tube in a centrifugal field, and when particles of different density are involved, then they will tend to accumulate at different levels in the tube (1).

Hitherto, the standard technique has involved centrifugation through a uniform aqueous medium. A preliminary centrifugation at 1000 *g* is applied which removes all the larger debris which is derived from cell walls and, it is said, nuclei. This may be followed by a second separation at 6000 *g* which removes chloroplasts when leaf material is involved. The third phase involves centrifugation with speeds up to about 20,000 *g* and induces the separation of mitochondria. The final treatment is designed to isolate microsomes, which are deposited when the field is at 60,000–100,000 *g*.

When this succession has been completed, cell wall, nuclear, chloroplast, mitochondrial, and microsomal fractions have been isolated and a supernatant residue is left. The supernatant is presumed to be free of all particulate matter and the protein that it contains is said to represent the soluble fraction of the tissue. Certainly, some of this protein is catalytically active, and the enzymes of the supernatant are referred to as soluble enzymes (44).

Although a variety of fractions may be isolated from the same homogenate it is only rarely that more than two are separated from the same preparation. Nuclei are usually isolated separately, since they tend to be disrupted by maceration techniques that are appropriate for other fractions. Chloroplasts again are normally treated separately since, when present, some are inevitably crushed and the fragments contaminate other fractions.

The centrifugation technique is valuable, but it has important limitations and some of the implications of the results obtained with it require emphasis. Since the separation of the different particles depends on differences in size and density, it is clear that any particular fraction is uniform only with respect to these physical characteristics and it is certainly not uniform cytologically. This is particularly important in connection with the mitochondrial fraction. Most of the particles in this conform to the general size and density of mitochondria. Most also give the appropriate staining reactions. Many, however, do not stain with Janus green B and are probably derived from the indeterminate group that have here been called proplastids. For similar reasons the microsome fraction is also probably contaminated with particles which are different from the majority. In this case the particles may be fragments of larger organelles. During maceration many mitochondria are undoubtedly dispersed and fragments from them are eventually deposited with the microsomes. The cytological heterogeneity of particular fractions is important since this may be the origin of the bewildering array of enzymatic properties that have been attributed to certain organelles. The cytological entity may have a comparatively restricted enzyme complement, but the isolated fraction may have a large variety because of the contaminants that it incorporates.

The soluble fraction occupies a peculiar status. The enzymes in the supernatant are probably in this phase in a soluble form. This does not, however, necessarily mean that they were originally in the cell in that form. The protein of the supernatant is quite simply that which is not derived from any particulate fraction, and it is therefore derived from what has here been called the ground phase. It may be recalled that this involves protein attached to the surface membranes, protein that contributes to the structural framework, and it may involve free protein in the fluid of the cytoplasm or even of the cell sap. How much of this is catalytically active is unknown. But the observations from the centrifugation procedure do not exclude the possibility that all components of this system carry enzymatic properties, whether they are strictly in solution in the original cell or not.

B. Enzymes of the Ground Phase of the Cytoplasm

These are the enzymes that are found in the supernatant after all the particulate fractions have been removed. The variety in this group is large. It involves certain hydrolytic enzymes, various phosphorylases, and all the enzymes of the glycolytic series.

There is some evidence that different enzymes of the supernatant may be derived from different parts of the cytoplasm. This evidence has been obtained particularly from studies of the catalytic properties of the external surface of the protoplast (9). It has frequently been shown that when cells are suspended in a substrate solution, end products of an enzymatic reaction may accumulate in the external medium at a rate greater than might be expected if the substrate molecule had to penetrate the external barrier. When tissues are suspended in a sucrose solution hexoses accumulate in the medium, and when they are exposed to organic phosphates, free phosphate ions are found in the external fluid. It is relevant that unlike bacterial and fungal cells green plant cells do not produce extracellular enzymes. The enzymes of the cell are firmly anchored in the protoplast and in conventional experimental situations they are not released into the external medium. Tissues are known, such as those of the glandular organs of insectivorous plants, which do secrete active enzymes. These, however, involve exceptional situations and do not invalidate the general conclusion that with normal parenchymatous tissues enzymes do not escape from the protoplast. Such being the case, the experimental observations necessarily indicate that the enzymatic reaction is at the surface of the protoplast, and the hydrolysis of the sucrose may be attributed to an invertase and that of the ester to a phosphatase in the external boundary layer.

The presence of enzymes in the surface is consistent with the structure of the diffusion barrier described above. If this consists of two layers of protein on the inner and outer surfaces of a phospholipid layer, then the enzymes would no doubt be components of the external protein layer. The incidence of surface enzymes is a structural feature of importance. It has frequently been claimed that activated transport of solutes across the diffusion barriers requires enzymatic reactions. The evidence clearly indicates that catalytic reactions are in fact a property of the external membrane, and the relation of these to absorption has been investigated in some detail with respect to sugar. The permeability of diffusion barriers to glucose is relatively low. Nevertheless, in certain cells glucose, is rapidly absorbed, and it has been suggested that this depends on a surface phosphorylation. The effect of heavy metals, and particularly uranium, on sugar absorption supports this interpretation. With yeast, uranium inhibits sugar absorption to the extent of 90%. The inhibition, however, may be relieved by increasing the external concentration of phosphate. This suggests that the uranium is absorbed on to emzymatic sites which are normally occupied by sugar and phosphate. When the phosphate concentration is increased, this ion displaces the heavy metal and exposes an appropriate enzymatic site for the absorption of sugar (72).

C. MITOCHONDRIA

The systems associated with mitochondria have recently been intensively studied with the appropriate fractions isolated from homogenates. The main conclusion that has emerged from a large number of investigations is that the mitochondria are the seat of oxidative activity and that all the enzymes associated with the aerobic phase of respiration are carried in these organelles.

A close association between mitochondria and aerobic respiratory activity was first suggested on the basis of observations of the effects of Janus green B staining. The immediate effect of the dye is to color the particles a characteristic deep blue, and this color persists if the tissue is exposed to air. On the other hand, when it is confined to anaerobic conditions, the color fades. This is similar to the effect of tissue on methylene blue in the absence of oxygen, and the decolorization is due to the same mechanism as that involved in the fading of the Janus green B. The colorless compound is a reduced form, and this is developed by the transfer of hydrogen to the dye when oxygen is not available. The results obtained with isolated mitochondria have fully confirmed the suggestion promoted by the dye reaction. When the particles are suspended in a solution of one of the cycle acids, they induce a rapid untake of oxygen with a corresponding dispersal of substrate. From this and other observations, it has been established that mitochondria carry (a) the enzymes of the acid cycle, (b) the electron transfer system, and (c) the system which promotes aerobic phosphorylation with the generation of ATP.

When isolated mitochondria from mung beans (*Phaseolus aureus*) (58) or from pea (*Pisum sativum*) seedlings (21) are suspended in a solution of single components of the acid cycle, other members of the organic acid cycle are generated. Indeed, the evidence has shown that all stages of the cycle including the incorporation of pyruvate are completed in the mitochondria and that these therefore carry all the appropriate enzymes.

The oxygen uptake that accompanies oxidation of cycle acids is highly sensitive to cyanide. Not only so, but it is reversibly inhibited by carbon monoxide. This substance, while depressing oxygen uptake in the dark, has little influence in the light. Collectively these effects indicate that terminal oxidation is due to cytochrome oxidase. The presence of various cytochromes in the mitochondria has been shown spectroscopically, and some evidence has been provided showing that these are accompanied by other intermediate carriers.

In the intact cell, the evidence is overwhelming that electron transfer through the cytochrome system is associated with aerobic phosphorylation. This function is also a property of mitochondria. When radioactive phosphate is supplied in the suspension medium in addition to ATP or ADP, the triphosphate that is recovered at the end of the reaction is found to be labeled, which indicates that the generation of ATP occurs in these particles (59).

Evidence has been assembled that suggests that certain synthetic reactions may be associated with the mitochondria. The synthesis of amino acids and of fats are two among many that have been assigned to them, but it may be repeated that this is not in fact a homogeneous fraction. While the majority of particles in the fraction are probably typical mitochondria, others may belong to different categories and they may carry different enzyme systems (36).

It has been shown above that the mitochondrion is structurally a highly organized system. Metabolically it is probably equally highly organized. When it is disrupted it loses a high proportion of its protein. It also loses a great many enzymatic activities associated with it. Some activities are unaffected, while others are markedly depressed. The protein that is dispersed is undoubtedly soluble material from between the cristae. At least some of this is enzymatically active, and the release of the protein therefore involves a dispersal of certain enzymes such as an acid phosphatase and glutamic dehydrogenase. Other enzymes such as those of the cytochrome system, succinic dehydrogenase, and several others, are unaffected. These are probably part of the protein that is incorporated in the structure of the cristae. They are insoluble and they are therefore unaffected by the disruption of the system (43).

In mitochondrial fractions from vertebrate tissues, it has been claimed that a group of particles may be identified which contain only hydrolytic, and particularly proteolytic, enzymes. Similar particles have not been reported from homogenates of plant tissues, but if they are present they may have the same significance. When death occurs particulate bodies disintegrate, the hydrolytic enzyme bodies are likely to disperse along with the rest, and the enzymes they contain will then be released into the cytoplasm and promote autolysis. It has always been something of a mystery how the living state is maintained with the large quantity of hydrolytic enzymes that the cell contains. If these are in fact segregated in small packets this explains at once the maintenance of the active state and the rapid induction of autolysis when death occurs (23).

D. MICROSOMES

The metabolic status of these bodies is more difficult to define than is that of mitochondria. Various enzyme systems have been attributed to them, but in many cases with doubtful justification. This fraction after isolation tends to be contaminated with fragments from disrupted mitochondria, and certain of the activities identified in microsome fractions may in fact be due to these bodies. On the other hand certain enzymes, and notably cytochrome c reductase, are certainly more abundant in the microsomes than they are elsewhere in the cell. It is possible that the primary metabolic significance of microsomes is a consequence of their high RNA content. This substance, it has been shown, is required in both protein synthesis and in the incorporation of individual amino acids into proteins. Relevant observations with plant microsomes are not available, but data with appropriate fractions from liver indicate that these bodies are active in promoting incorporation. If this is the case with liver, then it may well also be the case with plant material.

The resemblance between microsomes and virus particles has been mentioned above. A further similarity may be noted here. The virus particle is also an extremely active center of protein synthesis. In this case, infection leads to the formation and accumulation of further virus

nucleoprotein. In the virus particle, the RNA which it contains acts a
a template for the formation of a specific virus protein in the same wa
as the RNA in the microsome organizes the synthesis of specific cyto
plasmic protein. In fact the virus crystal may in certain connections b
considered simply as a "rogue microsome."

E. CHLOROPLASTS

The enzymes of chloroplasts have not been studied in detail, thei
general nature however may be inferred from the reactions that th
organelles sustain.

It is certain that chloroplasts promote the photolysis of water, and i
is highly probable that they incorporate the mechanism of the photo
synthetic fixation of carbon dioxide. Isolated chloroplasts in light induc
a cleavage of water with the evolution of oxygen. In the *in vitro* system
the reaction is continuous only when an appropriate hydrogen accepto
is provided. The nature of the mechanism involved in photolysis i
still unknown, but it may be of some significance that chloroplasts con
tain a variety of cytochromes, some of which are unlike those of th
mitochondria (38). There is no evidence that any respiratory function
are localized in chloroplasts, and it is improbable that these cytochrome
are associated with an oxidative phosphorylation.

Carbon dioxide fixation in photosynthesis is also a characteristic o
these bodies, and they therefore probably carry the enzymes associate
with this and with the conversion of the products of fixation to sugar
In addition, they undoubtedly carry the phosphorylases required in th
synthesis of starch from sugar (2).

F. NUCLEI

There is a wealth of information, much of it conflicting, on the en
zyme systems of mammalian nuclei, and from it only one firm con
clusion can be drawn—and that a negative one. It was at one time held
that the nucleus is the seat of respiratory activity. It is now quite cer
tain that this is not the case. The oxygen uptake of isolated nuclei i
negligible whatever the medium in which they are suspended, and they
apparently do not carry any oxidizing enzymes. Slight oxygen absorp
tion and traces of related enzymatic activity can undoubtedly be at
tributed to contamination with mitochondrial fragments.

The paucity of firmly established positive conclusions is a conse
quence of the experimental difficulties that nuclei present. They are
apparently particularly liable to absorb enzymes from the macerate
and in other circumstances to lose enzymes to it, which may be a consequence of the fact noted (see above) that the boundary membrane of

he nucleus is peculiar in being traversed by large pores. Fragmentary as the data are, they nevertheless suggest that a few catalytic systems may be more abundant in the nucleus than they are in the cytoplasm. Among the few are deoxyribonuclease, which degrades DNA hydrolytically, and arginase, which promotes the cleavage of arginine to ornithine and urea. The significance of this is obscure, but it may be of some importance that the substrates on which these enzymes act are themselves characteristic of the nucleus. DNA is probably confined to the nucleus, and arginine represents a large proportion of the basic nuclear proteins (56).

The results of only one investigation have been published in which the enzymes of plant nuclei have been investigated. The nuclei in this case were isolated from embryos of wheat (*Triticum aestivum*), and the surprising result was recorded that they are particularly rich in the enzymes of the glycolytic cycle. Embryonic tissues are composed of meristematic cells, and the presence of glycolytic enzymes may be characteristic of the nuclei of such cells. If this is the case, then the general inference regarding the enzymatic status in mature cells may require some amplification (79).

XVIII. The Distribution of Metabolic Activities

The different parts of the cell clearly involve different enzymatic systems. These, however, are certainly interdependent and the general outlines of the interacting system may be considered in terms of the metabolism of sugar and of nitrate ions.

Both these substances are absorbed either from other cells or directly from an external medium, and both, before they can reach the cytoplasm, must traverse the external plasmalemma. Nitrate probably traverses this structure without significant restraint and penetration into the cytoplasm probably does not require any enzymatic activity at the external surface. When it reaches the cytoplasm some of it is undoubtedly metabolized by being reduced and incorporated into amino acids and a variety of soluble nitrogen compounds, while some may be eventually discharged across the tonoplast into the vacuole. The nitrate ion or its reduction products may accumulate in the vacuole, and this may involve a movement against the concentration gradient. If the tonoplast has the general membrane structure, then it is likely that the activated movement of either the nitrate ion or of compounds derived from it will involve, either directly or indirectly, a reaction with catalytic protein. These activated movements across membranes will be discussed in a later chapter (Volume II, Chapter 4).

The sugar that is absorbed into the cytoplasm undoubtedly reacts at some point with a catalyst in the plasmalemma. This may involve a phosphorylation which promotes the flow into the cytoplasm. Whether this phosphorylation leads to the formation of the sugar ester which is discharged into the cytoplasm as such and is then available for glycolytic breakdown may be doubted. It is more probable that when the sugar is released at the internal surface of the plasmalemma it has been de-esterified and is in a state in which it can be acted on by the enzymes of the glycolytic sequence or of direct oxidation. Some of the sugar that reaches the cytoplasm is undoubtedly immediately dispersed in the first phase of respiration. Some, however, is certainly transported across the tonoplast and discharged into the vacuole. The movement across the tonoplast may involve reactions similar to those sustained by the plasmalemma. There may again be an enzymatic reaction at the external surface of the tonoplast which promotes an activated inward flow.

The matrix carries all the glycolytic enzymes, and these may be either on the framework or in the fluid by which it is bathed. The hexose is first phosphorylated with the production of fructose-1,6-diphosphate. The molecule is then split into two three-carbon fragments and each of these is ultimately converted into a molecule of pyruvic acid. The production of pyruvate involves several stages and these are all traversed in the ground phase of the cytoplasm. [For details regarding sugar absorption consult Rothstein (72).]

The subsequent metabolism of the pyruvic acid occurs in the mitochondria which are embedded in the cytoplasm. The products of glycolysis circulate in the fluid of the ground phase and they may diffuse to the mitochondria or be carried to them in a protoplasmic stream.

There is some evidence that certain enzymes are present on the external surfaces of the mitochondria. Since the mitochondrion is enclosed in a membrane involving protein layers on either side of a lopoid layer, this might indeed be expected. If this has the properties of other diffusion barriers then catalytic properties in the external protein are probable. Thus, the pyruvate when it comes into contact with the mitochondria may be transformed immediately. On the other hand there is again some evidence that a transport mechanism operates across the external membrane, and this may involve reaction of the pyruvate at the external surface with the enzymes of a system which promote internal accumulation.

In the body of the mitochondrion the products of glycolysis are exposed to enzymes on the surfaces of the cristae and between them. These enzymes promote the reactions of the cycle, the development of acids and their degradation through decarboxylation, dehydrogenation and electron transfer to oxygen. In the course of electron transfer ATP is generated, and this is probably discharged into the matrix between the baffles. [For details relating to mitochondria, consult Lindberg and Ernster (53).]

Ammonia, or other reduced forms of nitrogen, which are also present in the ground cytoplasm may be absorbed catalytically into the mitochondrion and there react with acids of the cycle with the production of amino acids. Alternatively the acids may leak out of the mitochondrion and react with ammonium in the mesoplasm, again with the formation of amino acids. Ultimately, whatever the seat of the primary reaction with the dicarboxylic acids, amino acids are available in the ground cytoplasm and it is probable that the transamination reactions which provide the variety of amino acids proceed in this phase.

The ATP and similar compounds which are generated in the mitochondria undoubtedly leak out, reach the ground cytoplasm and there become available to other organelles which are also embedded in this phase—the microsomes and the nucleus. Some ATP is probably absorbed into the nucleus and there provides for the synthetic reactions of this body.

Much of the ATP is, however, probably consumed in synthetic reactions of the ground cytoplasm and of the microsomes. In the presence of this compound appropriate enzymes may phosphorylate the amino acids or the nucleic acids of the microsomes. If the reaction is with the RNA, then the enzymes may be carried by the microsomes. Whatever the sequence, however, the amino acids which have been generated by reactions in the mitochondria may condense onto the microsomes and there become elaborated into proteins.

XIX. Nuclear Cytoplasmic Relations

The metabolic cycle of the cell is maintained with a pattern similar to that outlined. It depends on surface reactions in diffusion barriers, on particular reactions in the ground cytoplasm, on another set in the mitochondria, and on another set again in the microsomes. In this system the nucleus is not involved. It may absorb ATP from the cytoplasm, but it does not apparently contribute anything directly to the metabolic cycle. This is consistent with the general state of low catalytic activity that many nuclei seem to display and is consistent with a great deal of direct evidence on the influence of the nucleus on the activity of the cytoplasm. This evidence has been obtained primarily from enucleation experiments, in which the metabolic activity of nucleated and enucleated fragments are compared. This technique has been used extensively with certain animal cells, and it has also been used to a more limited extent with plant cells. The two types of fragment may be obtained in several ways. When normal parenchymatous cells are strongly and sharply plasmolyzed the protoplast may disrupt into several fragments, only one of which carries a nucleus. Enucleated cells may also be obtained with *Spirogyra* by centrifuging the filament. Under this treatment the nucleus is displaced to one end of the cell and divides in that position. At the same time the wall is formed in the zone that was occupied by the nucleus before the centrifugal treatment. The most valuable experimental material, however, is obtained from the alga *Acetabularia mediterranea.* This is a unicellular organism which has a tubular stalk, the cavity of which is continuous into a disklike head. When the stem is severed one unit is obtained with, and a second without, a nucleus.

With the protoplast fragments obtained by plasmolysis treatment, it has been observed that cell wall formation begins on the surface of the cytoplasm although it may not be completed. With enucleated cells of *Spirogyra* it has also been shown that the photosynthesis continues, the synthesis of tannins is sustained, and the cells may elongate. Enucleated fragments of *Acetabularia* have the same rate of oxygen uptake, they give the same rate of incorporation of radioactive phosphorus and the same rate of incorporation of radioactive carbon into proteins as other fragments which carry a nucleus. All these effects are observed immediately after the induction of the enucleated state, and they show that the nucleus is not a necessary constituent of the metabolic system and that the nucleus does not contribute anything on which the operation of the cycle depends (6).

Moreover the normal action of the cytoplasm may continue for a surprisingly long time after separation from the nucleus. Enucleated fragments of *Acetabularia mediterranea* for instance sustained normal respiratory activity for three months. Eventually, however, activity in the portion without a nucleus declines while the corresponding processes in the complete protoplast continue at a steady and undiminished rate. Clearly the experimental evidence indicates that while the nucleus has little or no effect on immediate matabolism it has a considerable effect on the maintenance of the metabolic apparatus. Further, it also indicates that the maintenance is mediated through some particular chemical substance. The long period of stability suggests that activity continues until a stock of some particular substance is exhausted and that declining activity is an indication of a decrease in the level of the hypothetical compound.

All the available evidence is consistent with the view that the substance that sustains cytoplasmic activity is RNA. Direct determinations of RNA content after enucleation are consistent with this interpretaion. With *Acetabularia* it has been shown that, while the immediate result of enucleation is to accelerate RNA synthesis, nevertheless the final effect is to depress the RNA content considerably. It is suggested that the initial enhancement is due to the removal of a competition from the nucleus for a precursor, since RNA is synthesized both in the nucleus and the cytoplasm. After some time the stock of precursor in the cytoplasm is depleted and the RNA level falls. In normal circumstances, it may be supposed that the RNA forms the template for the synthesis of specific proteins. After enucleation the template mechanism is not restored and the synthesis of specific proteins cannot therefore proceed. Consequently, with a failure in the regeneration of RNA, in time the elaboration of particular enzymes decreases and this occasions the decrease in general activity.

In terms of this interpretation the particular contribution of the nucleus to the cytoplasm is the maintenance of the level of RNA in the cytoplasm. The mechanism through which this action is exerted may be uncertain in *Acetabularia*. In other organisms, however, the evidence suggests that the effect is one which involves a direct contribution of RNA from the nucleus to the cytoplasm. In *Amoeba* for instance the RNA content of the cytoplasm begins to decrease immediately after enucleation. Cytological observations have been described which suggest the extrusion from the nucleus into the cytoplasm of basophilic bodies. These are unlikely to be composed of DNA since the evidence for cytoplasmic DNA is still not decisive. The nucleoli are known to contain large quantities of RNA and these are certainly expelled into the cytoplasm when mitosis occurs. It is possible, however, that nucleolar RNA is transferred to the cytoplasm even when the nuclear membrane is intact. It is relevant in this connection that the nuclear membrane is traversed by large pores and there is not therefore likely to be any structural restraint on the outward movement of a polynucleotide. Finally it has been shown that the turnover rate of RNA in the nucleus is greater than it is in the cytoplasm (even in *Acetabularia*) which is of course compatible with the position that RNA is synthesized in the nucleus (54).

The synthesis of RNA in the nucleus implies a probable supply of ATP. This, it has been suggested, is derived from the mitochondria, and it may be significant that the arrangement has frequently been described of the nucleus being surrounded by a cloud of mitochondria. It may be that ATP released from these is absorbed by the nucleus and in due course is consumed in the synthesis of RNA.

The mechanism through which RNA is synthesized is problematical. Biochemical data derived from staphylococcal preparations suggest that

RNA synthesis is mediated through DNA. If this is the case in the nucleus, then the DNA will act as a template for the synthesis of RNA and thus ultimately control the elaboration of specific proteins in the cytoplasm.

Certainly DNA occupies a decisive status in the whole economy of the cell. Since it is a characteristic component of the nucleus and of the chromosome, the possibility has frequently been mooted that it is the material of which the gene complex is composed. The constant association between the chromosomes and DNA suggests as much and there is independent evidence that genetical changes are in fact determined by changes in a DNA complex. Certain strains of pneumococcus produce smooth colonies in culture, but occasionally a mutant is observed which develops rough colonies. The smooth strain may however be induced to form rough colonies by treating it with certain extracts from the rough mutant. The induced roughness persists as a continuous genetical character. The smooth strain is, in fact, transformed into a rough strain by the extract treatment. The crude extract is a complex mixture, but the evidence indicates that the active principle in it is a DNA. The phenomenon suggests that the original mutation is due to a change in a DNA, and that when this modified acid is extracted and applied to organisms which do not carry it, it nevertheless becomes incorporated into the nucleic acid complement of the acceptor cell and becomes part of the genetical determination mechanism (45).

Several other instances of similar transformations depending on DNA in microorganisms have been described. Comparable situations have not been identified with higher plants or animals, but the evidence from microorganisms at least sustains the view that DNA is an important genetical determinant. This interpretation is consistent with the possibility elaborated above that the DNA controls the formation of the RNA. It may be supposed that the DNA has a particular surface configuration which determines that of the RNA. This diffuses into the cytoplasm and by virtue of the properties transmitted to it from the DNA it determines the catalytic properties of the proteins that are formed in the cytoplasm, and therefore determines the characteristics of the metabolic apparatus. Nuclear control of this synthesis is evidently continuous. It does not depend on the release of RNA at the time of mitosis. The intermediate nucleic acid is being continuously synthesized and continuously supplied to the cytoplasm throughout the interphase (56).

It may be emphasized that, while an effect of DNA on protein synthesis is widely recognized, it is not universally accepted that this is mediated through RNA. Some investigators hold that the effect is direct and that enzyme protein is synthesized on a DNA template. However, it still seems that the hypothesis given is that which assimilates most of the knowledge available on the effect of the nucleus into a single pattern.

Whether the action of DNA on the synthesis of enzyme protein is direct or through the mediation of RNA may be doubtful, but that it does have this function seems highly probable. This is further suggested by certain facts regarding the content and composition of DNA in various tissues. The character of an organism must ultimately be determined primarily by a particular catalytic pattern evoked in development. If this is the case then with a constant development the composition of the DNA might be expected to be constant. As noted above, this has been found experimentally to be the case. Whatever the tissue within any one species, the base composition of the DNA is invariably the same; and again, whatever the tissue, as between different species the composition is different. Again it is a significant fact that the amount of DNA per chromosome within any one species is constant and between different species it varies. Since the chromosome complement determines the character and therefore the catalytic pattern of an organism, the DNA of the chromosome might be expected to be constant. It has been shown that within any one species the diploid nucleus always carries the same quantity of DNA, and the diploid nuclei of different species incorporate different quantities. Not only so, but it has been shown that the tetraploid nucleus contains double the quantity of the diploid.

REFERENCES

1. Anderson, N. G. Techniques for the mass isolation of cellular components. *In* "Physical Techniques in Biological Research" (G. Oster and A. W. Pollister, ed.), Vol. 3, 299–352. Academic Press, New York, 1956.
2. Arnon, D. I., Allen, M. B., and Whatley, F. R. Photosynthesis by isolated chloroplasts: IV. General concept and comparison of three photochemical reactions. *Biochim. et Biophys. Acta* **20**, 449–461 (1956).
3. Barer, R. Phase contrast and interference microscopy in cytology. *In* "Physical Techniques in Biological Research" (G. Oster and A. W. Pollister, eds.), Vol. 3, pp. 29–90. Academic Press, New York, 1956.
4. Bennett, H. S. A suggestion as to the nature of the lepasome granules. *J. Biophys. Biochem. Cytol.* **2**, 185 (1956).
5. Bonner, J. "Plant Biochemistry," 537 pp. Academic Press, New York, 1950.
6. Brachet, J. "Biochemical Cytology," 516 pp. Academic Press, New York, 1957.
7. Brooks, S. C. The intake of radioactive isotopes by living cells. *Cold Spring Harbor Symposia Quant. Biol.* **8**, 171–180 (1940).

8. Brown, G. L., Callan, H. G., and Leaf, G. Chemical nature of nuclear sap. *Nature* **165**, 600–601 (1950).
9. Brown, R. Protoplast surface enzymes and absorption of sugar. *Intern. Rev. Cytol.* **1**, 107–118 (1952).
10. Brown, R. Isolation of nuclei from plant cells. *Nature* **168**, 941–942 (1952).
10a. Brown, R. Unpublished data (1957).
11. Brown, R., and Broadbent, D. The development of cells in the growing zone of the root. *J. Exptl. Botany* **1**, 249–263 (1950).
12. Brown, R., and Rickless, P. A new method for the study of cell division and cell extension with some preliminary observations on the effect of temperature and of nutrients. *Proc. Roy. Soc.* **B136**, 110–125 (1949).
13. Brown, R., and Robinson, E. Cellular differentiation and the development of enzyme proteins in plants. *In* "Biological Specificity and Growth" (E. G. Butler, ed.), pp. 93–118. Princeton Univ. Press, Princeton, New Jersey, 1955.
14. Caspersson, T. O. "Cell Growth and Cell Function," 185 pp. Norton, New York, 1950.
15. Chambers, R. Micrurgical studies on protoplasm. *Biol. Revs. Cambridge Phil. Soc.* **24**, 246–265 (1949).
16. Chambers, R., and Fell, H. B. Micro-operations on cells in tissue culture. *Proc. Roy. Soc.* **B109**, 380–402 (1931).
17. Chargaff, E. Isolation and composition of the deoxypentose nucleic acids and of the corresponding nucleoproteins. *In* "Nucleic Acids" (E. Chargaff and J. N. Davidson, eds.), Vol. 1, pp. 307–371. Academic Press, New York, 1955.
18. Chodat, R. "Principes de botanique," 744 pp. Georg, Geneva, 1907.
19. Danielli, J. F. "Cytochemistry," 139 pp. Wiley, New York, 1953.
20. Danielli, J. F., and Harvey, E. N. The tension at the surface of mackerel egg oil, with remarks on the nature of the cell surface. *J. Cellular Comp. Physiol.* **5**, 483–494 (1935).
21. Davies, D. D. The Krebs cycle enzyme system of pea seedlings. *J. Exptl. Botany* **4**, 173–183 (1953).
22. Davson, H., and Danielli, J. F. "The Permeability of Natural Membranes," 365 pp. Cambridge Univ. Press, London and New York, 1943 and 1952.
23. De Duve, C. The enzymic heterogeneity of cell fractions isolated by differential centrifuging. *Symposia Soc. Exptl. Biol.* **10**, 50–61 (1957).
24. Dounce, A. L. The isolation and composition of cell nuclei and nucleoli. *In* "Nucleic Acids" (E. Chargaff and J. N. Davidson, eds.), Vol. 2, pp. 93–153. Academic Press, New York, 1955.
25. Ephrussi, B. "Nucleo-Cytoplasmic Relations in Micro-Organisms," 127 pp. Oxford Univ. Press, London and New York, 1952.
26. Erickson, R. O., and Goddard, D. R. An analysis of root growth in cellular and biochemical terms. *Growth* **15**, Suppl., 89–116 (1951).
27. Farrant, J. L., Potter, C., Robertson, R. N., and Wilkins, M. J. The morphology of red beet (*Beta vulgaris L.*) mitochondria. *Australian J. Botany* **4**, 117–124 (1956).
28. Frey-Wyssling, A. "Submicroscopic Morphology of Protoplasm," 411 pp. Elsevier, Houston, Texas, 1953.
29. Fruton, S. F., and Simmonds, S. "General Biochemistry," 940 pp. Wiley, New York, 1953.
30. Gale, E. F., and Folkes, J. P. The assimilation of amino acids by bacteria: 20.

The incorporation of labeled amino acids by disrupted staphylococcal cells. *Biochem. J.* **59,** 661–675 (1955).
31. Gale, E. F., and Folkes, J. P. The assimilation of amino acids by bacteria: 21. The effect of nucleic acids on the development of certain enzymic activities in disrupted staphylococcal cells. *Biochem. J.* **59,** 675–684 (1955).
32. Galston, A. W., and Dalberg, A. Y. The adaptive formation and physiological significance of indoleacetic acid oxidase. *Am. J. Botany* **41,** 373–380 (1954).
33. Gicklhorn, J. Intracelluläre Myelinfiguren und ähnliche Bildungen bei der reversiblen Entmischung des Protoplasmas. *Protoplasma* **15,** 90–109 (1932).
34. Glick, D. "Techniques of Histo- and Cytochemistry," 531 pp. Interscience, New York, 1949.
35. Guilliermond, A. "The Cytoplasm of the Plant Cell," 247 pp. Chronica Botanica, Waltham, Massachusetts, 1941.
36. Hackett, D. P. Recent studies in plant mitochondria. *Intern. Rev. Cytol.* **4,** 143–196 (1955).
37. Heyes, J. K. Unpublished data from author's laboratory, 1957.
38. Hill, R. Reduction by chloroplasts. *Symposia Soc. Exptl. Biol.* **5,** 222–231 (1951).
39. Höber, R. The surface of the protoplast, its properties and its architecture. "Physical Chemistry of Cells and Tissues," Blakiston, New York, 1947.
40. Hodge, A. J., McLean, J. D., and Mercer, F. V. Ultrastructure of the lamellae and grana in the chloroplasts of *Zea mays L. J. Biophys. Biochem. Cytol.* **1,** 605–613 (1955).
41. Hodge, A. J., Martin, E. M., and Morton, R. K. The structure of some cytoplasmic components of plant cells in relation to the biochemical properties of isolated particles. *J. Biophys. Biochem. Cytol.* **3,** 61–70 (1957).
42. Hoffler, K. Über Kappenplasmolyse. *Ber. deut. botan. Ges.* **46,** 73–82 (1928).
43. Hogeboom, G. H. "Symposium on the Fine Structure of Cells," 825 pp. Interscience, New York, 1955.
44. Hogeboom, G. H., and Schneider, W. C. The cytoplasm. *In* "Nucleic Acids" (E. Chargaff and J. N. Davidson, eds.), Vol. 2, pp. 199–216. Academic Press, New York, 1955.
45. Hotchkiss, R. D. The biological role of the deoxypentose nucleic acids. *In* "Nucleic Acids" (E. Chargaff and J. N. Davidson, eds.), Vol. 2, pp. 435–473. Academic Press, New York, 1955.
46. Huggins, C., Tapley, D. F., and Jensen, E. V. Sulphydryl-disulphide relationships in the induction of gels in proteins by urea. *Nature* **167,** 592–593 (1951).
47. Hughes, A. "The Mitotic Cycle," 232 pp. Academic Press, New York, 1952.
48. Hume, M. On the presence of connecting threads in graft hybrids. *New Phytologist* **12,** 216–221 (1913).
49. Jordan, D. O. The physical properties of nucleic acids. *In* "Nucleic Acids" (E. Chargaff and J. N. Davidson, eds.), Vol. 1, pp. 447–492. Academic Press, New York, 1955.
50. Lepeshkin, W. W. "Kolloidchemie des Protoplasmas," 228 pp. Springer, Berlin, 1924.
51. Lessler, M. A. The nature and specificity of the Feulgen nucleal reaction. *Intern. Rev. Cytol.* **2,** 231–247 (1953).
52. Levitt, J. Investigations of the cytoplasmic particulates and proteins of potato tubers: II. Nitrogen, phosphorus, and carbohydrate contents. *Physiol. Plantarum* **7,** 117–123 (1954).

53. Lindberg, O., and Ernster, L. "Chemistry and Physiology of Mitochondria and Microsomes," 136 pp. Springer, Vienna, 1954.
54. Marshak, A. *Symposia Soc. Exptl. Biol.* **12,** (1958).
55. Marsland, D. A. Protoplasmic streaming in relation to gel structure in the cytoplasm. *In* "The Structure of Protoplasm" (W. Seifritz, ed.), pp. 127–161. Iowa State College Press, Ames, Iowa, 1942.
56. Mazia, D. Physiology of the cell nucleus. *In* "Modern Trends in Physiology and Biochemistry" (E. S. G. Barron, ed.), pp. 77–122. Academic Press, New York, 1952.
57. Mercer, F. V., Hodge, A. J., Hope, A. B., and McLean, J. D. The structure and swelling properties of Nitella chloroplasts. *Australian J. Biol. Sci.* **8,** 1–18 (1955).
58. Millerd, A., and Bonner, J. The biology of plant mitochondria. *J. Histochem. and Cytochem.* **1,** 254–264 (1953).
59. Millerd, A., Bonner, J., Axelrod, B., and Bandurski, R. S. Oxidative and phosphorylative activity of plant mitochondria. *Proc. Natl. Acad. Sci. U.S.* **37,** 855–862 (1951).
60. Mitchell, M. B., Mitchell, H. K., and Tissieres, A. Mendelian and non-Mendelian factors affecting the cytochrome system in Neurospora crassa. *Proc. Natl. Acad. Sci. U.S.* **39,** 606–613 (1953).
61. Moore, A. R. On the significance of cytoplasmic structure in the plasmodium. *J. Cellular Comp. Physiol.* **7,** 113–129 (1935).
62. Onslow, M. W. "The Anthocyanin Pigments of Plants," 314 pp. Cambridge Univ. Press, London and New York, 1925.
63. Overend, W. G., and Peacocke, A. R. *Endeavour* **16,** 90 (1957).
64. Pearsall, W. H., and Ewing, J. The diffusion of ions from living plant tissues in relation to protein iso-electric points. *New Phytologist* **23,** 193–206 (1924).
65. Pfeiffer, H. Experimental researches in the non-Newtonian nature of protoplasm. *Cytologia (Tokyo) Fujii Jubilee Vol.* pp. 701–710 (1937).
66. Plowe, J. Q. Membranes in the plant cell: I. Morphological membranes at protoplasmic surfaces. *Protoplasma* **12,** 196–240 (1932).
67. Plowe, J. Q. Membranes in plant cells: II. Localization of differential permeability in the protoplast (1932).
68. Porter, K. R. Observations on a submicroscopic basophilic component of cytoplasm. *J. Exptl. Med.* **97,** 727–749 (1953).
69. Preston, R. D. "The Molecular Architecture of Plant Cell Walls," 211 pp. Wiley, New York, 1952.
70. Rabinowitch, E. I. "Photosynthesis," Vol. 1, 599 pp. Interscience, New York, 1945.
71. Robinson, E., and Brown, R. Cytoplasmic particles in bean root cells. *Nature* **171,** 313 (1953).
72. Rothstein, A. Enzyme systems of the cell surface involved in the uptake of sugars by yeast. *Symposia Soc. Exptl. Biol.* **8,** 165–201 (1954).
73. Sanger, F. The chemistry of simple proteins. *Symposia Soc. Exptl. Biol.* **9,** 10–31 (1955).
74. Schmitt, F. O. Optical studies of the molecular organization of living systems. *J. Appl. Phys.* **9,** 109–117 (1938).
75. Schoenheimer, R. "The dynamic state of body constituents," 78 pp. Harvard Univ. Press, Cambridge, Massachusetts, 1942.
76. Scott-Moncrieff, R. J. A biochemical survey of some Mendelian factors for flower color. *J. Genet.* **32,** 117–170 (1936).

77. Sharp, L. W. "An Introduction to Cytology," 3rd ed., 567 pp. McGraw-Hill, New York, 1934.
78. Singer, C. J. "Short History of Science to the Nineteenth Century," 399 pp. Oxford Univ. Press, London and New York, 1941.
79. Stern, H., and Mirsky, A. E. The isolation of wheat germ nuclei and some aspects of their glycolytic metabolism. *J. Gen Physiol.* **36**, 181–200 (1953).
80. Steward, F. C., Caplin, S. M., and Millar, F. K. Investigations on growth and metabolism of plant cells: I. New techniques for the investigation of metabolism, nutrition, and growth in undifferentiated cells. *Ann. Botany (London)* [N. S.] **16**, 57–77 (1952).
81. Steward, F. C., and Mühlethaler, K. The structure and development of the cell-wall in the Valoniaciae as revealed by the electron microscope. *Ann. Botany (London)* [N. S.] **17**, 295–315 (1953).
82. Strugger, S. Die vitalfarbung des Protoplasmas mit Rhodamin B, und 6G. *Protoplasma* **30**, 85–100 (1938).
83. Swift, H. Cytochemical techniques for nucleic acids. *In* "Nucleic Acids" (E. Chargaff and J. N. Davidson, eds.), Vol. 2, pp. 51–92. Academic Press, New York, 1955.
84. Thompson, D'A. "On Growth and Form," 1116 pp. Cambridge Univ. Press, London and New York, 1942.
85. Tolbert, N. E., and Burris, R. H. Light activation of the plant enzyme which oxidizes glycolic acid. *J. Biol. Chem.* **186**, 791–804 (1950).
86. Watson, M. L. The nuclear envelope: its structure and relation to cytoplasmic membranes. *J. Biophys. Biochem. Cytol.* **1**, 257–270 (1955).
87. Weier, T. E., and Stocking, C. R. The chloroplast: structure, inheritance, and enzymology. *Botan. Rev.* **18**, 14–75 (1952).
88. Whistler, R. L., and Smart, C. L. "Polysaccharide Chemistry," 493 pp. Academic Press, New York, 1953.
89. White, P. R. "The Cultivation of Animal and Plant Cells," 239 pp. Ronald Press, New York, 1954.

CHAPTER TWO

Proteins, Enzymes, and the Mechanism of Enzyme Action

BIRGIT VENNESLAND

I. Introduction

A living organism may be regarded as an extraordinarily complex system of beautifully coordinated chemical reactions. Biochemical research is aimed at the eventual elucidation of all of these reactions, and of their various interrelationships. In the nineteenth century, the basic preparations for this great task were made by the organic chemists, who determined the structure and characteristics of the multitude of small molecules which may be regarded as the building blocks of life. During the half century following Büchner's discovery of cell-free fermentation (1897), the attention of biochemical investigators has been focused on the problem of determining the detailed nature of the reaction sequences in the metabolism of these small molecules. Numerous "metabolic maps" have been and are being worked out for the paths of synthesis and degradation of sugars, amino acids, fats, purines, pyrimidines, and hosts of related substances. The subject of the present chapter is the characterization of the agents—the enzymes—which command the chemical events of these reaction sequences.

The word *enzyme* (meaning *in yeast*) was coined by Kühne in 1867, but the scholar who focuses on the present meaning of the word has difficulty choosing a date to mark the first "discovery" of such a substance. Thus, the practical knowledge of fermentation processes is older than the recorded beginnings of civilization. As the new science of chemistry was developed from the end of the eighteenth century on through the nineteenth, we find that many of the great chemists of the early period occupied themselves with the problem of the action of enzymes. Their interest bears witness to the wealth of an earlier tradition, unorganized and unscientific—but rich in information. Plant sources—seeds and roots—were used as commonly as animal sources in these almost prescientific studies. Thus, in 1785, just two years after Spallanzani's observations on the liquefaction of meat by the gastric juice of birds, the liquefaction of starch by aqueous extracts of sprouted barley was noted by Irvine. In 1833, Payen and Persoz showed that the responsible agent, which they called diastase, was thermolabile, that it acted catalytically (i.e., a small amount could cause the decomposition of a large amount of starch), and that it could be concentrated and purified by precipitation with alcohol. The blueing of a tincture of guaiacum by a thermolabile, soluble material obtained from plant roots was observed by Planche in 1810, and the hydrolysis of the glucoside amygdalin by an extract of bitter almonds was described in 1830. The responsible agent was named emulsin by Liebig and Wöhler in 1837. Many years later Emil Fischer established the usefulness of emulsin as a reagent for determining the stereoconfiguration of glucoside bonds. Berzelius, Liebig, and Pasteur, illustrious names in science, were all intensely interested in various aspects of the problem of the nature of enzyme action. Around this problem revolved the great nineteenth-century argument about "vital force." The controversies of this period have now been resolved, and the start of the truly modern period may be said to begin with the general recognition that "ferments," "diastases," or "enzymes" can all be separated from intact cells and identified as proteins.[1]

The first demonstration of the protein nature of an enzyme was pro-

[1] References, and a more detailed discussion of the historical development of enzymology, may be found in the treatises of Lieben (63) and of Hoffmann-Ostenhof (45).

vided by Sumner's preparation (1926) of crystalline urease from jack beans (113). The combined efforts of hundreds of enzymologists in subsequent years has not yet brought to light any clear-cut example of an enzyme which is not protein in nature. This is not surprising, since the general properties of heat lability, stability to dialysis, and sensitivity to pH, which have at various times been included almost in the definition of the word enzyme, are actually the properties of native, undenatured proteins.

It will save time and trouble to define an enzyme as a protein which acts as a catalyst. In this definition, the word catalyst has its usual meaning of a substance which promotes a reaction without itself being consumed in the reaction. Furthermore, the reaction catalyzed should be defined as a specific chemical change, and not, for example, as a physiological process.

The above definition is that which is generally assumed in the use of the word "enzyme" by the practicing enzymologist. It represents the result of a natural evolution of the original definition, which did not include the restriction that an enzyme must be a protein. This restriction is introduced to eliminate unnecessary argument about the naming of any category of substances which might have high molecular weight, catalytic action, and perhaps even possess some of the other generally recognized properties of enzymes, but which might not be protein in nature. By definition, such substances would be excluded from the category of enzymes. The intention in specifying further that the reaction catalyzed should be completely defined as a specific *chemical* change, is to exclude such processes as transport and other more complex physiological phenomena. It is recognized, of course, that such restrictions are arbitrary. They have been introduced for the sake of clarity and simplicity and should not be regarded as a denial of the obvious similarities of a protein such as hemoglobin to the proteins included in the category of enzymes.[2]

The catalytic action of proteins accounts in large part for their functional importance within the living cell. There are, of course, proteins which to our knowledge possess no catalytic action but serve

[2] Dixon and Webb (24b, page 5) have defined an enzyme as "a protein with catalytic properties due to its power of specific activation." They point out that "the second half of the definition rules out such non-enzymic proteins as cytochrome c, which indeed is a catalytic protein, but by virtue of its action as a carrier and not by activating any other substance." There is much to be said for this definition. Though the cytochromes are very generally regarded as enzymes, and will be treated as enzymes in this chapter, the distinction between cytochrome c and other enzymes, as pointed out above, may well be kept in mind.

a structural function. The fibrous proteins of hair (keratin) and silk (fibroin) constitute typical examples. Other proteins such as those of seeds, eggs, and milk appear to be accumulated mainly as food deposits for the young growing organism. If however, we focus our attention on the protein which is present within the cytoplasm of a living cell, we feel it is appropriate to enquire whether most, if not all, of this protein may not be at least potentially enzymatic in nature. Virtanen (133) has suggested that this may be true for some microorganisms. The question cannot be answered with certainty, but accumulating evidence suggests that for some cell types, a large proportion of the protein is enzymatic. For example, a yeast cell, which may be regarded as specialized for alcohol fermentation, contains very substantial quantities of the enzymes required to catalyze this reaction sequence. Thus, it has been estimated that the so-called oxidizing enzyme (i.e., the triose-phosphate dehydrogenase), alone, constitutes more than 5% of the total protein of yeast (42). Since the cell must contain hundreds of enzymes, it is striking that one of these enzymes—even a very important one—can amount to such a high proportion of the protein present. In a later section (see page 168), the speed with which enzymes operate is related to the number of enzymatic steps required to synthesize a new organism and the time required for the process (i.e., generation time). Calculations of this sort can only be gross estimates, but one can pick *reasonable* numbers and arrive at the conclusion that much of the cell protein of a rapidly proliferating bacterium may be enzymatic in nature. Of course there is no reason to suppose that structural function and enzymatic function are mutually exclusive. Proteins must provide an important structural component of the cell architecture, contributing both to form and to function of nucleus, cytoplasm, granules, and membranes. Any enumeration of protein function must include, also, the action of protein as a metabolite which participates in the metabolic processes in addition to catalyzing them (109).

II. Protein Structure

A. AMINO ACIDS AND PEPTIDE CHAINS

Since enzymes are proteins, enzyme chemistry may be regarded as a special branch of protein chemistry. The problems encountered in the elucidation of the structural chemistry of enzymes are in part identical with the problems of elucidating the structure of the proteins. These substances are large, complex molecules consisting of chains of α-amino acids linked together by peptide bonds between the carboxyl groups and the α-amino groups. The backbone of protein structure is thus the peptide chain (I):

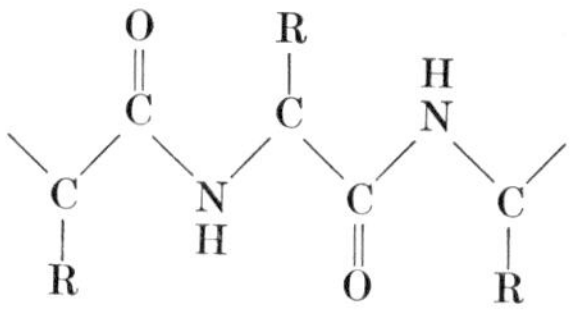

```
        O       R
        ‖       |       H
        C       C       N
 \    /   \   /   \   /   \    /
  C        N        C        C
  |        H        ‖        |
  R                 O        R
```

(I)

where R represents one of the residues of the various naturally occurring amino acids.

Table I lists the names and formulas of the amino acids which occur very generally in proteins. All of these amino acids have the L-configuration. If cysteine and cystine are regarded as equivalent, because of their easy interconversion, then there are eighteen amino acids that are very widely distributed and are apt to be part of the molecular structure of any one particular enzyme.

In addition to amino acids, proteins are very likely to contain a certain number of amide groups. Ammonia forms amide links,

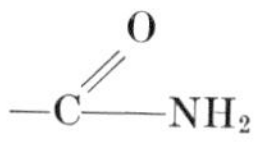

```
      O
     //
 —C——NH2
```

with the distal carboxyl groups of the aspartic and glutamic acid moieties. Cross links between peptide chains or links forming loops in a peptide chain are generally formed by the disulfide of cystine (II).

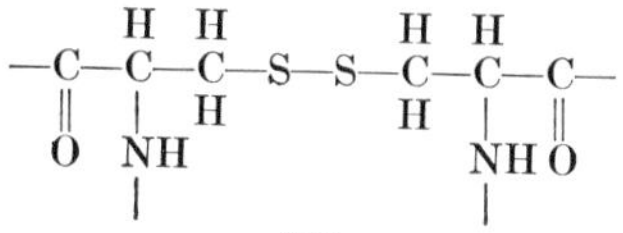

```
     H  H          H  H
 —C—C—C—S—S—C—C—C—
  ‖  |  H       H  |  ‖
  O NH             NH O
     |              |
```

(II)

Phosphate may also be bound to the protein, generally at the β-hydroxyl group of serine, and Perlmann (90) has shown that diesters of phosphate likewise occur, so that phosphate may serve in the same way as disulfide, as a bridge between peptide chains (III).

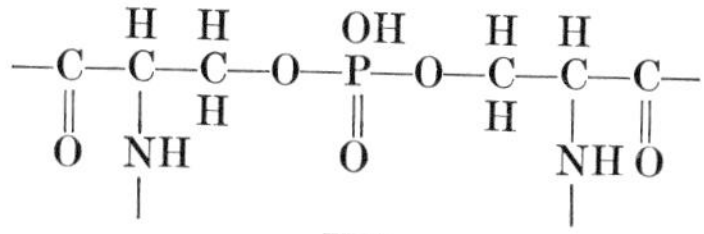

```
     H  H      OH     H  H
 —C—C—C—O—P—O—C—C—C—
  ‖  |  H      ‖      H  |  ‖
  O NH         O        NH O
     |                   |
```

(III)

A great variety of other materials may also be bound to the protein molecule. When such non-amino acid constituents can be shown to

TABLE I
THE AMINO ACIDS OF PROTEINS[a]

Name	Formula
Glycine	H HC—COOH NH_2
Alanine	H CH_3C—COOH NH_2
Valine	CH_3 \\ H CHC—COOH / NH_2 CH_3
Leucine	CH_3 \\ H $CHCH_2C$—COOH / NH_2 CH_3
Isoleucine	CH_3 \\ H CHC—COOH / NH_2 C_2H_5
Serine	H H HC——C—COOH OH NH_2
Threonine	H H CH_3C—C—COOH OH NH_2
Cysteine	H H HC——C—COOH SH NH_2
Cystine	—S—S— Form of cysteine
Methionine	H H HC—CH_2C—COOH SCH_3 NH_2
Aspartic acid	H COOH—CH_2C—COOH NH_2
Glutamic acid	H COOH—CH_2CH_2C—COOH NH_2
Lysine	H H HC—$CH_2CH_2CH_2C$—COOH NH_2 NH_2
Arginine	H H $NH_2CNCH_2CH_2CH_2C$—COOH ‖ NH_2 NH

TABLE I (*Continued*)

Name	Formula
Phenylalanine	C_6H_5—CH_2—CH(NH_2)—COOH (benzene ring—CH_2—C(H)(NH$_2$)—COOH)
Tyrosine	HO—C_6H_4—CH_2—C(H)(NH_2)—COOH
Histidine	HC═C—CH_2C(H)(NH_2)—COOH; ring: HC—N═CH—NH—C
Tryptophan	benzene ring fused: —C—CH_2C(H)(NH_2)—COOH; C═C, N
Proline	H_2C—CH_2; H_2C CH—COOH; N—H
Hydroxyproline[b]	HOC(H)—CH_2; H_2C CH—COOH; N—H

[a] Additional amino acids (e.g., hydroxylysine, thyroxine) occur in proteins but have a more limited distribution and so have not been included here. An even larger group of amino acids have been shown to occur free in plant tissues. An excellent, up-to-date summary of information on this subject can be found in recent reviews (110, 112).

[b] This amino acid has a more restricted distribution in plant proteins than the others listed.

play a functional role in the action of an enzyme, they are called prosthetic groups (see heading III,B). But the list of known possible prosthetic groups does not give an adequate notion of the variety and quantity of non-amino acid substances which the protein molecule may contain. Carbohydrates and lipids may occur in great abundance. In fact some of the lipoproteins contain more lipids than amino acids (18, 48).

There is an enormous range of molecular size which may be ex-

TABLE II
MOLECULAR WEIGHTS OF PROTEINS

Protein	Mol. wt.[a]
Insulin	6,000
Cytochrome c	13,000
Papain	21,000
Pepsin	34,000
Peroxidase (horse radish)	44,000
Hemoglobin (horse)	68,000
Triosephosphate dehydrogenase (yeast)	120,000
Ascorbic acid oxidase (summer squash)	146,000
Alcohol dehydrogenase (yeast)	150,000
Edestin	309,000
Urease (jack beans)	480,000
Clostridium botulinum toxin	900,000
Tomato bushy-stunt virus	10,600,000
Tobacco-mosaic virus	40,000,000

[a] The figures are rounded to the nearest thousand.

TABLE IIIA
AMINO ACID COMPOSITION OF SOME PROTEINS OF LOW MOLECULAR WEIGHT[a]

Amino acid	Insulin (99) (M = 6000)	Ribonuclease (43) (M = 14,000)	Lysozyme (31) (M = 15,000)	Papain (105) (M = 20,700)
Alanine	3	12	10	13
Arginine	1	4	11	9
Aspartic acid	3	16	20	17
Half-cystine plus cysteine	6	8	10	8
Glutamic acid	7	12	4	17
Glycine	4	3	11	23
Histidine	2	4	1	1
Isoleucine	1	3	6	9
Leucine	6	2	9	9
Lysine	1	10	6	8
Methionine	—	4	2	—
Phenylalanine	3	3	3	4
Proline	1	5	2	9
Serine	3	15	10	11
Threonine	1	10	7	7
Tryptophan	—	—	8	5
Tyrosine	4	6	3	17
Valine	5	9	6	15
Amide N	6	17	18	19

[a] The figures represent the number of residues per molecule.
M = molecular weight.

hibited by protein molecules, as illustrated by the representative figures assembled in Table II. Among the smallest, well-defined proteins is the hormone, insulin, with a molecular weight of 6000. (In solution insulin exists more often as a dimer, with a molecular weight of 12,000.) At the other extreme of size are the viruses, which have particle weights of several millions. The plant viruses are nucleoproteins containing ribonucleic acid and are smaller and simpler in structure than the viruses which attack bacteria and animal cells. The molecular weights of most enzymes fall between those of the protein hormones and those of the viruses.

TABLE IIIB
AMINO ACID COMPOSITION[a] OF SOME PLANT SEED PROTEINS (123)

Amino acid	Edestin (*Cannabis sativa*)	Squash seed globulin (Cucurbitaceae)	Zein (Gramineae)
Alanine	48	—	118
Arginine	96	93	10
Aspartic acid	90	—	35
Half-cystine plus cysteine	12	9	7
Glutamic acid	141	—	183
Glycine	—	—	—
Histidine	16	14	9
Isoleucine	36	34	38
Leucine	58	61	161
Lysine	16	21	0
Methionine	16	15	16
Phenylalanine	32	41	44
Proline	36	—	91
Serine	60	—	67
Threonine	32	24	29
Tryptophan	7	9	0
Tyrosine	24	24	29
Valine	56	56	34
Amide N	127	—	216

[a] The figures are residues of amino acid per 10^5 gm protein.

Chemical methods of analysis are now available whereby the amounts of the different amino acids present in a purified protein can be determined with reasonable accuracy. Table IIIA gives the amino acid composition of the hormone, insulin, and of three different enzymes, for which relatively good data are available. The amino acid composition of insulin is, in fact, known with certainty. It should be clear that the smaller the protein molecule, the more accurate will be the information about the number of residues of any particular amino acid present in the molecule. The enzymes listed in Table IIIA are all

relatively small molecules which can be obtained in a high state o
purity by fairly simple procedures. Table IIIB gives the amino aci
composition of some representative plant seed proteins. More detaile
data may be found in several reviews (14, 70, 123). The figures o
Table IIIB are incomplete and necessarily less accurate than those o
Table IIIA. Except for the seed proteins, there is a dearth of goo
data on the composition of individual proteins from plants. Stewar
and Thompson (111) have assembled the available data on the amin
acid composition of the proteins in bulk of various plants.

B. First Level of Organization

The structural characterization of a protein involves the determina
tion of the number of peptide chains present in the molecule, the deter
mination of the sequence in which the amino acids are linked in thos
chains, and the determination of the position of cross linkages betwee
chains or between two parts of one chain, such as may be formed b
disulfide bonds and sometimes by phosphate. These structural feature
are dependent on relatively stable, covalent bonds, and the structura
characteristics so defined are often called the first level of organiza
tion of the protein molecule (69).

The procedures employed for determining these aspects of protei
structure have been summarized in excellent reviews (35, 98). Mentio
will be made here only of a few methods, such as the procedures in
volving dinitrofluorobenzene (DNB), the reagent of Sanger (IV).

$$\text{F-}C_6H_3(NO_2)_2 + H_2N\text{—} \rightarrow \text{—NH-}C_6H_3(NO_2)_2 + HF$$

(IV)

This compound reacts with $—NH_2$ groups, with the elimination o
hydrofluoric acid and the formation of relatively stable, pigmente
dinitrophenyl derivatives. The derivatives of the various amino acid
can readily be distinguished. If an intact protein is treated with thi
reagent the *N*-terminal amino acids will react. The protein may the
be hydrolyzed without removal of the pigment, and the *N*-termina
amino acids can be identified. "End-group analysis" carried out in thi
way has been used extensively within recent years to give a wealt
of new information, and the end groups of a great number of protein

have been determined. If allowances are made for certain procedural difficulties, this method tells how many peptide chains are present in the molecule, as well as the identity of the amino acid residue located at the *N*-terminal end of the chain.

The enzyme carboxypeptidase, which specifically hydrolyzes carboxy-terminal amino acid residues, has been used to determine the nature of the amino acid present at the carboxy-terminal end of the chain. Other enzymes with proteolytic action have been employed to break the protein into fragments. The basic procedure of sequence analysis is, in fact, to break the protein into fragments in a variety of ways, to analyze the fragments, and to reconstruct the original structure by identifying areas of overlap. Partial acid hydrolysis, or hydrolysis by several of a variety of proteolytic enzymes (e.g., trypsin, chymotrypsin, pepsin, subtilisin) may be used to effect the fragmentation. The various proteolytic enzymes have certain specificities, or preferences for splitting particular peptide bonds, and a knowledge of these specificities is sometimes a necessary prerequisite for making full use of the proteolytic enzymes as reagents in sequence analysis. At present the action of trypsin is the most reliable way of splitting a peptide chain at specific peptide bonds. This enzyme attacks only those bonds which are derived from the carboxyl group of the amino acids lysine and arginine.

Figure 1 shows a diagram of the structure of beef insulin, which has been completely determined at the first level of organization (98, 99). Amino acid sequence in a peptide chain is indicated by an abbreviated notation (13) in which each amino acid is designated by the first three letters of its name, except for isoleucine (Ileu), cysteine (CySH), and a half cystine residue (CyS—). By convention, the left-hand end of the formula commences with the free amino group. Of particular interest to the physiologist are the species differences that have been established (see page 197).

The success of Sanger's attack on the problem of insulin structure has had noteworthy consequences in stimulating work on more difficult structural problems. The pituitary hormones have also been amenable to structure studies, and, at the time of this writing, work is in active progress on the determination of the structure of the enzymes ribonuclease and lysozyme (5). These are relatively small and stable enzymes, whose ease of purification and availability in relatively large amounts caused their selection for detailed study. If the complete determination of the first level of organization of these enzyme proteins is successful, then an extension of the methods employed to other enzymes would appear to be within the realm of possible achievement, though the enormous amount of painstaking labor involved should not be underestimated.

One of the structural problems which is of particular interest in connection with enzymes is the determination of what segment of the molecule is essential for enzyme activity and what portions can be dispensed with; and closely related to this is the characterization of the active site or sites where the substrate is bound and catalytic action

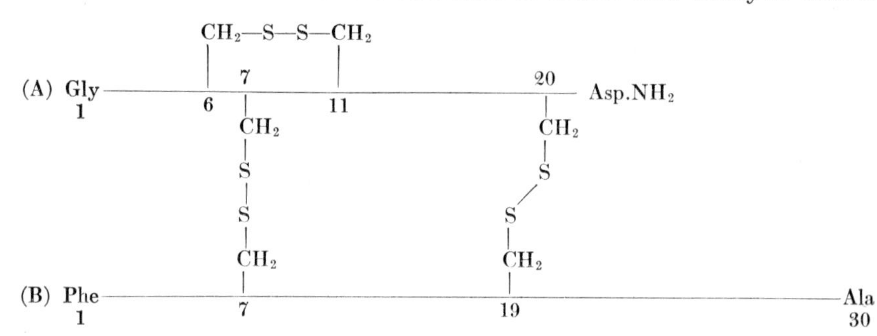

Relationship of the two peptide chains

NH₂ S S S NH₂ NH₂ S NH₂
Gly.Ileu.Val.Glu.Glu.Cy.Cy.Ala.Ser.Val.Cy.Ser.Leu.Tyr.Glu.Leu.Glu.Asp.Tyr.Cy.Asp.
1 2 3 4 5 6 7 8 9 10 11 12 13 14 15 16 17 18 19 20 21

Sequence of A chain

NH₂ NH₂ S S
Phe.Val.Asp.Glu.His.Leu.Cy.Gly.Ser.His.Leu.Val.Glu.Ala.Leu.Tyr.Leu.Val.Cy.Gly.Glu. . .
1 2 3 4 5 6 7 8 9 10 11 12 13 14 15 16 17 18 19 20 21
Arg.Gly.Phe.Phe.Tyr.Thr.Pro.Lys.Ala.
22 23 24 25 26 27 28 29 30

Sequence of B chain

FIG. 1. Structure of beef insulin.

occurs. Some recent experimental approaches to these problems will be discussed later in this chapter.

C. SECOND AND THIRD LEVELS OF ORGANIZATION

Protein molecules in their native state have well-defined shapes as well as sizes. Some, for example, are long rods; others are globular. This shape of the native protein molecule must depend on the manner in which the peptide chains are coiled or folded. This has been called the second level of organization of a protein. A third level of organization is sometimes also recognized, which is concerned with the manner in which peptide chains are packed together in the whole molecule. The second and third level of organization of a protein are closely interrelated and may be considered together as different aspects of the same problem (26, 27, 68, 69).

1. Denaturation

The specific coils and loops and packing patterns of the peptide chains are determined largely by hydrogen bonds, van der Waals' forces, and interactions between electrical charges. Because these bonds are readily broken, the structural characteristics dependent on them are readily lost or altered. This is what occurs during denaturation of a native protein (92). In this process, covalent bonds are generally not broken, so the first level of organization of the protein molecule remains intact. The term native protein is used to denote a protein which presumably possesses the same structure that it had in its original environment, i.e., in the tissue or material from which it was isolated. Any change in properties of this protein may be termed a denaturation. Common denaturing agents include heat, extremes of pH, and high concentrations of certain reagents such as urea. The denaturation process may be reversible, in the sense that a substance with the properties of the original native protein can be regenerated from the denatured protein under appropriate conditions; or the denaturation may involve irreversible changes. Any one type of protein may undergo both types of denaturation, depending on the treatment used. There must be, in such cases, at least more than one denatured state. The term, "denatured protein," thus has a certain ambiguity. One does not think of a denatured form of a protein as one specific or particular structure, but rather as a group of possible structures, whereas the native form of the protein is regarded as being more unique.

In general, denatured protein is less soluble than the original native protein, and this change in solubility can be used to follow the process. Another criterion of denaturation is loss of enzyme activity. Because the capacity of a protein to act as a catalyst is frequently (but not always) dependent on the secondary and tertiary level of organization of the molecule, it is obviously of particular interest to the enzyme chemist to know the peculiar structural characteristics of the native, active enzyme protein and the nature of the structural changes which occur on denaturation.

Many refined and elaborate physical tools and techniques have been applied to obtain at least a partial solution of the problem of the fine details of protein structure. Information about the size of the molecule, its electric charge, and its shape, can be obtained by a variety of procedures such as, for example, measurement of (a) sedimentation rate in a gravitational field (ultracentrifugation), (b) rate of diffusion, (c) rate of movement in an electric field (electrophoresis), (d) osmotic pressure, (e) viscosity, (f) light-scattering, (g) double refraction of flow, and (h) rotation of polarized light. The data from the physical measurements are, of course, combined with information obtained by chemical analysis. Discussion of the manner of application of these various procedures is quite outside the scope of this chapter, which is limited necessarily to a concise survey of the general conclusions emerging from research in this area.

2. *Helical Structures*

One of the most useful and powerful tools employed for the study of protein structure has been X-ray analysis (6, 68). In a few limited instances X-ray data have made it possible to reach specific conclusions regarding the arrangement of the peptide chains in a protein. The case of the insoluble fibrous protein, keratin, may be taken as an example. Astbury, who pioneered in this area, was the first to classify fibrous proteins into three groups, depending on the kind of X-ray diffraction patterns exhibited by the different fibers (6). Keratin (wool) fibers normally give a so-called α-pattern. The α-keratin has the structure of a fairly compact coil called the α-helix. This structure was first suggested by Pauling and Corey (87) as a particularly stable, and therefore plausible, configuration for the peptide chains of proteins generally. This helical structure is in accord with the precise dimensions and geometry of the fundamental peptide chain residue, as determined from crystal-structure studies of amides, amino acids, and simple peptides. The amide group must be planar. There is about 50% double-bond character in this C—N amide bond, and the bond distance is consequently shorter (1.32 A) than the normal single bond length of 1.47 A. The favored configuration is the *trans* form shown in diagram (V):

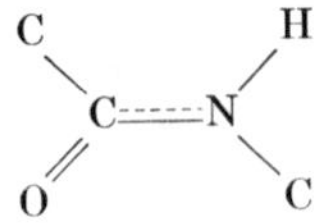

```
C           H
  \        /
   C-----N
  //       \
O           C
```

(V)

The α-helix is a coiled structure which contains 3.6–3.7 amino acid residues per turn and in which each peptide C═O group is hydrogen-bonded to the N—H of the fourth residue beyond. Figure 2 shows a diagram of a left-handed and a right-handed α-helix. The structure may be indicated by the chemical sequence (VI):

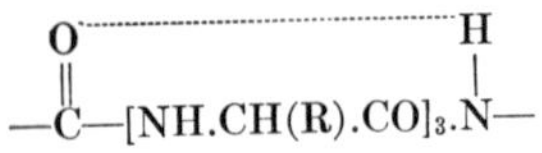

```
 O.........................H
 ‖                         |
—C—[NH.CH(R).CO]3.N—
```

(VI)

Other types of helical structure are also possible, but, of these, the α-helix is currently thought to be the most important. The synthetic polypeptide, poly-γ-methyl-L-glutamate, gives X-ray diffraction patterns which fit the α-helix almost exactly. For naturally occurring globular proteins, however, the structure is more complicated.

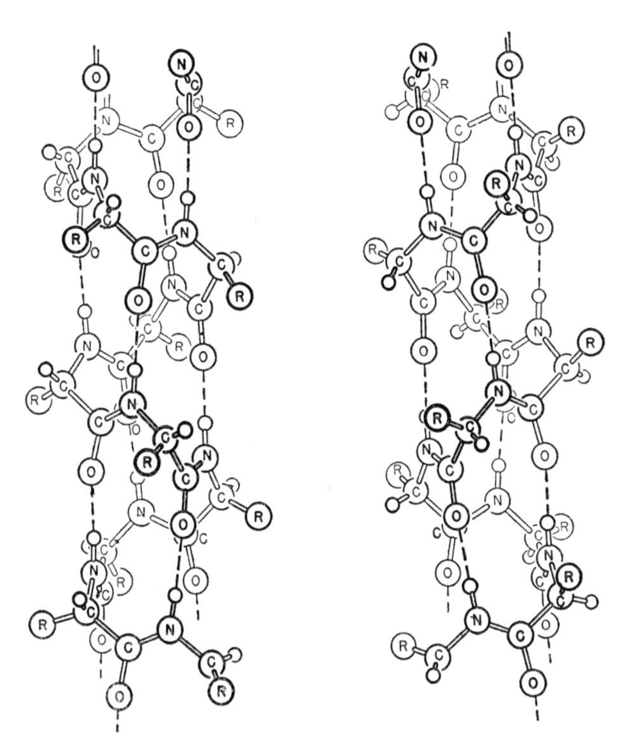

FIG. 2. Perspective drawing of a segment of a left-handed α-helix and of a right-handed α-helix. Note that the two are mirror images if the R groups are removed from the α-carbon atoms and replaced by hydrogen atoms. However, when the R groups are in place, in the L-configuration as shown, then the two helices are no longer mirror images. Reprinted from J. T. Edsall [(27), Fig. 8], based on drawing provided by the courtesy of Drs. R. B. Corey and L. Pauling.

Fibers of α-keratin (wool) can be stretched considerably beyond their original length. After such stretching, the X-ray diffraction picture is altered to the so-called β-pattern. The conversion of α-keratin to β-keratin involves an uncoiling of the helix to give a structure of extended peptide chains in parallel arrangement. Globular proteins appear to have a structure similar in part to that of the α-type fibrous proteins, whereas on denaturation some globular proteins may show a capacity to form fibers of the β-keratin type. Thus the denaturation of the globular protein has a certain similarity to the conversion of α- to β-keratin and may be regarded as a kind of unwinding or uncoiling of a more compact structure which is at least partly helical in nature. This picture of denaturation is only approximate, since the helix by no means suffices to describe the globular protein structure completely, as already pointed out.

A most important factor contributing to the stability of the α-helix is the total effect of all the hydrogen bonds between C═O and N—H groups (see Fig. 2). The hydrogen bond is regarded as resulting from the attraction between the positive end of one dipole and the negative end of another. It is formed in proteins between O and N—H (e.g., N—H · · · O), or between O and OH (e.g., O—H · · · O). Such hydrogen bonds have an energy of about 5–7 kcal per mole, which is considerably less than the energies of 25–100 kcal per mole that are characteristic of most single covalent bonds. The effect of many hydrogen bonds is additive, however, and so can become quite large. (Since the O and OH groups of water molecules may also be hydrogen-bonded to N—H and O groups, the energy responsible for stabilizing the protein helix is actually the difference between the energy content of the system when the C═O and N—H groups are hydrogen-bonded to water, and the energy content of the same system when the hydrogen bridges are formed between the C═O and N—H groups of the peptide chain.) Hydrogen bonds may also link the C═O and N—H groups of neighboring peptide chains, in the extended, so-called "pleated sheath" structures, and the phenolic OH of tyrosine may in some instances be hydrogen-bonded to the carboxyl group of an aspartic or a glutamic residue. It is therefore not surprising that reagents such as urea and guanidine act to cause protein denaturation. The urea readily forms hydrogen bonds itself. In high concentrations it competes successfully for the C═O and N—H groups of the peptide chain, breaking the hydrogen bonds which stabilize the helical structure and thus causing an uncoiling. Such denaturation can often be reversed by diluting out the urea. Denaturation by urea usually results in loss of enzyme activity, but this is not always so (92). Ribonuclease, for example, has a compact globular structure which is disrupted in high concentrations of urea, without loss of enzyme activity (5).

3. *Surface Films*

Denaturation of proteins can also occur in surface films. Proteins show a marked tendency to spread at the surface of water (15, 19, 96). Under some circumstances, the molecule unrolls completely to form a monolayer. The backbone of the polypeptide chain lies in the surface, and the protein molecule has assumed a fibrous form. Such films may form a "two-dimensional gas." The thickness is about 9.5 A, and the area occupied by 1 mg of protein may be greater than 1 square meter (15). A profound change is obviously necessary in the secondary and tertiary structure of the protein molecule to convert the globular protein to the thin, flat layer which constitutes the film. The formation of a film is therefore accompanied by a protein denaturation which is usually irreversible. Hence the foaming or frothing which occurs when a gas is bubbled rapidly through an enzyme solution is associated with a gradual loss in enzyme activity.

Spreading in a film does not always lead to loss of biological activity, however. Thus insulin retains activity when spread as a monomolecular film, and some enzymes, such as saccharase, can be spread as monolayers without loss of activity (15, 92). In the latter case there appears to be some question, however, whether a genuine monolayer was formed. Spreading is a complex phenomenon and is by no means fully understood. It has been suggested that the structure of cell membranes may be partly determined by proteins (24), and the large number of interfaces present in living cells certainly implies that the properties of proteins in surfaces have great physiological importance (19, 24).

4. *Unmasking of Reactive Sulfur Groups*

A phenomenon which is also in keeping with the idea that denaturation is to be regarded as an uncoiling or unfolding of the molecule, is the change in chemical reactivity of the —SH groups which sometimes accompanies denaturation. In a native, globular protein, some of the —SH groups of the cysteine residues may be covered or protected in such a manner that they are not susceptible to oxidizing agents like ferricyanide, or reagents like silver ions *p*-chloromercuri-benzoate. When denaturation occurs, however, the —SH groups are exposed and the —SH titer increases (92). Of course, if the native structure of the protein is stabilized by disulfide (—S—S—) bonds, as is the case for the enzyme ribonuclease and for the fibrous protein keratin, reduction of these bonds to —SH may lead to denaturation. Although the enzyme activity of ribonuclease survives denaturation by urea, reduction of the disulfide bridges leads to loss of enzyme activity (9). In this connection, we may note, however, that dependence of enzyme activity on the integrity of certain —SH groups is a frequent finding. This phenomenon is discussed later in this chapter.

5. *Bound Water*

Water constitutes an important part of the natural environment of intracellular proteins and plays a role also in the structure of the protein molecule. A certain amount of water is bound very firmly (26) This amount generally varies from 4 to 10 gm H_2O per 100 gm dr protein. When the first increments of water are added to a thoroughl dried protein, there is an actual volume contraction, and a considerabl amount of heat (3–6 kcal per mole H_2O) may be liberated. This firml bound water is held by hydrogen bonds to specific ionic and pola groups of the amino acid side chains. A larger number of water mole cules are more loosely associated with the protein. Fully half of th weight of a protein crystal in equilibrium with its mother liquor ma be water, but some of this water may be bound only in the sense tha it fills holes or spaces in the crystal structure. The determination of th exact amount and location of all of the water bound to a protein mole cule in solution is a very difficult problem (26). Water constitutes th largest part, by weight, of the structure of gels, as discussed in th following section.

6. Gels

A protein gel is a three-dimensional network of protein fibers whic has the properties of a solid rather than a fluid, in spite of the fact tha it contains a high proportion of water to solid matter. Gel formation i a complex phenomenon (30, 139). The aggregation of protein fiber to form a three-dimensional network requires cross linkages betwee fibers at more than one point of the protein molecule. In many gel hydrogen bonds are thought to be responsible for the cross linkage This explains why gels of fibrin and gelatin are dispersed by high con centrations of urea. In the case of egg white, serum albumin, and serur globulin, however, urea induces gel formation. Here an unrolling c the globular protein must precede the gel formation, and it has bee shown that small amounts of —SH groups enhance the rate of gellin (47). This has been explained in terms of a series of *trans*-sulfuratio reactions of the general type:

$$R{-}S{-}S{-}R' + R''{-}SH \rightarrow RSH + R''{-}S{-}S{-}R'$$

The gel formation is thought to proceed as a chain reaction, induced b the added SH reagent, as pictured in diagram (VII):

RSH + S—S + S—S + S—S ··· ⟶ R—S—S SH + S—S + S—S ····

R—S—S S—S SH + S—S ···· ⟶ R—S—S S—S S—S SH ····

(VII)

Phenomena such as this may be of interest in relation to the reported changes in —SH groups which occur in association with the process of cell division (76, 108). The importance of water as a structural component of cytoplasm is undoubtedly related, at least in part, to the imbibition and binding of water by protein, and the study of artificial systems such as gelatin has provided a model for the more complex phenomena encountered.

Extensive studies have been made of the swelling of gelatin by uptake of water and of the similar swelling of the collagen structures from which gelatin is derived (11). The swelling phenomena are divided customarily into two groups: (a) the swelling due to addition of acids and bases, and (b) the swelling induced by neutral salts. The first type of swelling is associated with Donnan effects due to the ionization of acidic and basic groups in the protein. There is a minimum of this swelling at the isoelectric point of the protein in salt-free media. The amount of swelling increases with lower and higher pH to a maximum which is followed by a decline at the pH extremes. Both acid and alkaline swelling are decreased by salts. The second type of swelling, due to neutral salts, is associated with a breaking of ionic and hydrogen-bond cross links by the added salt ions, with the resulting provision of more room for water molecules. Water can enter gel structures by free diffusion, and the amount which enters is determined in part by the space available.

III. Classification and Nomenclature of Enzymes[3]

A. TYPES OF REACTIONS CATALYZED

There is no well-defined, generally accepted system for naming or classifying enzymes. It seems likely that some concerted action may be taken within the reasonably near future to bring some order into the present chaos. In the meantime, the absence of a coherent and complete system of classification or nomenclature need not disturb us; it is characteristic of most fields of knowledge which are expanding rapidly. As new enzymes are discovered, names for these enzymes must be coined, and it is the usual custom to form the new name by adding the suffix *-ase* to a stem which denotes the type of substrate which the enzyme acts upon, or the type of reaction catalyzed, or both. Hoffmann-Ostenhof (44) has suggested a rational nomenclature and has proposed that enzymes should be grouped into five main classes: (1) Hydrolases;

[3] There are few references in Section III and IV to the literature prior to 1950. For detailed earlier documentation, the reader may refer to appropriate chapters in Sumner and Myrbäck (115).

(2) Transferases; (3) Oxidoreductases; (4) Lyases and synthases; (5) Isomerases and racemases.

These classes are distinguished, in part, on the basis of the number of components of the catalyzed reaction: 4 for the first three classes, 3 for the fourth, and 2 for the fifth class. Thus, enzymes belonging to the first three of these classes catalyze reactions which may be symbolized by the equation:

$$A + B \rightleftharpoons C + D$$

For enzymes of class 1, B is H_2O, and the general type equation may be written:

$$R—R' + HOH \rightleftharpoons R—H + R'OH$$

The arrow from right to left is dotted in, to indicate that the equilibrium from left to right is generally favored. For enzymes of class 2, the general type equation may be written:

$$R—A + R'—B \rightleftharpoons R—B + R'—A$$

For enzymes of class 3, it is difficult to write a general type equation that covers all cases, but the group is adequately distinguished by the stipulation that a transfer of hydrogen or oxygen or electrons must be involved. Enzymes belonging to class 4 catalyze reactions of the general type:

$$A \rightleftharpoons B + C$$

The lyases catalyze reactions from left to right, and the synthases catalyze reactions from right to left. The enzymes of class 5 catalyze reactions of the type:

$$A \rightleftharpoons B$$

We may compare the classification of Hoffmann-Ostenhof, with the grouping given in a current text (36):

A. Hydrolysis-Condensation or Replacement
   - Proteinases, Peptidases, and Amidases
   - Esterases
   - Thiol Esterases
   - Phosphatases and Transphosphorylases
   - Glycosidases
   - Transglycosidases

B. Phosphorolysis-Condensation
   - Phosphorylases

C. Cleavage or Formation of C—C Linkages
   - Decarboxylases
   - Aldolases

D. Hydration-Dehydration and Related Processes
Hydrases and Related Enzymes

$$\begin{array}{c} | \quad | \\ -C-C- \\ | \quad | \\ H \quad OH \end{array} \rightarrow \begin{array}{c} | \quad | \\ -C{=}C- \end{array}$$

(OH may be NH_2 or SH)

E. Oxidation-Reduction
Dehydrogenases
Oxidases
Peroxidases and Catalases

(It should be understood that different texts will group the various enzyme reactions in different ways.) In the above list, group *E* corresponds to class 3 of Hoffmann-Ostenhof; groups *C* and *D* are both included in class 4; there is no group corresponding to class 5; and, though groups *A* and *B* together correspond to classes 1 and 2 together, the subdivision is different in the two classifications.

It is, as a matter of fact, difficult to construct an unambiguous and straightforward system of classification on the basis of the type of reaction classified. For example, the distinction between classes 1 and 2 of Hoffmann-Ostenhof breaks down with increasing frequency, as more recent studies show that many enzymes can cause both hydrolyses and transfer reactions. Furthermore, the distinctions between various kinds of hydrolytic enzymes may fail when detailed studies show that proteinases (i.e., proteolytic enzymes) may split certain types of amide bonds and even ester bonds (40). Finally, there are enzyme reactions which must be formulated as combinations of the apparently different reaction types (e.g., the reaction catalyzed by the malic enzyme, which is both an oxidation-reduction and a decarboxylation-carboxylation reaction, and so belongs in both class 3 and class 4 of Hoffmann-Ostenhof).

If it is desirable to classify enzymes on the basis of the type of reaction catalyzed, then it seems that the detailed reaction mechanism is a better criterion than more superficial characteristics. Unfortunately, we do not know enough about detailed reaction mechanism to use it as a criterion in more than a few cases. Progress in our knowledge of enzymes must be measured, however, in terms of reaction mechanism, and it is on this basis that the subsequent discussion will be developed.

B. Prosthetic Groups

Some enzymes contain only amino acids in their molecules. Others contain other chemical moieties in addition. The term prosthetic group is sometimes used for any substance attached to a protein which is nc amino acid in nature. We shall here use the term in a more restricte sense to indicate a chemical moiety which is not an amino acid an which is necessary for, and often can be shown to participate in, er zyme function.

The better-known prosthetic groups include:

a. Iron porphyrins such as heme and related compounds.

b. Derivatives of riboflavin, mainly riboflavin monophosphate an flavin adenine dinucleotide. These may or may not be associated wit metal ions such as iron, copper, manganese, or molybdenum.

c. Diphosphothiamine, usually associated with magnesium ions.

d. Pyridoxal phosphate and related compounds.

To the above list we may add a fifth group of metal ions alone (e.g Cu, Zn).

In many cases, the functional role of the prosthetic groups is at lea partially understood and the presence of a particular prosthetic grou connotes a specificity for certain reaction types. With the possible ex ception of diphosphothiamine, all of the prosthetic groups listed abov can readily be shown to undergo nonenzymatic reactions which ar similar to the characteristic reactions catalyzed by the enzymes c which they form a part. The prosthetic group alone can thus provide model for the enzyme reaction. The attachment of the prosthetic grou to a particular protein, however, results in a large increase in reactio rate and a narrowing of specificity to one particular reaction of one o a few very closely related substrates.

The main difficulty attending the classification of enzymes on th basis of their prosthetic group content is that the identity of the pros thetic group may be difficult to determine if the enzyme is availabl only in a crude and very impure mixture. It may be particularly diff cult to prove the *absence* of any prosthetic group whatever. Or it ma not be easy to determine whether a component of the enzyme shoul be classified as a prosthetic group or not. Carboxypeptidase was know in crystalline form for some time before zinc was identified as a cha acteristic portion of the molecule (126); and it is still not entirely clea how the zinc functions in the enzyme reaction. If, on the other han the prosthetic group has intense and characteristic light-absorptio bands, identification may be relatively simple, particularly if change in the absorption bands occur during the action of the enzyme, thereb indicating the nature of the chemical change undergone by the pros thetic group. Thus the cytochromes, which contain heme as a prostheti group, were known for many years mainly in terms of the changes i the absorption spectra of cell suspensions and crude tissue homogenate

. COENZYMES (OR COFACTORS)

The word "coenzyme" was coined by Duclaux in 1897, to designate ialyzable substances essential for enzyme activity. There is a close nalogy between a coenzyme (or cofactor) and a prosthetic group. It primarily the firm binding of the prosthetic group to the protein hich differentiates prosthetic groups from coenzymes. Simple anions r cations may function as cofactors or coenzymes. Thus chloride ions re necessary for activity of the α-amylases, and Mg^{++} is required by all f the so-called kinases (i.e., the enzymes which catalyze a transfer of hosphate from adenosine triphosphate to some acceptor other than vater). Other coenzymes are organic compounds. There appears to be difference in function between a cofactor like chloride ion or mag- esium ion and some of the organic cofactors. The latter can usually e shown to undergo cyclic structural changes during the enzyme ction, which cannot be the case for chloride or Mg^{++}. A rather similar ituation obtains in the case of prosthetic groups, in that there is a dif- erence in apparent function between a metal ion such as Zn^{++} which annot be shown to undergo cyclic change, though it may appear to be ssential for activity, and a prosthetic group such as heme or flavin vhich can be shown to be alternately oxidized and reduced. Some in- estigators prefer to recognize this distinction by using different terms o designate the two types of prosthetic groups or cofactors. We have voided these formal distinctions here, mainly because they have not et come into general use.

Those prosthetic groups and coenzymes which undergo cyclic changes luring enzyme action, are analogous in many respects to the substrates f the enzyme. The firm binding of prosthetic group to protein differ- ntiates the prosthetic group from both substrate and coenzyme, but a ather different criterion differentiates coenzyme from substrate. The lassic example of a coenzyme—coenzyme I, cozymase, or diphospho- yridine nucleotide—was originally discovered and named as a sub- tance necessary for fermentation. Addition of only small amounts of ozymase would enable the protein components of yeast extract to fer- nent large amounts of sugar (provided Mg^{++}, phosphate, and adenylic cid were also added). In such a system the coenzyme is clearly dif- erentiated from the substrate. The latter is turned over in large quan- ity compared to the amount of coenzyme required. But the fermenta- ion mixture is of course a whole set of enzyme reactions, and when hese are broken down into individual components it becomes apparent hat the coenzyme is indeed a substrate for enzyme action. It undergoes o net change in the over-all reaction because the coenzyme is alternately reduced at one step in the reaction sequence and reoxidized a a later step, being thus regenerated to act again. In other words, if we focus on the individual enzyme reaction, the coenzyme cannot be clearly differentiated from the substrate. But if we examine the natura reaction sequence of which the individual enzyme reaction is one com ponent, then we find a small amount of coenzyme undergoing a cycli change, whereas the substrate undergoes a large net change.

There are three substances which have been called "coenzymes" from the time of their first discovery. These are coenzyme I (cozy mase), coenzyme II, and coenzyme A. Coenzymes I and II are both pyridine nucleotides and function by being alternately oxidized and re duced. The structure of the oxidized form of diphosphopyridine nucle- otide (DPN), or coenzyme I, is shown in formula (VIII). Coenzyme II

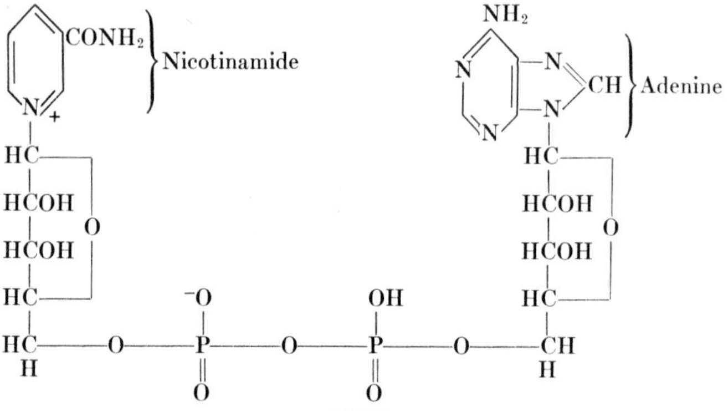

$CONH_2$ Nicotinamide NH_2 Adenine

(VIII)

or triphosphopyridine nucleotide (TPN) is identical with coenzyme I except that it contains an extra phosphate group at C-2 of the ribose moiety attached to adenine. The mechanism of action of the pyridine nucleotides is discussed in Section IV,C.

Coenzyme A, "the acetylating coenzyme," was originally discovered as a cofactor for acetylation reactions (66). It functions in these re- actions by accepting an acetyl group at S from a donor in one enzyme reaction, and passing the acetyl group on to an acceptor in the next. The structure of coenzyme A (CoA) is shown in formula (IX).

Note that both DPN and TPN, as well as CoA are *nucleotide* derivatives. It does not appear to be accidental that these substances have such a structure, which relates them to the components of ribo- nucleic acid. There are, in fact, a host of other compounds which are also nucleotides or nucleotide derivatives and which likewise could be said to function as coenzymes, in the same sense that DPN, TPN, and CoA function as coenzymes. These other substances have not always been so closely associated with the word coenzyme as the three sub-

```
    NH2
     |
N/‾‾‾‾\-N≷
|       |   >CH
\__N__/-N/                 O-
        |                 /
       HC------|       P=O
        |      |  O/    \
      HCOH_(   |          OH                    Pantetheine
        |  \   O             _____________________________________________
       HC   \  |              Pantothenic acid           Thioethanolamine
        |      |             ________________________   __________________
       HC------|   O      O      CH3     O                 O
        |          ||     ||      |      ||                ||
       HC—O—P—O—P—O—CH2CCHOHC—NCH2CH2C—NCH2CH2SH
       H       |      |       |          H           H
               O-     O-      CH3
                             (IX)
```

stances mentioned specifically. We have in mind the 5-mono, di-, and triphosphates of adenine, guanine, cystosine, and uracyl. Not only is the orthophosphate moiety transferred from one compound to another by way of these substances, but compounds such as uridine diphosphate glucose and cytidine diphosphate choline are obligatory intermediates in the metabolism of carbohydrates and phospholipids—substances which might at first sight appear to have little obvious connection with the nucleic acids. It appears that Nature has chosen, in a great many instances, to require that a substrate be converted to a nucleotide derivative before it can enter the "metabolic pool." In other words, enzymes tend to act upon nucleotide derivatives. Even ortho- and pyrophosphate may in fact be regarded as derivatives of nucleotides and as coenzymes, with no violation of the definition we are using here. The list of coenzymes includes also glucose-1,6-diphosphate, the coenzyme for phosphoglucomutase, and 2,3-diphosphoglycerate, the coenzyme for the mutase which interconverts 2- and 3-phosphoglycerate. These latter coenzymes will be discussed in Section IV,F,6 of this chapter. It should be understood that no attempt has been made in this chapter to discuss or even to list *all* substances which may be classified as coenzymes.

IV. Enzyme Reaction Mechanisms

A. Oxidation-Reduction Enzymes Containing Firmly Bound Prosthetic Groups

The biological processes of oxidation involve a series of oxidation-reduction reactions in a so-called respiratory chain, beginning with the removal of hydrogen atoms and/or electrons from substrate and ending with the transfer of electrons to the ultimate acceptor, molecular oxygen. A number of enzymes with firmly bound prosthetic groups play a prominent role in this chain. These include various heme proteins and flavoproteins. Since the role of these substances is discussed in detail in another chapter of this treatise, the discussion here is limited to a few aspects of the problem of mechanism. During function, the prosthetic groups of these proteins usually undergo a cyclic reduction and reoxidation. Both the hemes and the flavins are pigments, and the change in color or absorption spectrum which attends the change in the oxidation-reduction state provided an early clue to the mode of action of these substances (50a, 137, 138).

1. Heme Proteins

The structure of heme is shown in formula (X).

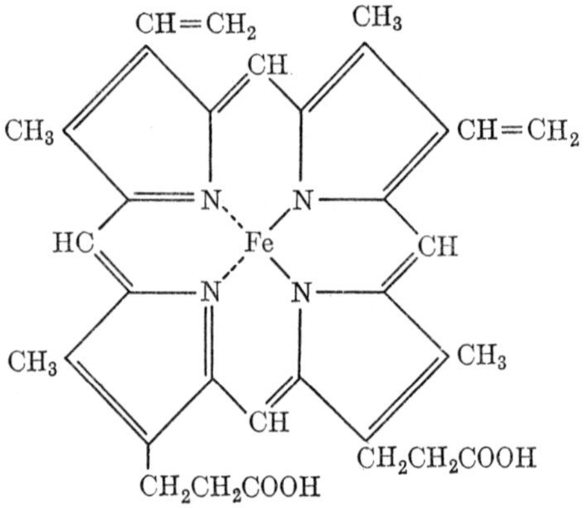

$CH{=}CH_2$ CH_3
CH
CH_3 $CH{=}CH_2$
N N
HC Fe CH
N N
CH_3 CH_3
CH
CH_2CH_2COOH
CH_2CH_2COOH

Heme (iron protoporphyrin)
(X)

Because of the coordinated double-bond system, the four pyrrole rings and their CH bridges lie in a plane. The iron lies in the plane joined to the four nitrogen atoms. It has two coordination positions, one above and one below the plane, and these are available to combine with some group on the protein or with water or anions.

The heme proteins include the cytochromes, catalase, and peroxidase. Of the cytochromes, the most thoroughly studied is cytochrome c which, unlike other members of this group, is readily soluble, and so has been purified extensively. The heme of cytochrome c is bound to the protein by thioether bonds. These are not readily broken, and the molecule can be hydrolyzed partially by acid or by proteolytic enzymes to give pigmented fragments containing parts of the peptide chain of the protein (121). Analysis of these fragments has led to the conclusion that the sequence of amino acids in the vicinity of the heme has the structure shown in (XI).

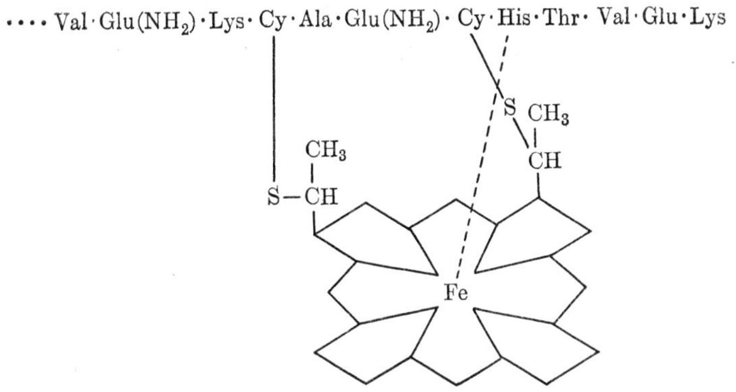

.... Val·Glu(NH_2)·Lys·Cy·Ala·Glu(NH_2)·Cy·His·Thr·Val·Glu·Lys

CH_3 CH_3 S—CH S CH Fe

(XI)

The heme group in this protein is visualized as lying in a crevice in the protein, with both of the extra coordination positions of iron occupied, probably by histidine N. This accounts for the lack of autooxidizability of the reduced cytochrome. Electrons may reach the Fe (which alternates functionally between Fe^{+++} and Fe^{++}) by way of the imidazole ring (121). Magnetometric measurements, which can be used to determine the presence of unpaired electrons, have been particularly useful for structure studies of cytochromes and other heme proteins, since the iron atom, under different conditions, may have 0, 1, 3, or 5 unpaired electrons.

The cytochromes are one of four groups of proteins containing heme prosthetic groups. Another group, the hemoglobins, function in oxygen transport. The other two groups are the peroxidases and the catalases, which are sometimes considered together as one group because they have many characteristics in common. It is the protein moiety of the various enzymes which confers specificity on the catalyst, since the prosthetic group is the same.

The peroxidases are very efficient catalysts for the oxidation of a variety of reducing substances by peroxides. The type reaction may be written:

$$H_2O_2 + H_2A \rightarrow 2H_2O + A$$

The absorption spectrum of the peroxidase shows characteristic changes during the reaction (17), and these changes have been interpreted as being due to intermediates which are formed by combination of the enzyme with the peroxide (i.e., enzyme-substrate complexes). Another interpretation is that the intermediates are higher oxidation states of the hemoproteins, in which a more complicated oxidation process than electron transfer has occurred. There are two intermediate compounds which can be detected, and George (37) has suggested that they are, respectively, substances in which Fe has a charge of 5+ and of 4+. The reaction sequence is then represented as:

$$Fe_{Per}^{+++}(H_2O) + H_2O_2 \rightarrow Fe_{Per}^{V}O^{+++} + 2H_2O$$

$$Fe_{Per}O^{+++} + AH_2 \rightarrow Fe_{Per}^{IV}O^{++} + AH\cdot + H^+$$

$$Fe_{Per}O^{++} + AH_2 + H^+ \rightarrow Fe_{Per}^{+++}(H_2O) + AH\cdot$$

(In this reaction sequence, Roman numerals are used to represent the 5+ and 4+ oxidation steps, and the subscript "Per" identifies the enzyme as peroxidase.) The first reaction is a 2-equivalent oxidation of peroxidase by H_2O_2. The next two steps are single equivalent reductions as a result of which AH is oxidized and Fe_{Per}^{+++} is regenerated. The two radicals (AH·) which are formed, may be considered to dismute to give A and AH_2.

Catalase causes a decomposition of H_2O_2 to O_2 and water: $2H_2O_2 \rightarrow 2H_2O + O_2$. This reaction may be regarded as a dismutation or oxidation-reduction between two molecules of H_2O_2. That is, the reaction is analogous to the peroxidase action, except that AH_2 is another molecule of O_2H_2. Under certain conditions catalase also acts as a peroxidase, causing the oxidation of substrates such as alcohols by H_2O_2. The peroxide must be generated slowly, to obtain this peroxidase action, otherwise the peroxide competes successfully with the alcohol.

The ability to decompose peroxide is not peculiar to catalase. Ionic iron alone has catalatic action. Heme, the prosthetic group of catalase is also effective without the protein, and other heme proteins, such as hemoglobin, also decompose peroxide. The action of catalase is far faster, however, than that of these other substances.

Starting with the knowledge that the action of catalase must be determined by the manner in which the protein combines with the heme, Wang (136) has constructed low-molecular weight catalase models, which far surpass the activity of substances such as iron, heme, and hemoglobin, though they do not reach the extraordinarily high activity of catalase itself. The most active model is a complex between ferric ion and triethylenetetramine ($H_2NCH_2CH_2NHCH_2CH_2NHCH_2CH_2NH_2$). The four nitrogen atoms of the amine occupy four coordination positions of the iron, leaving two positions free for the attachment of the peroxide. The successful construction of models of this sort helps to provide an insight into the structural requirements of the enzyme, which cannot here be fully explored. The suggestion that nonenzymatic catalysis may serve as a model for enzymatic catalysis is not of recent vintage (60), but it is only recently that knowledge has progressed to a point where a number of successful models have been constructed (39, 107, 119) (see also page 162). One is led by the study of models to the obvious question: Why should the enzyme molecule be so very large if a relatively small molecule can perform the catalytic function of the enzyme quite effectively? This is a question to which we will return later, when the structural characteristics of other enzymes have been considered.

2. *Flavoproteins*

Like the heme proteins, the flavoproteins also function by being alternately oxidized and reduced, as shown in the equation (XII)—

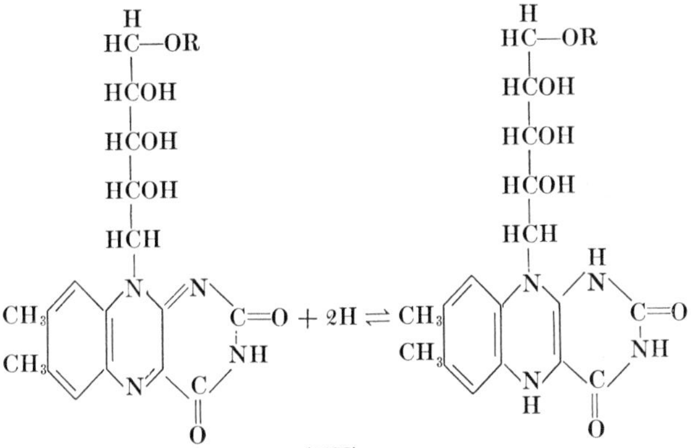

H
HC—OR
HCOH
HCOH
HCOH
HCH
CH_3, CH_3, N, N, N, N, C=O, NH, C, O

+ 2H ⇌

H
HC—OR
HCOH
HCOH
HCOH
HCH
CH_3, CH_3, N, N, H, N, N, H, C=O, NH, C, O

(XII)

[where R stands for the phosphate of riboflavin mononucleotide (FMN) or for the adenine ribose pyrophosphate moiety of flavin adenine dinucleotide (FAD)].

Free riboflavin is an oxidation-reduction pigment which reacts reversibly with other oxidation-reduction dyes. At acid pH a "semiquinone" intermediate is formed. That is, the normally two-equivalent oxidation-reduction reaction can proceed in two separate one-equivalent steps (12, 78, 140), forming a free-radical intermediate with an odd number of electrons. Like so many oxidation-reduction dyes, reduced riboflavin is auto-oxidizable (oxidized by O_2) and the oxygen used in the auto-oxidation is reduced to H_2O_2.

The flavins are prosthetic groups of a great variety of enzymes. Combination with the protein confers considerable specificity on the reactions catalyzed. Various hydrogen donors which may reduce the flavoprotein include amino acids, CoA derivatives of fatty acids, and the reduced pyridine nucleotides. The different flavin enzymes also show specificity for oxidants. Some react directly with molecular oxygen, forming H_2O_2, as does the free flavin. Others react only slowly or hardly at all with O_2, but may be oxidized by cytochromes, nitrate nitrite, quinones, and a variety of other reagents. Most of the flavoproteins which do not react readily with O_2 contain metal ions as firmly bound constituents of the enzymes (71, 83). Iron, copper, molybdenum and manganese have all been identified as constituents of various flavoproteins. The role of the metal in the enzyme reaction is not completely understood. In only one case, that of nitrate reductase, which contains molybdenum, has the metal been shown to undergo valency change from Mo^{5+} to Mo^{6+} during enzyme action. The flavoproteins, like the cytochromes, are an important constituent of the respiratory apparatus associated with particulate structures and are discussed in more detail in other chapters.

3. Copper Proteins

A number of oxidizing enzymes have been found to contain copper alone as a prosthetic group. Ascorbic acid oxidase and phenolase are typical examples (129). These enzymes are widely distributed in the plant kingdom (73). They are "true oxidases" in that they work directly with molecular oxygen. The mode of action of phenolase has been studied with isotopic O^{18} by Mason and his associates (72, 74), who have made the important discovery that the oxygen of O_2 attacks the substrate directly in the phenolase reaction. The substrate is a phenol, which acquires an extra hydroxyl group, and the O of this hydroxyl group has its origin in the O_2, not in the OH of the medium. The reaction is basically a four-electron oxidation. The enzyme contains two Cu^+ ions, which are converted to Cu^{++} when the phenol is hydroxylated. The two Cu^{++} ions must then be reduced to Cu^+ before the enzyme can go through another cycle. This reduction may be effected by the hydroquinone product which is thereby converted to a quinone. Or the reduction of Cu^{++} may be effected by another reducing agent, which then appears to be "co-oxidized" with the phenol. The sequence may be pictured as shown in equation (XIII).

$$\begin{matrix} Cu^+ \\ \wr \\ Cu^+ \end{matrix} + O_2 + \text{phenol (C}_6\text{ ring–OH)} + 2H^+ \longrightarrow \begin{matrix} Cu^{++} \\ \wr \\ Cu^{++} \end{matrix} + \text{HO–C}_6\text{ ring–OH}$$

$$\begin{matrix} Cu^{++} \\ \wr \\ Cu^{++} \end{matrix} + \text{HO–C}_6\text{ ring–OH} \longrightarrow \begin{matrix} Cu^+ \\ \wr \\ Cu^+ \end{matrix} + \text{O=C}_6\text{ ring=O} + 2H^+$$

(XIII)

3. ENZYMES CONTAINING THIAMINE OR PYRIDOXINE DERIVATIVES

The enzymes of this group catalyze reactions involving a splitting or formation of carbon-carbon bonds.

Diphosphothiamine (also called cocarboxylase or thiamine pyrophosphate) has the structure shown in formula (XIV).

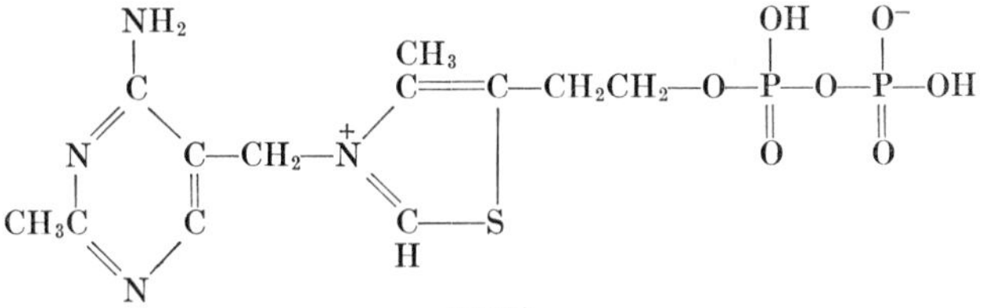

Pyrimidine ring (N, C–NH_2, C–CH_2–, C, N, CH_3C) linked by CH_2 to the thiazolium ring: $\overset{+}{N}$, C(–CH_3)=C–CH_2CH_2–O–P(OH)(=O)–O–P(O^-)(=O)–OH, C(H)–S

(XIV)

Enzymes containing this prosthetic group act characteristically on substrates which contain the grouping

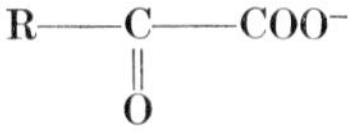

$$R\text{—}\underset{\underset{O}{\|}}{C}\text{—}COO^-$$

or

$$R\text{—}\underset{\underset{O}{\|}}{C}\text{—}\underset{\underset{OH}{|}}{\overset{\overset{H}{|}}{C}}\text{—}R'$$

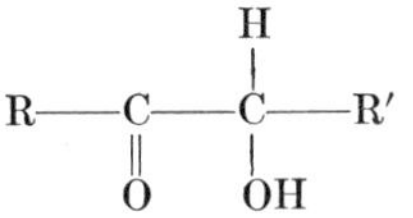

Substrates of the first group (i.e., α-keto acids) such as pyruvate, are decarboxylated, and those of the second group, such as ribulose diphosphate (with tranketolase) also undergo a splitting of the C—C bond of the

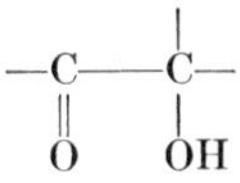

$$\text{—}\underset{\underset{O}{\|}}{C}\text{—}\underset{\underset{OH}{|}}{\overset{|}{C}}\text{—}$$

group. The manner of action of diphosphothiamine is not completely understood, although it has been investigated extensively.

The formulas for pyridoxal phosphate and pyridoxamine phosphate are shown in formula (XV).

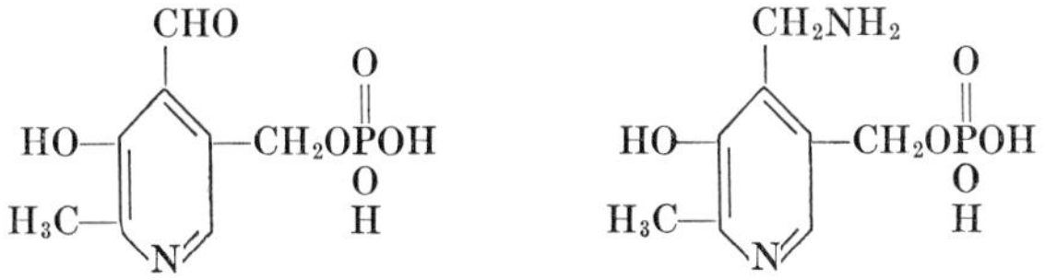

Pyridine ring with CHO, HO—, H_3C—, N, and —$CH_2OP(=O)(OH)OH$ (drawn as $CH_2O\overset{\overset{O}{\|}}{P}OH$ / O / H)

Pyridoxal-5-phosphate

Pyridine ring with CH_2NH_2, HO—, H_3C—, N, and —$CH_2OP(=O)(OH)OH$ (drawn as $CH_2O\overset{\overset{O}{\|}}{P}OH$ / O / H)

Pyridoxamine-5-phosphate

(XV)

Enzymes which contain these substances as prosthetic groups include, among others, the transaminases, the amino acid decarboxylases, and the amino acid racemases. A wide variety of reactions are catalyzed, but the substrates are generally α-amino acids. Snell and his collaborators have made a detailed study of the nonenzymatic reactions between pyridoxal and amino acids. In aqueous solution, if certain metal ions such as Cu^{++}, Fe^{++}, or Al^{+++} are present, and particularly at higher temperatures, the amino acids undergo most of the various reactions which can be catalyzed by the enzymes which contain pyridoxal phosphate as a prothetic group. Of course, the nonenzymatic reactions are not specific. All the reaction types may occur in the same solution, to give a variety of reaction products, and a great variety of different amino acids may react. In the case of the enzyme reactions, on the other hand, each enzyme is specific for one or a few amino acids, and completely specific for reaction type. Nevertheless, it seems likely that the basic mechanisms of the nonenzymatic and enzymatic reactions have features in common, and we have here an instance where a model for an enzyme reaction appears to have been particularly well chosen.

On the basis of the results obtained with the nonenzymatic reactions, Metzler *et al.* (77) have proposed a general mechanism for pyridoxal-catalyzed reactions. According to this proposal, a Schiff base is formed and stabilized by chelation with a metal ion. The bonds attached to the α-carbon atom of the original amino acid are labilized in this chelate and may be broken in a variety of ways. The equation (XVI) shows

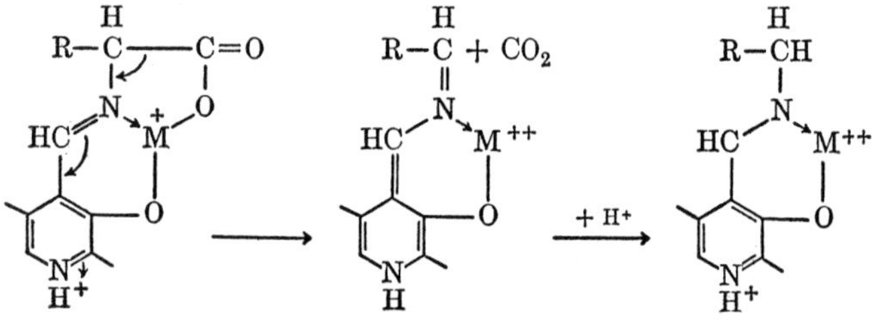

R—C + CO_2 → + H^+ →

(XVI)

the mechanism for one of the possible reactions, a decarboxylation. In the enzymatic reaction, the protein may take the place of the metal ion. It is also possible that some if not all of the pyridoxal phosphate enzymes contain metal ions.

C. Pyridine Nucleotide-Linked Dehydrogenases

1. General Description

Many biological oxidations begin, at the substrate level, with an oxidation of the substrate by a pyridine nucleotide. The present discussion will be concerned primarily with the enzymes which act with DPN, i.e., with the so-called DPN-linked dehydrogenases. (The TPN-linked dehydrogenases have been shown to behave similarly.) The reactions catalyzed by these enzymes may be formulated as shown in the equation (XVII):

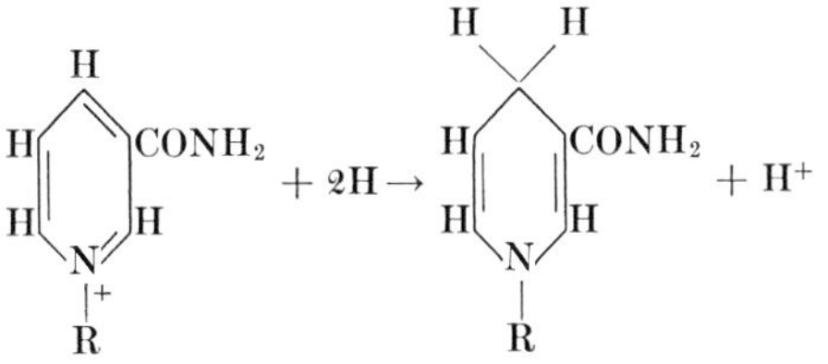

$$\text{(pyridinium ring: H, H, H, H, } CONH_2\text{, } N^+\text{–R)} + 2H \rightarrow \text{(dihydropyridine ring: } H_2\text{, H, H, H, } CONH_2\text{, N–R)} + H^+$$

(XVII)

The nicotinamide moiety of the pyridine nucleotide is oxidized and reduced by the removal or addition of hydrogen. In a typical dehydrogenase reaction, the two hydrogen atoms have their origin in the substrate of the enzyme, which is frequently an alcohol or an aldehyde.

The actual oxidative process in the respiration of sugar begins with a reduction of the nicotinamide moiety of DPN or TPN. Thus, in the Embden-Meyerhof path of glucose degradation, DPN is reduced by D-glyceraldehyde-3-phosphate, in the presence of triosephosphate dehydrogenase, and in the so-called "shunt" pathway, it is TPN which is reduced by glucose-6-phosphate in the presence of glucose-6-phosphate dehydrogenase.

The oxidation of triose in the triosephosphate dehydrogenase reaction may be formulated by equation (XVIII).

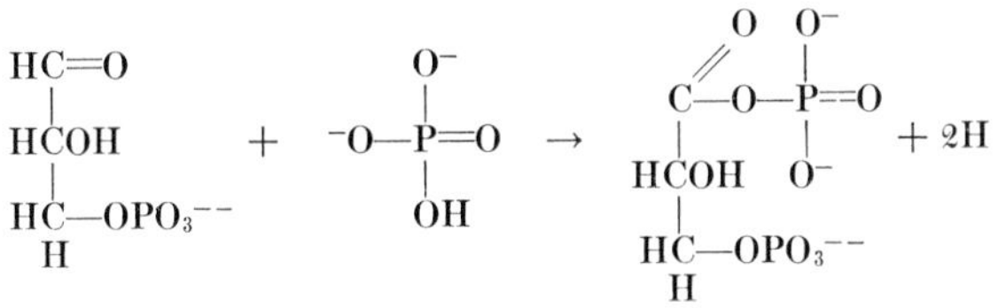

$$\begin{array}{l} HC{=}O \\ | \\ HCOH \\ | \\ HC{-}OPO_3^{--} \\ H \end{array} + \begin{array}{c} O^- \\ | \\ {}^-O{-}P{=}O \\ | \\ OH \end{array} \rightarrow \begin{array}{l} \quad O \quad O^- \\ \;\,/\!/ \quad\;\; | \\ C{-}O{-}P{=}O \\ | \qquad\quad | \\ HCOH \quad O^- \\ | \\ HC{-}OPO_3^{--} \\ H \end{array} + 2H$$

(XVIII)

In this equation, the products include the two hydrogen atoms necessary for the reduction of DPN. Of course, these hydrogen atoms do not appear as atomic hydrogen. One of them comes from the carbonyl carbon atom of the triose. The aldehyde must actually furnish a proton and two electrons, or the equivalent of a hydride ion, H^-. The H^+ may be considered to be furnished by the orthophosphate ion or by the water of the medium. The fact that the reaction can be balanced with H^+ and H^- in no sense shows how the oxidation of the substrate actually occurs. One can formulate all oxidation-reduction reactions in terms of a transfer of electrons, which may or may not be accompanied by a loss or addition of the elements of water. In these formal terms, the aldehyde suffers a loss of two electrons and a hydrogen ion. The reduction of DPN requires two electrons and a hydrogen ion. The question is how this oxidoreduction reaction actually takes place (132).

2. *Direct Transfer of Hydrogen*

With the use of deuterium as a tracer, it has been possible to show that the enzyme reaction involves a direct transfer of a hydrogen atom from the aldehyde to the DPN (67, 130, 131). That is, the extra hydrogen atom at the para position of the reduced DPN is the *same* hydrogen atom that was removed from the triose. Since there is no such reaction in the absence of the specific enzyme, the enzyme must function by holding the triose and the DPN together in some very special way which facilitates the transfer of a proton and two electrons or of a hydride ion. An alternative possibility might be that the substrate donates a hydride ion to some nonexchangeable position on the protein, from which the hydrogen, in turn, is transferred to DPN. By nonexchangeable, we mean that the hydrogen must be donated to form a new C—H bond, since H bound to O, N, or S exchanges very rapidly with H^+ of the medium. It is difficult to imagine what group on the protein might function to accept and transfer nonexchangeable hydrogen, and direct transfer between substrate and DPN is regarded as the more probable mechanism (132). The precise manner in which phosphate enters the triosephosphate dehydrogenase reaction has been in sharp dispute for some time. Current majority opinion favors the view that the aldehyde group of the triose phosphate combines first with an —SH group in the enzyme, and hydrogen is transferred from this complex to DPN, to give reduced DPN and a thiolester. The phosphoglyceryl group is then transferred from the —SH group of the enzyme to phosphate (24b, 94, 95).

All of the DPN-linked alcohol and aldehyde oxidations which have been examined to date occur with a direct transfer of hydrogen. With aldehydes, the H on the

$$\begin{array}{c}\mathrm{HC{=}O}\\ |\end{array}$$

group is transferred, and with alcohols, an H is transferred from

$$\begin{array}{c}\mathrm{H}\\ \mathrm{—C—OH}\\ \mathrm{H}\end{array}$$

or from

$$\begin{array}{c}\mathrm{H}\\ \mathrm{—C—OH}\\ |\end{array}$$

The hydrogen on the hydroxyl must drop off as an H^+ ion when the carbonyl group is formed as a result of the oxidation of the primary or secondary alcohol. Besides triosephosphate dehydrogenase, the reactions which have been examined include those catalyzed by the dehydrogenases for ethanol, acetaldehyde, L-lactate, L-malate, D-glycerate, α-glycerophosphate, L-glutamate, glucose, a β-hydroxysteroid, and isocitric dehydrogenase (28, 62, 130–132).

The substrates for the pyridine nucleotide dehyrogenases are not all alcohols and aldehydes. Reduced pyridine nucleotides may be oxidized quite specifically by flavoproteins. In reactions of this sort, deuterium cannot be applied very easily to determine whether a direct transfer of hydrogen is involved because the extra hydrogen of the reduced flavin is attached to nitrogen, and so exchanges very rapidly with the hydrogen ions of the medium. In this connection, it is of interest that the demonstrated absence of direct hydrogen transfer has been used as a partial basis for the correct prediction that an enzyme will be found to be a flavoprotein. Dihydroörotic dehydrogenase catalyzes the oxidation of dihydroörotate to orotate, as shown in reaction (XIX). In this reaction,

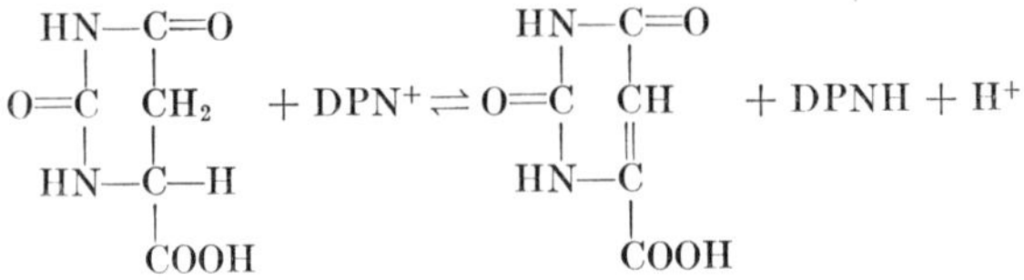

```
     HN—C=O                          HN—C=O
     |  |                            |  |
   O=C  CH2    + DPN+ ⇌ O=C  CH        + DPNH + H+
     |  |                            |  ||
     HN—C—H                          HN—C
        |                               |
        COOH                            COOH
  Dihydroörotic acid                 Orotic acid
                       (XIX)
```

two hydrogen atoms are removed from two neighboring carbon atoms, forming a carbon-carbon double bond—a rather unusual reaction for a pyridine nucleotide-linked reaction. Application of deuterium to the study of the reaction demonstrated that there was no detectable transfer of hydrogen between substrate and DPN (38). Subsequent purification then showed that the enzyme contained a flavin prosthetic group (H. C. Friedmann and B. Vennesland, unpublished observations).

3. *Steric Specificity*

The steric specificity of enzyme reactions has long been a well-known fact (33). Thus, certain plant glucosidases were used in the early days of organic chemistry to determine whether glucosides had an α- or β-configuration, and peptidases or proteolytic enzymes act only on peptide bonds between amino acids of the natural, or L-configuration. Further, those DPN-linked dehydrogenases which act on secondary alcohols (e.g., malic dehydrogenase and lactic dehydrogenase), were known almost from the time of their discovery to act on only one of the two stereoisomeric forms of these compounds. The steric specificity of enzyme reactions is usually extremely high for the particular position which is attacked in the enzyme reaction, that is, for the carbon atom where a bond is broken and a new bond is formed. This implies that the molecules are oriented in space in a very particular way when reaction takes place. At carbon atoms removed from the site of actual chemical change, steric specificity may be less marked.

TABLE IV
STERIC SPECIFICITY FOR DPN (62)

Dehydrogenase	Source	Steric specificity
Alcohol (with ethanol)	Yeast; *Pseudomonas;* liver; wheat germ	α
Alcohol (with isopropyl alcohol)	Yeast	α
Acetaldehyde	Liver	α
L-Lactate	Heart muscle	α
L-Malate	Pig heart; wheat germ	α
D-Glycerate	Spinach	α
Dihydroörotate	*Zymobacterium oroticum*	α
α-Glycerophosphate	Muscle	β
3-Phosphoglyceraldehyde	Yeast; muscle	β
L-Glutamate	Liver	β
D-Glucose	Liver	β
β-Hydroxysteroid	*Pseudomonas*	β
DPNH-cytochrome c	Rat liver mitochondria; pig heart	β
TPNH (transhydrogenase)	*Pseudomonas*	β
β-Hydroxybutyryl CoA	Heart muscle	β

There are two hydrogen atoms at the reduced para position of the nicotinamide ring of DPN. The carbon atom of this position is therefore not asymmetric. If one deuterium atom is introduced at this position, the carbon atom does become truly asymmetric, however. The use of deuterium has therefore made it possible to show that the hydrogen transfer caused by pyridine nucleotide dehydrogenases is not only direct, but also stereospecific for the DPN. The nicotinamide ring has two sides, and the transfer of hydrogen caused by a particular enzyme occurs either to one side or to the other side, but not indiscriminately to either side. It is not known which side is which, but the side used by yeast alcohol dehydrogenase has been termed the α-side, and the side used by the triose dehydrogenase has been termed the β-side. Table IV lists the various DPN-linked dehydrogenase reactions for which the steric specificity has been determined. It is apparent from the table that an approximately equal number of α-specific and β-specific enzymes have been found to date.

4. *Zinc*

Several of the pyridine nucleotide dehydrogenases have been shown to contain zinc firmly bound in the molecule, and it has been suggested that all such enzymes contain zinc (126, 127). Any such generalization at the present time would, however, appear to be premature. The enzymes investigated include the dehydrogenases for alcohol, lactate, glutamate, glucose-6-phosphate, glycerophosphate, and malate (127). The latter three enzymes were found to have considerable amounts of other metal constituents also, and for these enzymes the question is open whether the zinc is present as a specific and necessary constituent of the enzyme.

The quantitative determination of zinc is associated with certain practical difficulties. The best and most extensive data are available for alcohol dehydrogenase, where the presence of zinc is indisputable. Yeast alcohol dehydrogenase has been reported to bind four molecules of DPN and to contain four atoms of zinc per molecule (127). Thus there would appear to be one atom of zinc per active site, and Vallee and his associates, who pioneered in this field, have suggested that the zinc acts to facilitate the binding of DPN. More extensive investigation of the problem by Wallenfels and Sund (135), have revealed that the situation is somewhat more complicated and that the zinc content of the enzyme is variable, with up to five atoms of zinc bound firmly and a considerably larger number more loosely associated with the protein. There has been a considerable amount of stimulating discussion of the possible details of the reaction mechanism of the alcohol dehydrogenase reaction. As in so many other cases, it seems easier to formulate hypotheses in this area than it is to prove them. The question of the function of zinc must still be regarded as an open problem.

It is of interest also that zinc has been known since the middle of the nineteenth century to be a stimulant to the growth of fungi, and its essentiality for virtually all plants is now established. If zinc is a component of such important enzymes as some of the pyridine nucleotide dehydrogenases, a ready explanation of the need of plants for zinc is provided. Many of the trace metals necessary in plant nutrition have been shown to be essential components of enzymes (this topic will be developed in Volume III).

D. Enzyme-Reaction Kinetics

1. Enzyme Assay

The word enzyme has an operational connotation. We recognize and measure an enzyme in terms of the reaction it catalyzes. All practical operations in enzymology are eventually dependent on an available assay method for measuring how much enzyme is present. The quantity or amount of the enzyme is measured by determining the rate of the reaction catalyzed. Such rates are often called "units" of enzyme activity. Although "units" are always reaction rates, that is, a change in concentration (or amount per unit volume) during a given time, there is no uniformity in the conventions used for calculating their numerical value. One investigator may express "units" in grams per liter per hour, another in micromoles per milliliter per minute. Since concentration changes of substances with characteristic absorption spectra are often determined by measuring changes in light absorption with a Beckman spectrophotometer, the ΔOD, or change in optical density observed under specific conditions, is often used as a measure of change of concentration. It is clear, however, that the assay method must be capable of measuring these "units" quantitatively, and the first concern of the experimenter is therefore to find a set of conditions under which the rate of reaction of an enzyme is directly proportional to the amount of enzyme present.

The purity of an enzyme is expressed as its "specific activity," which is calculated as the number of "units" present in a given amount of protein (or nitrogen) or a given amount of dry weight. The activity of a purified enzyme is sometimes expressed as its turnover number. This is simply the number of molecules of substrate which are acted upon by one molecule of enzyme in one minute, generally under conditions which are optimal for reaction. Thus, for the reaction $A \rightarrow B$, the turnover number of the enzyme catalyzing the reaction is the number of molecules of A which one molecule of enzyme can convert into B in one minute. We may regard the turnover number as the "frequency" with which the enzyme cycle can operate. Turnover numbers of enzymes vary widely in magnitude, as illustrated by the representative figures assembled in Table V.

One may, as a stimulating exercise, examine the possible relationships between turnover number and generation time of, for example, a microorganism. We will assume that most of the protein of a bacterium is enzymatic protein and attempt to estimate the average turnover number of these enzymes within the cell. Our assumptions are not

TABLE V
TURNOVER NUMBERS OF ENZYMES

Enzyme	Turnover number[a]
Cholinesterase	18,000,000
Catalase	5,000,000–19,000,000
Triosephosphate isomerase	1,000,000
Urease	460,000
Phosphoglyceric kinase	320,000
Lactic dehydrogenase	31,000
Alcohol dehydrogenase	29,000
Triosephosphate dehydrogenase	27,000
Phosphoglucomutase	17,000
Enolase	10,000
Diaphorase	9,000
D-Amino acid oxidase	2,000
Pyruvic decarboxylase	850
L-Amino acid oxidase (snake venom)	3,000
L-Amino acid oxidase (kidney)	6
Liver alcohol dehydrogenase	220

[a] The figures in this table are taken from Hoffmann-Ostenhof (45), where more detailed documentation can be obtained.

necessarily correct, and our figures can only be the crudest estimates. An attempt to make such a calculation is nevertheless instructive.

Assume that the average enzyme molecule of a bacterium contains 1000 amino acid residues. (With a mean residue weight of 112, this would give a molecular weight of 112,000.) Assume further that there are an average of ten enzymatic steps required per amino acid residue in the over-all process whereby the amino acid is formed from the available food molecules and incorporated into protein. There are then 1000×10 or 10,000 enzymatic steps required to make the protein. Consider now that in one generation time for the cell in question, each protein molecule will be duplicated. Generation times as short as 9 minutes have been reported for bacteria, and 20-minute generation times are common. To be conservative, we will select the latter figure. The enzymatic steps per minute, 10,000/20 or 500 may be regarded as a kind of average turnover number for all the enzymes involved in making protein. Since lipids, carbohydrates, and nucleic acids must also be synthesized, and these are approximately equal to the protein in bulk, we may add another 500 necessary enzymatic steps for the synthesis of nonprotein material. This gives us an average turnover number of 1000 for all the enzymes. Such a figure may seem low when compared with known turnover numbers for purified enzymes (see

Table V), but we must remember that these turnover numbers listed in Table V are determined under optimal conditions far removed from an equilibrium point, with the enzyme saturated with substrate. There is little reason to believe that all enzymes operate under such conditions *in vivo*. In fact, one may surmise that in some of the reaction sequences of metabolism, many of the enzymes operate close to equilibrium points, and so will have relatively low *net* turnover numbers. Also, the slowest steps in a metabolic sequence will determine the over-all net rates. A net turnover number of 1000 is therefore not necessarily low. It is also believed that the above estimates are conservative. The figure of ten steps per amino acid must include the steps necessary to generate the energy to make the protein precursors. If the organism is growing anaerobically on peptone, glucose, and salts, we may assume about five steps per high-energy phosphate bond, which is required to incorporate the amino acid into the protein, and at least one step for hydrolysis of peptone. Even if many of the required amino acids are present preformed, they will not be present in the right proportions, so extra synthetic steps are required to make at least some of the amino acids. Of course, if the organism must manufacture its amino acids from ammonia and glucose, many more enzymatic steps are required, but the generation time under such circumstances also becomes longer.

2. *Enzyme-Substrate Dissociation Constant*

As a general rule, the measured rate of an enzyme reaction shows a characteristic dependence on the substrate concentration. If rate measurements are made at a series of different substrate concentrations with the same quantity of enzyme, one often finds that the magnitude of the initial velocity, v, increases with increasing concentrations of substrate, S, until a maximum velocity, V, is reached, beyond which further increase in substrate concentration has no effect on the measured velocity of the reaction. The relationship between S, V, and v, is often defined by the equation $K_M = S(V/v - 1)$ where K_M is a constant known as the Michaelis constant.

The derivation of this equation is very simple. The enzyme reaction is assumed to begin with the rapid, reversible combination of the enzyme, E, with the substrate, S, to form the enzyme substrate complex, ES. This is the first step in the reaction sequence

$$E + S \rightleftharpoons ES \xrightarrow{k} E + \text{product}$$

The rate-determining step in the enzyme reaction is assumed to be the conversion of ES to free enzyme and product. The rate constant for this second, rate-limiting reaction is k. The Michaelis constant, K_M, is defined as the dissociation constant for the reversible conversion of ES to E and S. That is,

$$K_M = \frac{(E)(S)}{(ES)}$$

(where parentheses are used to indicate concentrations).

The amount of S is assumed to be so large relative to E, that only a negligible amount of S can be removed as ES.

Since
$$v = k(ES)$$
$$(ES) = v/k$$

If all of E is combined as ES, the velocity has its maximum value, V.

Therefore, $V = k(E + ES)$ or $(E) = V/k - (ES)$.

Substituting for (ES),

$$(E) = V/k - v/k = (V - v)/k$$

Substituting for (E) and (ES) in the equation for K_M,

$$K_M = (V - v)/k \times k/v \times S \text{ or } K_M = (V/v - 1)S.$$

More conveniently, the equation is used in a linear form to simplify the task of determining whether a set of experimental data actually fit the equation. The details of these operations need not concern us here. The points to remember are that K_M is, operationally, equal to the substrate concentration when the velocity is half of the maximum attainable value, and theoretically, at first approach, it is the enzyme-substrate dissociation constant.

The assumptions underlying the simple derivation given above are not always justified. The fact that a given set of data fit the equation is not evidence for the validity of the assumptions. For example, the velocity of formation of ES from E and S is not necessarily faster than the velocity of the further reaction of ES. Under these circumstances, the first step may be partially rate-limiting. The data may still fit the equation, but the K_M value calculated is not the true enzyme-substrate dissociation constant.

$$E + S \underset{k_2}{\overset{k_1}{\rightleftharpoons}} ES \overset{k_3}{\rightarrow} E + \text{product}$$

If k_1, k_2, and k_3 are used to indicate the velocity constants of the various reactions as shown above, then

$$K_M = \frac{k_2 + k_3}{k_1}$$

A simple derivation for the above equation may be found in Neilands and Stumpf (82), which also contains a straightforward treatment of the practical problem of determining and calculating K_M. Note that the term K_M is always used to refer to the constant which may be calculated from the *experimental* data. This is the convention used by enzymologists. The *theoretical* significance of K_M may vary with the circumstances.

The rate-limiting step in an enzyme reaction is not necessarily the first or second step in the simple reaction sequence to which this discussion has been limited. A later step, such as the dissociation of the product from the enzyme surface, may also be rate-limiting. K_M may then become a more complicated function of the velocity constants of the various reactions involved [see, for example (120)].

It is self-evident that if the enzyme reaction consists of an interaction of two molecules, $A + B \rightleftharpoons A' + B'$, the situation is likewise more complicated. In general, reactions of the latter sort are handled experimentally by saturating the enzyme with one substrate and then varying the concentration of the other. The case of the pyridine nucleotide dehydrogenases provides an example. Here the enzyme may be considered to have four substrates, i.e., the oxidized and reduced forms of DPN or TPN, as well as the oxidized and reduced forms of the substrate proper. K_M values may be determined experimentally for all four substrates.

If the only rate which can be measured experimentally is the rate of disappearance of the substrate of the reaction, or the rate of formation of the final product, kinetic data alone may not permit an evaluation of the theoretical significance of an experimentally determined Michaelis constant. If, however, some intermediate in the reaction can also be measured, then some of the rate constants of the intermediate steps may possibly be evaluated separately, and more definitive conclusions may be drawn than is otherwise possible. Alberty (1, 2) has treated the general problem of enzyme reaction kinetics in detail.

The enzyme substrate complex should not be regarded as a hypothetical entity invented to provide physical meaning for a mathematical equation which happens to fit some data. Various lines of independent evidence add reality to *ES*. For example, *ES* may have an absorption spectrum different from the sum of free *E* plus free *S*. Some of the pyridine nucleotide dehydrogenases provide examples. Reduced DPN has a well-defined absorption band with a peak at 340 mμ. There is a shift in the position of this band when the reduced DPN combines with liver alcohol dehydrogenase (16, 122, 122a). Such shifts do not occur with all of the dehydrogenases. In the case of triosephosphate dehydrogenase, the combination of oxidized DPN with protein is accompanied by the formation of a new absorption band (95). This latter enzyme also binds DPN sufficiently firmly so that it can be shown to sediment with the protein in the ultracentrifuge, and an independent evaluation of the enzyme-DPN dissociation constant can be obtained by centrifugation procedures (128). So we see that even though the substrate is not linked to enzyme by covalent bonds and dissociates from the enzyme freely, the reality of the combination of enzymes with substrate can frequently be demonstrated.

3. *Effect of Temperature*

There are, in general, two different ways in which temperature influences an enzyme reaction (104). We may consider, first, the effect of temperature on any chemical reaction. This is most simply described in terms of the Q_{10} or temperature coefficient. Most chemical reactions have a Q_{10} of approximately 2 or 3.

$$Q_{10} = \frac{\text{Reaction velocity at } T^\circ + 10^\circ}{\text{Reaction velocity at } T^\circ}$$

(where T° is the temperature)

Since enzyme reactions consist essentially of a sequence of chemical reactions, they would be expected to have similar temperature coefficients. This is in fact the case, but only within a limited range of temperature. As the temperature is raised, heat denaturation of the protein commences and inactivation of the enzyme occurs. The gradual loss in enzyme activity therefore counteracts the normal increase in reaction velocity, and the apparent Q_{10} value drops and may assume a negative value. In other words, enzymes have an optimum temperature, at which maximum reaction velocity is observed. The position of this optimum will vary with the manner in which the enzyme assay is carried out. Since the enzyme inactivation takes place over a period of time, the initial velocity will be faster than the velocity at a later period. Temperature optima are therefore usually not reproducible unless the manner of determining them is duplicated exactly.

The measurement of the dependence of reaction rate on temperature gives data from which one may calculate the so-called "activation energy" of the reaction. The calculation is based on the Arrhenius equation, which indicates the manner in which the velocity constant, k, of a reaction varies with the temperature:

$$d \ln k/dT = E/RT^2$$

where R is the gas constant, T is the absolute temperature, and E is the activation energy, a constant characteristic for the reaction. If the above equation is integrated and if R is expressed in calories, we obtain the expression:

$$\log \frac{k_2}{k_1} = 0.219E \left(\frac{1}{T_1} - \frac{1}{T_2} \right)$$

where k_1 is the velocity constant at T_1, and k_2 is the velocity constant at T_2. From this equation it is evident that a plot of log k against $1/T$ should give a straight line with the slope of $-0.219E$. Calculation shows that for a reaction which proceeds twice as fast at 32°C as at 22°C, the activation energy is 12,000 calories, a typical value for a chemical reaction. Though the rates of enzyme reactions have activation energies (and consequently temperature coefficients) of the same order of magnitude as other chemical reactions, an enzyme always lowers the activation energy of the reaction which it catalyzes. Thus, the activation energy, E, for the hydrolysis of sucrose by hydrogen ions (HCl) is 26,000 calories; but for the hydrolysis of sucrose by malt invertase, E is 13,000 calories. Similarly, the activation energy for the hydrolysis of ethyl butyrate by hydrogen ions is 13,200 calories, and the hydrolysis by pancreatic lipase has an activation energy of 4200 calories (64, 104).

When the heat-denaturation of an enzyme commences, and the measured reaction rate is affected by the enzyme inactivation, then a constant value for E cannot be obtained. That is, in this temperature range, the plot of log k against $1/T$ does *not* give a straight line. If a reaction is complex, for example if it occurs as a sequence of several reactions with different temperature coefficients, then, also, E as calculated from the data will not be constant.

The activation energy, E, is regarded as the energy increment which a molecule must acquire in order to be converted to some other stable form. It is pictured as the height of the energy hump in the accompanying diagram (Fig. 3), which shows the change in energy content of a molecule A, in the process of conversion to B.

The heat denaturation of a protein may also be treated as a chemical reaction for which the dependence of rate on temperature may be determined. Such measurements have shown that E for heat denaturation of a protein has a characteristically high value, lying in the range 40,000 to 100,000 calories per mole (92). At 50°C, these values correspond to temperature coefficients (Q_{10} values) of 7 and 125, respectively. Q_{10} values up to 600 have been reported. Other chemical reactions with such high temperature coefficients do not proceed at appreciable rates at 50°. Some explanation for these unusual circumstances is required. The answer is found in the conclusion that the heat denaturation of a protein involves an unusually large entropy (S) change (29). The entropy component may under these circumstances be regarded as a measure of change from order to disorder. Thus the temperature coefficient of heat denaturation provides evidence that there is a change from a highly ordered arrangement of the molecule in its native state to a disordered arrangement in the denatured state. Historically, an important line of evidence for the conclusion that enzymes are proteins was provided by the demonstration that, for crystalline pepsin, the activation energies were identical for the process leading to loss of enzyme activity on heating and for the process of heat denaturation as measured by loss of solubility (84). The practical consequence of the high activation energy for heat denaturation of a protein is that the onset of protein denaturation is very abrupt. There is only a small

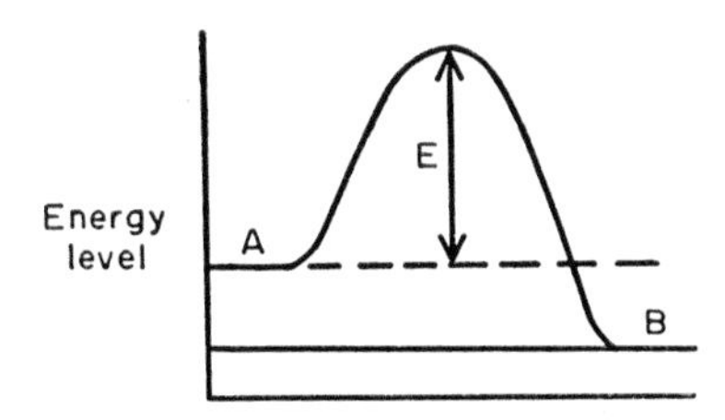

FIG. 3. Change in energy (E) content of a molecule (A) in the process of conversion to B.

temperature range, sometimes only 2° or 3°, within which the reaction is not either too fast or too slow to be measured accurately. A more detailed treatment of the effect of temperature on enzyme reactions may be found in a review by Stearn (106).

4. *Effect of pH*

The hydrogen ion concentration of the medium in which an enzyme reaction occurs may influence the reaction in a variety of ways (1, 3). There is usually a pH range within which the enzyme is relatively stable, but above and below which the protein is denatured, with consequent loss of enzyme activity. Then, there may be an effect of pH on the substrate. If the latter contains acidic or basic groups, the ionic form in which the substrate is present will depend on the pH. If, for example, the substrate is a weak acid HA, it will dissociate to give A^-, and the enzyme may act only on A^- and not on HA (or vice versa). Under these circumstances, enzyme activity will be negligible at pH's where virtually all of the substrate is present as HA, the form on which the enzyme does not act. The pH may also have a marked effect on the equilibrium of an enzyme-catalyzed reaction. Such effects are particularly striking in the DPN-linked dehydrogenase reactions. In the reduction of DPN by an alcohol, for example, a hydrogen ion is formed, and this hydrogen ion must be included in the expression for the equilibrium constant. Thus, for the reaction: $CH_3CH_2OH + DPN^+ \rightleftharpoons CH_3CHO + DPNH + H^+$, ($DPN^+$ indicates oxidized DPN, and the DPNH indicates reduced DPN), the equilibrium constant,

$$K = \frac{(CH_3CHO)(DPNH)(H^+)}{(CH_3CH_2OH)(DPN^+)}$$

A change of pH of one unit is equivalent to a tenfold change in (H^+), so it is clear that pH can have a marked effect on the extent to which DPN will be reduced by ethanol (93a, 122).

Finally, the pH can affect the enzyme reaction by determining the ionization state of the protein. This effect is analogous in some respects to the effect of pH on the ionic state of the substrate. The active configuration of the enzyme may require that a hydrogen ion be associated at a particular site, and thus the enzyme may be converted reversibly from active to inactive form by altering the pH of the medium. Above and below certain hydrogen ion concentrations an irreversible denaturation of the protein is also apt to occur. Enzymes, generally, show characteristic pH optima which are determined by one or several of the factors already mentioned (1).

E. INHIBITORS OF ENZYME ACTION

Enzymes are inhibited by an enormous variety of chemical reagents. Some of these are fairly specific, in the sense that they inhibit only a few closely related enzymes. Such inhibitors are used for diagnostic purposes, to obtain information about the essential components of enzyme systems. Thus the inhibition of an oxidation reaction by carbon monoxide and the relief of that inhibition by light is an almost diagnostic test for cytochrome oxidase. Chelating or complexing agents which combine with certain metals may also be used to show the necessity of a metal ion for the reaction which is inhibited (e.g., inhibition by CN^- implies that heavy metals such as iron or copper are required; inhibition by diethyl dithiocarbamate implies that copper ions are necessary).

Another group of inhibitors such as iodoacetate, *p*-chloromercuribenzoic acid, and heavy-metal ions (e.g., Cu^{++}, Hg^{++}) act by substituting on or oxidizing —SH groups. The state of the —SH groups in the protein molecule has received considerable attention from enzymologists because the activity of the enzyme is so often dependent on the presence of unsubstituted, reduced —SH (9). Thus, the proteolytic enzyme, papain, has long been known to show full activity only when a reducing agent is added. Each molecule contains one —SH group which is necessary for enzyme action (32). The pyridine nucleotide dehydrogenases are, to the author's knowledge, all dependent on —SH groups. In fact, if all enzymes were classified into two groups according to whether or not intact —SH groups were required for activity, one would probably find that the list of enzymes not dependent on —SH was the shorter of the two lists. Different enzymes show considerable variability in the susceptibility of their —SH groups to inactivation. Some are so sensitive that they cannot be diluted with distilled water without loss of activity unless some reducing agent such as cysteine or thioglycollate is added to the medium. With others, —SH-dependence may be demonstrable only with a few special reagents. If an enzyme molecule contains several —SH groups, they are not necessarily all required for activity. The function of the —SH group in the enzyme action is not entirely clear. Possibly the active —SH groups of different enzymes have quite different functions. In some instances the —SH appears to be involved in the binding of the substrate by the enzyme. In other instances it has been suggested that the —SH participates more directly in the catalytic process of the enzyme reaction.

The action of a particular inhibitor may or may not be competitive with the substrate. By competitive inhibition, we mean an inhibition which is prevented or reversed by the addition of the substrate. If the degree of inhibition is a function of the ratio of the concentration of inhibitor to concentration of substrate, and not of the absolute amount of inhibitor added, and if the degree of inhibition is independent of the order in which inhibitor or substrate are added to enzyme, then the system is freely reversible.

Many reagents which cause freely reversible competitive inhibitions are analogs of the substrate, i.e., substances with structural features similar to, but not identical with, the natural substrate of the enzyme. Such inhibitors act by displacing the substrate from its natural combining site. They undergo no further reaction, but simply block the approach of the substrate to the enzyme. The study of a series of such inhibitors may indicate quite clearly what particular chemical groups of the substrate function in the binding of the substrate to the enzyme. Furthermore, the action of toxic substances can sometimes be explained by their chemical similarity to certain metabolites. The enzymes which normally act on the metabolites combine with the structurally similar toxic substances and are thereby inhibited (93, 143).

The judicious use of enzyme inhibitors and the study of their mode of action has provided the enzymologist with a broad avenue of approach to the problem of enzyme mechanism. Thus carbon monoxide and cyanide have been invaluable in studies of components of the respiratory chain. More recently, the study of the action of the so-called "nerve gases" on various hydrolytic enzymes has opened a new chapter in enzymology (see page 190).

Some enzyme inhibitors occur in nature. The powerful trypsin inhibitor present in soybeans may be taken as an example. This substance was discovered by Kunitz and has been investigated extensively (40, 61). It is a protein of molecular weight 24,000, which is the same as the molecular weight of trypsin. The two proteins combine in equimolar amounts at physiological pH's, to form a complex which is enzymatically inactive. Trypsin inhibitors are present in other leguminous seeds as well as in pancreas and egg white, to name but a few sources. One may inquire what the physiological role of the trypsin inhibitor in beans might be, since the substance would not be expected to come into natural contact with trypsin—unless, indeed, being eaten is regarded as a natural event in the life history of the bean. Evidence has been obtained, however, that there are proteins in the soybean with proteolytic activity which can be inhibited by trypsin inhibitor (118). It seems reasonable to surmise a possible relationship between inhibitor and protein metabolism during growth of the plant (4).

Other naturally occurring enzyme inhibitors similar to trypsin inhibitor but less intensively studied have been found to be heat labile. When the inhibitor is more sensitive to heat than the enzyme inhibited, an apparent activation of the enzyme by high temperatures may result (117).

Antibodies to enzymes may also be regarded as examples of naturally formed inhibitors. Particularly interesting are a group of metabolites which block the reaction sequence which leads to further formation of that metabolite. In some cases, such inhibition may reflect a simple mass action effect, but in other cases it appears to depend on the inhibition of an enzyme which acts at some point prior to the reaction where the metabolite is actually formed (144).

F. Group Transfer

1. General Formulation

Koshland (52–54) has pointed out that most enzyme reactions can be formulated very simply as group transfer, substitution, or displacement reactions of the general type: $B\text{-}X + Y \rightarrow B\text{-}Y + X$. This equation is intended to illustrate a reaction consisting of a transfer of some group

B from a donor, X, to an acceptor Y. To cause this reaction, it is necessary to break only one bond and to form one new bond.

The importance and convenience of formulating enzyme reactions as "group transfers" was perhaps first appreciated for the case of phosphate transfer reactions (7, 65, 94). It is generally recognized now, however, that there is nothing unique about the reactions involving phosphate transfer, except for their great variety and strategic location in the reaction sequences of intermediary metabolism. In the equation above, B may represent phosphate, or any of a large number of other groups, as, for example, hydrogen or a pair of electrons, or acyl, or methyl. An exhaustive list would include most of the known enzyme reactions. [We need only except addition or elimination reactions (lyases or synthases) of the type catalyzed by fumarase,

$$COO^{-}.CH_2CHOH.COO^{-} \rightleftharpoons COO^{-}{\cdot}CH{:}CH{\cdot}COO^{-} + HOH$$

which cannot conveniently be classified as displacement reactions.]

2. *Hydrolytic Reactions*

The manner in which a particular reaction fits the general formulation is sometimes self-evident, as, for example, in the pyridine nucleotide dehydrogenase reactions where a hydrogen atom can clearly be shown to be transferred from substrate to cofactor. The hydrolytic reactions may be regarded as a type of group transfer in which the acceptor, Y, is water. The hydrolysis of ethyl acetate in the presence of lipase can be visualized as a nucleophilic attack of OH^- on the carboxyl carbon atom of the ester bond, as shown in the equation (XX).

$$CH_3CH_2{-}O{-}\underset{\substack{\vdots\\ H\ddot{O}}}{\overset{O}{\overset{\|}{C}}}CH_3 \rightarrow CH_3CH_2OH + \underset{\substack{| \\ OH}}{\overset{O}{\overset{\|}{C}}}CH_3$$

(XX)

The alcoholate group, $CH_3CH_2O^-$, is displaced by the entering OH^-. The reactions in which water is ionized or an alcoholate group picks up a hydrogen ion and acetic acid ionizes to acetate are secondary spontaneous reactions known to occur almost instantaneously without catalysis. But the breaking of the old C—O bond with the formation of the new one cannot occur without help. There is an energy barrier to such a change. It is this energy barrier which the enzyme circumvents in some way, and it is bonds of this "hard-to-break" sort to which reference is made when we speak of formulating the reaction as a breaking of only one old bond and the formation of one new one.

The similarity of hydrolytic reactions to other group transfer re actions is brought out particularly strongly by the fact that a consider able number of hydrolytic enzymes are not specific for water and car catalyze transfer reactions as well as hydrolyses. In 1910, Willstätte and Stoll (141, 141a, 141b) reported that when green leaves were ex tracted with ethanol to obtain the pigment chlorophyll, and the leave

$$\text{Phytyl—O—}\overset{\overset{\text{R}}{|}}{\text{C}}\text{=O} + CH_3CH_2OH \longrightarrow CH_3CH_2\text{—O—}\overset{\overset{\text{R}}{|}}{\text{C}}\text{=O}$$

Ethyl chlorophyllide

$$\text{Phytyl—O—}\overset{\overset{\text{R}}{|}}{\text{C}}\text{=O} + HOH \longrightarrow \text{HO—}\overset{\overset{\text{R}}{|}}{\text{C}}\text{=O}$$

Free chlorophyllide

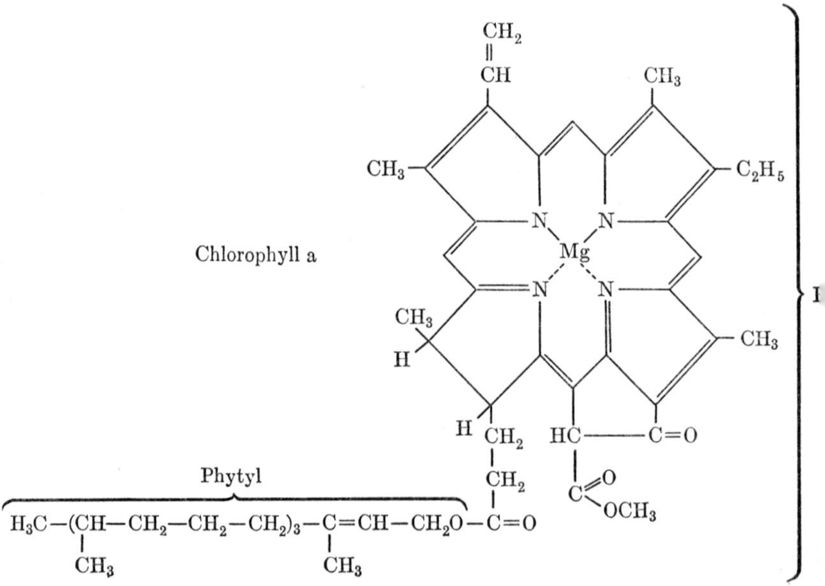

Chlorophyll a

CH_2 = CH; CH_3; CH_3; C_2H_5; N; N; Mg; N; N; CH_3; H; CH_3; H; CH_2; HC—C=O; CH_2; $C{=}O$, OCH_3

Phytyl

$$H_3C\text{—}(\underset{\underset{CH_3}{|}}{CH}\text{—}CH_2\text{—}CH_2\text{—}CH_2)_3\text{—}\underset{\underset{CH_3}{|}}{C}\text{=CH—}CH_2O\text{—C=O}$$

(XXI)

were allowed to steep in the solvent for some time, the chlorophyl suffered a change which consisted of the replacement of the phyty alcohol group by ethanol. The heat-labile enzyme responsible for caus ing this change was named chlorophyllase. The reaction catalyzed i shown (XXI). Other alcohols can be substituted for ethanol to give th corresponding esters. However, if the reaction is carried out in aqueou acetone, or in ether saturated with water, the water hydrolyzes th orophyll to free chlorophyllide. In other words, water can substitute alcohol in the absence of the alcohol. The ability to act in high con-ntrations of organic solvents is characteristic for some lipases, but is erwise an unusual property for an enzyme. In actual fact, the ases are thought to act at interfaces between an aqueous phase and a -solvent phase in which the substrate of the enzyme is dissolved.

Within recent years, a great variety of hydrolytic enzymes have been und capable of acting as transferases. Table VI is a summary, com-ed by Morton (79), of the various types of transfer reactions which

TABLE VI

SOME HYDROLASES WITH ASSOCIATED TRANSFERASE ACTIVITY

Enzyme	Source	Typical donor	Typical acceptor
d phosphatases	Human prostate gland	Phenyl phosphate	Glycerol
	Citrus fruits	p-Nitrophenyl phosphate	Methanol
	Malt	Phenyl phosphate	Cytidine
caline phosphatases	Intestine	Phenyl phosphate	Glucose
	Milk	Phenyl phosphate	Glucose
onuclease	Pancreas	Cyclic nucleotide	Cytidine
lycosidase	Emulsin	Phenyl-β-glycoside	Methanol
ctase	Yeast	Lactose	Lactose
vertases	Yeast	Sucrose	Sucrose
N-ase	Spleen	Coenzyme I (DPN)	Isonicotinamide
oteinases	Plant and animal	Benzylglycyl (or tyrosyl)-amide	Hydroxylamine
ptidases	Kidney	Glutathione	Glycine
	Cabbage	Glycylglycine	Phenylalanine

cur with different hydrolytic enzymes. The donor, listed in column is the *B-X* of Koshland's generalized reaction equation, and the ceptors of the last column can all act as *Y*. In every case, water can so act as *Y*. The acceptors are substances of the type HOR, and in the se of water, R is H.

Many of the phosphatases, for example, can cause a transfer of phos-ate from one phosphate ester to an acceptor such as glycerol, to form other phosphate ester. The hydrolysis and transfer reactions may cur simultaneously, and we think of the acceptor, HOR, as competing ith water for a particular site on the donor molecule. It is pertinent enquire, in cases of this sort, whether the acceptor, *Y*, is activated y the enzyme at all, or whether the activating action of the enzyme ay not be restricted to the donor molecule (79).

3. *Location of Bond-Splitting*

Many group transfer reactions present ambiguities of choice as to position of bond-breaking. If *B-X* has the general formula ROR′ a *Y* has the formula HOR″, then it is not self-evident from the chemi identification of the products ROR″ and HOR′ whether the *B-X* bo which is broken is at R or at R′. More specifically, in the previo formulation (XX) of the hydrolysis of an ester, the attack of nucleophilic group, OH^- was pictured as occurring on the carboxyl ca bon atom, so that the bond breaking occurred as shown in the figu on the left (see formula XXII) and not at the carbon atom of the al hol as shown in the figure on the right (see formula XXII).

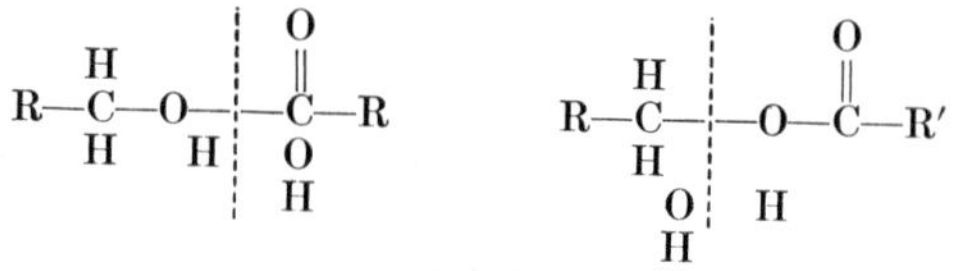

```
               ¦  O                            ¦        O
      H        ¦  ‖                      H     ¦        ‖
  R—C—O—¦—C—R                  R—C—¦—O—C—R′
      H     H ¦  O                       H     ¦
               ¦  H                          O ¦  H
                                             H
```

(XXII)

One might enquire whether this latter mechanism, shown in the figu on the right, should not also be considered. The reaction can certain be formulated in this way on paper with no difficulty. The choice the C═O carbon atom as the site of attack by the entering OH^- is bas on clear-cut experimental evidence. If such a reaction is carried out water containing heavy oxygen and the products of the hydrolysis a examined for their O^{18} content, the O^{18} is found in the acid carbox group, and not in the alcohol OH group (53).

One may sometimes make an educated guess about the location bond-splitting by examination of the specificity of the enzyme reactio In general, the enzyme tends to be more specific for the structure close to the site where splitting occurs. The criterion of specificity is parti ularly applicable if one of the carbon atoms of the C—O—C group an asymmetric carbon atom. This is true in the case of reactions cat lyzed by glycosidases, where the reaction may be written as show (XXIII).

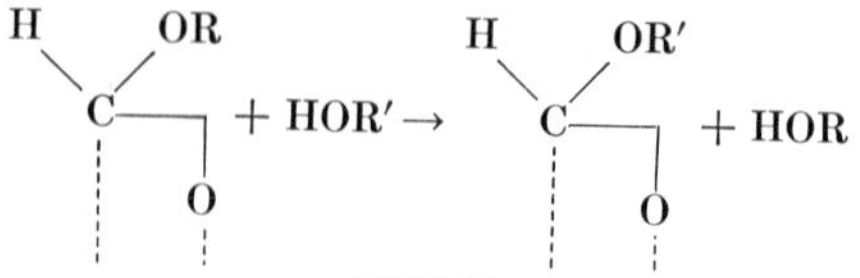

```
 H     OR                      H     OR′
  \   /                         \   /
   C———┐   + HOR′ →              C———┐   + HOR
   ¦   |                         ¦   |
   ¦   O                         ¦   O
   ¦   ¦                         ¦   ¦
```

(XXIII)

The glucoside carbon atom shown in this equation is asymmetric. may have α- or β-configuration. Now it is generally found that a parti ar glycosidase acts on only one of these two stereomeric forms. That it either attacks the substrate with the α-configuration or it attacks ly the substrate with the β-configuration, but it does not act on both. is is an indication that splitting occurs next to the glycoside carbon om

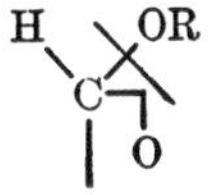

H OR
C
| O

his conclusion is supported by data obtained with O^{18} and by other idence which will be summarized later.

4. *Single and Double Displacements*

The displacement or transfer reactions in terms of which the enzyme actions are formulated have their prototype in organic chemistry in e form of nucleophilic displacement reactions (XXIV) on carbon.

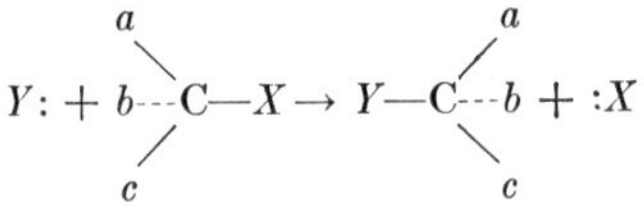

$$Y: + b \cdots \underset{c}{\overset{a}{C}} - X \rightarrow Y - \underset{c}{\overset{a}{C}} \cdots b + :X$$

(XXIV)

he nucleophilic group is visualized as approaching the carbon atom om the side directly opposite the position of the group X. As Y approaches, X recedes. The molecule goes through a transition state in hich the bonds to a, b, and c all lie in a plane, and if the carbon atom asymmetric, as in the case shown here, the displacement occurs with n inversion of configuration. If, however, two displacement reactions ccur on the carbon atom, in sequence, then one will find the original onfiguration restored, since two inversions result in retention of onfiguration.

Enzyme reactions which involve breaking a bond to an asymmetric arbon atom, such as those catalyzed by the glycosidases or glycoside ransferases, may occur either with inversion or with retention of coniguration. We may, accordingly, classify these reactions into two roups: namely, single-displacement reactions, which occur with inersion of configuration, and double-displacement reactions, which ccur with retention of configuration (52, 53). Mechanistically, the ingle displacement is visualized as a direct transfer of B from X to Y, n the enzyme surface. That is B-X and Y are visualized as being held n juxtaposition on the enzyme surface in such a way that the transfer f B from X to Y is facilitated, as shown on the left in the diagram XXV). In the double-displacement reaction, shown in the diagram

$$\boxed{X \cdots\cdots B \cdots\cdots Y} \qquad \overset{\cdot \cdot B \cdot \cdot}{X \qquad Y}$$

(XXV)

on the right, B is transferred first to a particular receptor group on th[e]
enzyme surface, and then donated to Y. That is, there are two reaction[s].
In the first, some group on the enzyme acts as Y. In the second, th[e]
enzyme is displaced by the Y substrate:

$$B\text{-}X + :\text{En} \rightarrow B\text{-En} + X$$

$$B\text{-En} + :Y \rightarrow B\text{-}Y + :\text{En}$$

As an example of a glycosidase which causes inversion of configuration, we may cite β-amylase, which acts on an α-glucoside bond to form
a β-glucoside as shown (XXVI).

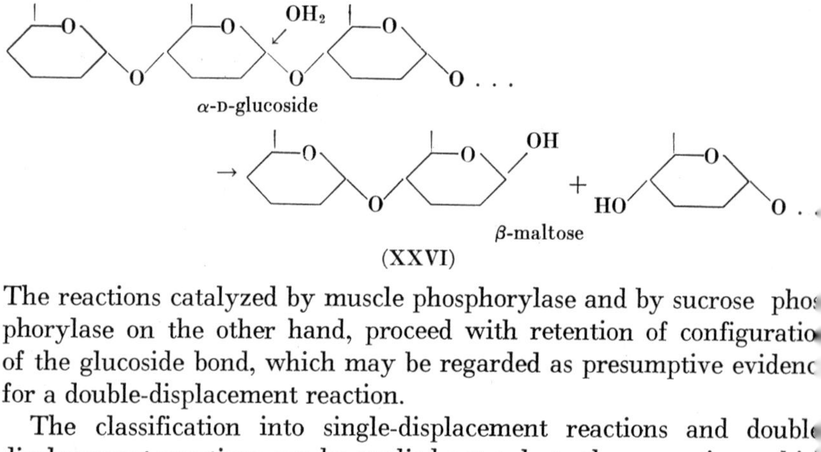

α-D-glucoside

β-maltose

(XXVI)

The reactions catalyzed by muscle phosphorylase and by sucrose phosphorylase on the other hand, proceed with retention of configuration
of the glucoside bond, which may be regarded as presumptive evidence
for a double-displacement reaction.

The classification into single-displacement reactions and double-
displacement reactions can be applied not only to those reactions which
involve substitution on an asymmetric carbon atom, but to all substitution reactions. When there is no asymmetric carbon atom, however,
it is not always easy to determine whether a reaction should be
classified as a single or as a double displacement. We may interject
here also, that the discussion up to this point has been deliberately over-
simplified. There are other categories of reactions possible, in addition
to single and double displacements, but these other categories do not
appear to be necessary to describe the available data on enzymes which
cause hydrolysis or group transfer.

5. *The Occurrence of "Exchange" Reactions*

Another procedure which has been employed extensively to obtain information about the mechanism of enzyme reactions is the measurement

so-called "exchange" reactions (53, 79). If an enzyme substrate, B-X incubated with labeled, free X in the absence of the normal acceptor there might be no net change in the total number of molecules of X present, but one may find that B-X becomes labeled: $B\text{-}X + X^* \rightarrow$ $X^* + X$.

It should be noted that the occurrence of an exchange reaction does t, in and of itself, permit unequivocal conclusions about mechanism. iere are two alternative explanations possible. The occurrence of exange may indicate that the reaction is a single displacement but that e enzyme has a very low specificity for Y; that is, in the reaction -B-Y|, free X may substitute for Y, |X-B-X|. The alternative interetation is that the reaction occurs as a double displacement, and at the enzyme-substrate intermediate is kinetically stable. The inrmation about exchange must be combined with other information order to permit a choice between the alternative explanations of a uble displacement with a stable intermediate of the type B:En or of a igle displacement with low specificity for X or Y.

One way of getting other information is to carry out direct studies the specificity of the reaction for Y (79). If the specificity is very w, the reaction might be a single-displacement reaction. An example provided by alkaline phosphatase, which acts on substrates of the pe $ROPO_3^{--}$. R may be any of a great variety of substances. Transrs as well as hydrolyses are catalyzed, and free R may act as Y. he enzyme catalyzes the reaction:

$$HOPO_3 + H_2O^{18} \rightarrow HO^{18}PO_3 + H_2O$$

Iere, R or Y may be regarded as HO.

In cases where the specificity for Y is very high, exchange may be garded as evidence for a double displacement. Specificity studies do ot always give unequivocal conclusions, however. Table VII shows a ımmary compiled by Koshland (53) of representative studies with venty-five different enzyme reactions, twelve of which gave positive esults for the occurrence of exchange, and thirteen of which did not. of the twelve which gave positive results, only three, triosephosphate ehydrogenase, sucrose phosphorylase, and glutathione synthetase, howed specificity patterns of the sort which permitted the conclusion hat a stable enzyme-substrate intermediate was formed. Chymotrypsin nd acetylcholinesterase, which appear in the table, are also thought o cause double-displacement reactions, but the evidence for this conlusion was obtained by another procedure described in a later section.

The conclusion that bacterial sucrose phosphorylase proceeds as a louble-displacement reaction is not dependent on specificity studies

TABLE VII
ISOTOPIC EXCHANGE REACTIONS OF TYPE *BX* WITH *X** (53)

Enzyme	Substrate	Labeled compound	Exchan[ge] observe[d]
Sucrose phosphorylase	Glucose-1-phosphate	P^{32}-phosphate	+
	Sucrose	C^{14}-fructose	+
Muscle phosphorylase	Glucose-1-phosphate	P^{32}-phosphate	−
Thymidine phosphorylase	Deoxyribose-1-phosphate	P^{32}-phosphate	−
Maltose phosphorylase	Glucose-1-phosphate	P^{32}-phosphate	−
DPN synthetase	ATP	P^{32}-pyrophosphate	−
Alkaline phosphatase	KH_2PO_4	H_2O^{18}	+
Myosin	ATP	ADP^{32}	−
	KH_2PO_4	H_2O^{18}	−
5′-Nucleotidase	AMP	C^{14}-adenosine	−
	KH_2PO_4	H_2O^{18}	−
Spleen DPN-ase	DPN	C^{14}-nicotinamide	+
Neurospora DPN-ase	DPN	C^{14}-nicotinamide	−
Purine nucleosidase	Adenosine	C^{14}-adenosine	−
β-Glucosidase	Glucose	H_2O^{18}	+
Chymotrypsin	Benzoyltyrosylglycinamide	C^{14}-glycinamide	+
	Phenylalanine	H_2O^{18}	+
Papain	Benzoylglycinamide	$N^{15}H_3$	+
Acetylcholinesterase	Acetic acid	H_2O^{18}	+
Lipase A	Butyric acid	H_2O^{18}	+
Triosephosphate dehydrogenase	Acetyl phosphate	$KH_2P^{32}O_4$	+
Glutathione synthetase	ATP	ADP^{32}	+
Acetyl kinase	ATP	ADP^{32}	−
	Acetyl phosphate	C^{14}-acetate	−
Pyruvate	Phosphopyruvate	C^{14}-pyruvate	−

alone. The discovery and study of this enzyme, by Doudoroff and as[-]sociates (25, 42), provided the first example of an enzyme which con[-]tained no known prosthetic group and yet could be proved, beyon[d] reasonable doubt, to form a stable enzyme-substrate intermediat[e]. Sucrose phosphorylase converts α-glucose-1-phosphate plus fructose t[o] sucrose and inorganic phosphate. The reaction is reversible an[d] proceeds with *retention of configuration* at the glucoside bond. Thi[s] enzyme also catalyzes the exchange of inorganic phosphate wit[h] glucose-1-phosphate, in the absence of fructose:

$$\text{Glucose-1-PO}_4^{--} + \text{HP}^{32}\text{O}_4^{--} \rightarrow \text{Glucose-1-P}^{32}\text{O}_4^{--} + \text{HPO}_4^{--}$$

In the above reaction, arsenate may be substituted for labeled ortho[-]phosphate. The result is an arsenolysis or a hydrolysis of glucose-1 osphate induced by arsenate. The explanation is that arsenate can bstitute for inorganic phosphate to give glucose-1-AsO_4^{--}, which is stable enough to undergo spontaneous hydrolysis. All the above facts e completely consistent with, and in fact demand, a double-displaceent mechanism, with a glucosyl-enzyme intermediate.

The pyridine nucleotide dehydrogenase reactions have been dis-ssed previously as though they were single-displacement reactions. he fact that deuterium labeling can be used to show a direct transfer hydrogen from substrate to pyridine nucleotide in no way elimi-ates the possibility that this transfer might occur by way of some sidue on the protein. This possibility appeared unlikely because it hard to imagine what kind of group on the protein could accept hydride ion and donate it to an acceptor without the occurrence of nsiderable exchange with the medium. In the case of alcohol dehydro-nase, more definitive evidence against reduction and oxidation of me group on the protein has been provided by experiments which ow that the enzyme does not catalyze oxidation-reduction reactions etween two pyridine nucleotide molecules, except in the presence of me small amount of the substrate (50). Thus, alcohol dehydrogenase n cause a transfer of hydrogen from ethanol to deamino DPN as well s to DPN. But there is no transfer of hydrogen between DPN and eamino DPN in the presence of alcohol dehydrogenase unless a little thanol or acetaldehyde is also present.[4] If the protein itself were educed and oxidized, it is difficult to see why ethanol or acetaldehyde ould be required to facilitate the interaction of DPN and deamino DPN. We might, of course, suppose that some particular structural con-guration of the enzyme, which was essential for catalytic action, was tabilized by, or otherwise dependent on, the simultaneous presence of oth ethanol and pyridine nucleotide. Such a possibility is exceedingly ifficult to eliminate, and the degree to which it will be regarded as a ikely possibility might vary in individual cases.

6. Stable Enzyme-Substrate Compounds

The best evidence which can be obtained for the occurrence of a ouble-displacement reaction is the isolation of the intermediate com-ound formed by the donation of some group from substrate to enzyme. As an example of a case where this has been successfully done, we may ite the definitive investigation of Najjar and Pullman on phospho-

There are other enzymes (i.e., the transhydrogenases) which catalyze a direct oxido-eduction between two different pryridine nucleotides, and a direct transfer of ydrogen occurs between substrates in such reactions also (97). These enzymes are pecific for pyridine nucleotides and do not operate with other substrates.

glucomutase (80). This enzyme causes the reversible interconversi of glucose-1-phosphate and glucose-6-phosphate to give an equilibriu mixture of these two compounds. The enzyme requires, as cofactor primer, glucose-1,6-diphosphate. The function of the cofactor is phosphorylate the enzyme. That is, a phosphate group is transferr from the cofactor to a particular position on the enzyme molecu which has been identified as the β-hydroxyl group of a serine moie (4a, 56). If the enzyme is already phosphorylated, the cofactor need n be added since it is generated in the reaction. The phosphorylated e zyme can transfer the phosphate to position 1 of glucose-6-phospha or to position 6 of glucose-1-phosphate. The glucose-1,6-diphospha may then donate the phosphate of either position to rephosphoryla the enzyme. Two different, reversible reactions occur, as shown in tl equations:

$$\text{Glucose-1,6-diphosphate} + \text{E} \rightleftharpoons \text{glucose-1-phosphate} + \text{E-phosphate}$$

$$\text{Glucose-1,6-diphosphate} + \text{E} \rightleftharpoons \text{glucose-6-phosphate} + \text{E-phosphate}$$

It is clear that an equilibrium mixture of the substrates will result, a few moles of enzyme act on many moles of substrate.

G. THE PROBLEM OF THE ACTIVE SITE

Pauling has suggested that enzymes act by stabilizing a transitic state, which may be visualized as a strained conformation throug which the atoms must pass to go from one relatively stable structu to another relatively stable structure (86). The statement that enzym act by lowering the activation energy of a reaction may be regarde as another way of saying the same thing. The activation energy is tl well-known "energy hump" over which the system must travel to g from one stable state to another. One must, of course, guard again any illusion that statements like the above say all that can be sai about mechanism. To say that an enzyme lowers the activation energ of a reaction is equivalent to saying that it acts as a catalyst, a stat ment already made in the definition of the word enzyme. The proble of reaction mechanism must be visualized as a search for the structur chemical characteristics of the enzyme which provide a basis for i catalytic properties and its specificity.

The great size of the average enzyme molecule poses a formidabl obstacle to the determination of structure. There does not seem to b any *a priori* reason, however, why the catalytic properties of the en zyme should be dependent on large size. Wang's model for catalas which must be regarded as partially successful, is quite small (see pag

58). Furthermore, Smith and his associates have been able to remove
vo-thirds of the amino acids from the proteolytic enzyme papain with-
ut loss of enzyme activity (5). Koshland has suggested that the
eason for the size of the enzyme molecule may perhaps be sought not
ı the structural characteristics necessary for the catalytic function,
ut rather in a kind of evolutionary necessity. There may be a distinct
volutionary advantage in the fact that different protein molecules with
ıe same catalytic function may be put together in a wide variety of
ifferent ways (54).

If the object is to determine the structural basis for catalytic action,
ne approach is obviously to degrade the enzyme molecule with pro-
olytic enzymes and then to seek the smallest fragment which still re-
ıins enzyme actvity. Changes in specificity might occur during such a
egradation, as has been found by Perlmann in her degradation studies
f pepsin (89). Koshland has suggested that the problem of enzyme
ructure may be subdivided into two rather different problems (55).
ne part of the enzyme molecule may be responsible for its catalytic
ction, another part for its specificity for particular substrates. By and
rge, the structural features responsible for specificity may be re-
arded as functioning mainly by binding substrate. These structural
atures would be expected to be quite different for enzymes with dif-
erent substrate specificities. The portion of the enzyme molecule which
romoted the catalytic action might on the other hand be very similar
r identical for enzymes whose catalyzed reactions can be formulated
ı a similar manner. Of course, the subdivision above is formal only
nd should not be regarded as the denial of a very particular and
ecessary spatial relationship between the catalytic center and the
tructural portions responsible for specificity. Interaction may also occur
etween a binding site and a catalytic site, as suggested by the results
f extensive studies which have been made with acetylcholinesterase
131).

When an enzyme contains a prosthetic group such as heme, the
ctive site of catalysis is defined by the site of the prosthetic group. In
ıch a case, the investigation of the active site must most probably
ıvolve a study of the structure of the peptide chains which are adjacent
› that prosthetic group. Investigations of this sort, made with cyto-
hrome c, have already been mentioned (see page 157).

When there is no prosthetic group, the location of the "area" of the
active site" would appear to be more difficult. Nevertheless, it has been
ossible, with some enzymes, to identify the active site by "labeling" it
vith certain reagents (8). These reagents are a group of phosphate
erivatives with the general formula shown (XXVII),

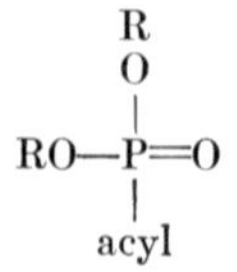

$$RO-\overset{\overset{\displaystyle R}{\displaystyle O|}}{\underset{\underset{\displaystyle acyl}{|}}{P}}=O$$

(XXVII)

where R is an alkyl or aryl group, and "acyl" is an acidic group suc
as halogen, nitrophenol, or another phosphate.

Compounds of this group include the so-called "nerve gases" and
number of very potent insecticides. Their toxicity to insects and highe
animals alike has been related to their inhibition of acetylcholinesteras
an enzyme essential for nerve function.

Most of the experimental work has been carried out with diisopropy
fluorophosphate (often abbreviated DFP). This substance is an ex
tremely potent inhibitor for a group of enzymes with esterase action
In addition to cholinesterase this group includes the proteolytic en
zymes, trypsin and chymotrypsin, which are known to hydrolyz
certain ester, as well as certain peptide, bonds (40). (Proteolytic en
zymes without esterase action, e.g., pepsin or papain, are apparentl
not inhibited by DFP.)

Balls and Jansen (8) and their collaborators have studied in detai
the action of DFP on chymotrypsin, selecting this particular enzym
because of the relative ease with which the protein could be obtained i
pure condition. They have shown that the inhibitor reacts stoichio
metrically with the enzyme, according to the equation (XXVIII),

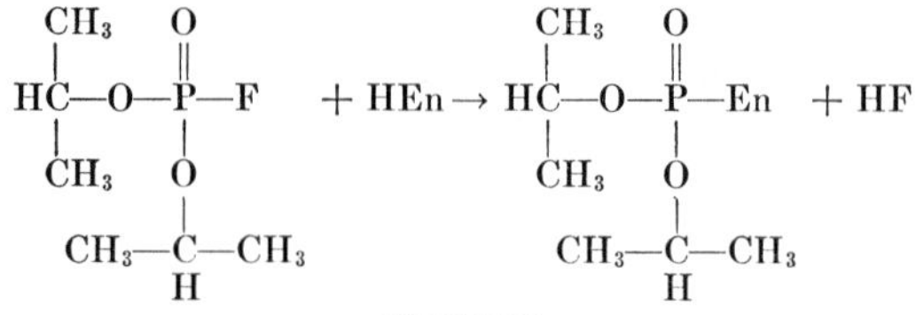

$$(CH_3)_2HC-O-\underset{\underset{\displaystyle O-CH(CH_3)_2}{|}}{\overset{\overset{\displaystyle O}{\|}}{P}}-F + HEn \rightarrow (CH_3)_2HC-O-\underset{\underset{\displaystyle O-CH(CH_3)_2}{|}}{\overset{\overset{\displaystyle O}{\|}}{P}}-En + HF$$

(XXVIII)

with the liberation of HF and the formation of an inactive protei
molecule containing the isopropyl phosphate. One mole of inhibito
combines with one mole of enzyme. Similar results have been obtaine
with trypsin and with cholinesterase.

The interpretation of these results is that the substrate and the in
hibitor both combine with the same nucleophilic site on the enzyme, bu
that the substrate-enzyme complex is readily hydrolyzed by water
whereas the inhibitor-enzyme complex is not so hydrolyzed. The activ
enzyme may sometimes be regenerated by displacing the inhibitor wit
suitable nucleophilic reagents, but the enzyme holds the inhibitor by a
covalent bond which is sufficiently strong to survive hydrolysis of the

enzyme to peptide fragments containing the bound inhibitor. The use of inhibitor labeled with radioactive phosphate, P^{32}, has facilitated the separation and identification of such fragments. In all cases investigated, the inhibitor has been found on the β-hydroxyl group of a serine moiety (20, 100, 101, 102).

It should be emphasized that individual free amino acids do not combine with DFP. The arrangement of amino acid residues in the protein molecule must therefore be responsible for the reactivity of the β-OH group of the serine. There is some question whether serine represents the initial site of binding, evidence having been advanced to indicate that the nitrogen of the imidazole ring of histidine may represent the initial point of attack of the inhibitor, with subsequent transfer to the more stable position on serine [see Dixon and Neurath (24a) for summary]. Consideration of the evidence for histidine on the one hand, or serine on the other, as the initial "site of action," is outside the scope of this chapter.

The sequence of amino acids for a considerable portion of the peptide chain containing diisopropylphosphorylserine has been determined for the enzyme chymotrypsin (20, 100, 125). Evidence has recently been obtained from a rather unexpected source that this amino acid sequence must be closely associated, somehow, with the catalytic action of the enzyme. We may recall that the enzyme phosphoglucomutase has been shown to act by receiving (and donating) phosphoryl groups from (and to) glucose-1-phosphate and glucose-6-phosphate and that the site which specifically combines with the phosphate is the β-OH group of a serine moiety (4a, 56). This enzyme is also inhibited by DFP (56), and the "active site" of phosphoglucomutase contains the same six amino acids in the same sequence as they occur in chymotrypsin (55). This sequence is: Asp.Ser.Gly.Glu.Ala.Val. Koshland has suggested that the common sequence of amino acids around serine is involved in making the otherwise inert side chain reactive, and that a common bond-breaking mechanism exists in these DFP-sensitive enzymes, which appear superficially to be so different in their action (esterase, peptidase, mutase). The structural features responsible for the specificity of the various enzymes must be further along the peptide chain from the reactive site, perhaps in adjacent coils, which may of course bring them close, gometrically, to the serine.

V. Physiological Aspects of Enzymology

A. ACTION OF ENZYMES WITHIN THE CELL

To the biologist, the main reason for studying enzyme reactions *in vitro* is the assumption that the information so gained can be applied to elucidate physiological processes. In the author's opinion there little cause for concern that the purified enzymes with which the en zymologist works are mere artifacts formed in the process of cell destruc tion. Such an attitude has done more to hinder advance than to help i There is nonetheless need for evidence that enzymes demonstrated *i vitro* really do function as such *in vivo*. Furthermore, the investigatc should keep an open mind and recognize that the properties of a enzyme may be altered to some extent during the isolation and pur fication procedures. It is also important to recall that the condition under which the enzymes are operating within the cell are almos certain to be different from the conditions which the enzymologist ha found to be convenient for their assay and experimental study.

What are some of these differences most likely to be? First, we mus recall that the concentration of enzymes in the cytoplasm may b quite different from the concentrations used in typical assay systems Thus, if we prepare a solution of DPN at about the average concentra tion at which it is present intracellularly and add to it a dehydrogenas with its substrate, in an amount convenient for assay, only a smal amount of the DPN may be bound by the protein. Within the cell however, a large proportion of the DPN is present in the form of DPN bound to protein (16, 46). It is the high concentration of protein whicl is responsible for the high proportion of bound DPN. Consideratio should be given also to the effect of protein concentration on the equi librium point of the reversible reaction catalyzed by the enzyme. Th statement is frequently made that an enzyme undergoes no net chang during the reaction which it catalyzes and has no effect on the equi librium point of the reaction. This is true if the number of molecules o enzyme present is small, compared to the number of molecules o substrate. It should be clear from the foregoing discussion, however that the catalytic properties of enzymes are a consequence of the cycli reaction sequence whereby the original form of the enzyme is alway regenerated. The enzyme actually participates very directly in the chemical changes of the reaction it catalyzes, and if very large amount of enzyme are used so that enzyme and substrate are present in ap proximately equimolar amounts, then very large changes may be notec in the apparent equilibrium points of the reactions so catalyzed. The true equilibrium points do not change. We are speaking of apparen equilibrium points calculated from total amounts (i.e., both free and en zyme-bound) of substrates present. If the dissociation constants of the "substrate-enzyme" complex and of the "product-enzyme" complex are very different, a high concentration of enzyme can cause a change in the direction in which the reaction appears to be favored. The magni-ude of such effects has been calculated and verified experimentally in the case of a number of DPN-linked dehydrogenase reactions (46, 122, 28).

Cori (21) has called attention to certain experimental facts which imply that even soluble enzymes appear sometimes to behave, within the cell, as though they were compartmentalized, or separated from each other. From studies of the metabolism of nitrogen compounds in plants, Steward and his collaborators (109) have quite independently come to similar conclusions about the necessity for separate phases or compartments. There is experimental evidence also that the kinetics of coupled enzyme reactions cannot necessarily be predicted from the rate constants which are observed when the individual enzyme reactions are tested separately. Let us take, for illustration, a specific example. In the anaerobic fermentation of sugar to lactate, there are two oxidation-reduction reactions. In the first, DPN is reduced by triosephosphate in the presence of triosephosphate dehydrogenase. In the second, the reduced DPN is reoxidized by pyruvate in the presence of lactic dehydrogenase. The pyruvate is derived from the oxidation product of triose without any further oxidation-reduction reactions intervening. The DPN thus acts to couple two dehydrogenase reactions, which take place as shown in equations *a* and *b*.

$$\text{Triosephosphate} + \text{DPN}^+ + \text{P}_i \rightleftharpoons \text{DPNH} + \text{diphosphoglycerate} \qquad (a)$$

$$\text{Pyruvate} + \text{DPNH} \rightleftharpoons \text{DPN}^+ + \text{lactate} \qquad (b)$$

In these equations, DPN^+ represents oxidized DPN, and DPNH represents reduced DPN. Reaction (a) takes place in the presence of triosephosphate dehydrogenase, and reaction (b) takes place in the presence of lactic dehydrogenase. The reactions were originally assumed to be coupled by a process of diffusion of DPN^+ and DPNH from one enzyme to the other enzyme. But if the rate of the coupled reaction is measured directly, it appears to be too fast to be explained in this way. This was first demonstrated by Cori *et al.* (23) and has been confirmed by Nygaard and Rutter (85). The kinetic data indicate that DPNH bound to triosephosphate dehydrogenase is oxidized as fast as, or even a little faster than, the DPNH not bound to the enzyme protein. A possible functional significance of the steric specificity of hydrogen transfer to DPN now becomes apparent. We may recall that Table IV shows that triosedehydrogenase uses the β-side of DPN and lactic dehydrogenase uses the α-side. In these terms, the possible geometry of the coupled reaction is not difficult to visualize. The DPN may fit between the two enzymes like the filling of a sandwich, accepting a hydrogen atom from the substrate on one side and passing a hydrogen atom to the othe substrate on the other side, without ever dissociating completely fron either enzyme.

There are insufficient data on the kinetics of coupled systems to per mit an extended generalization to other DPN-linked enzymes, but on is struck by the fact that certain other dehydrogenase reactions whicl serve to provide oxidants for DPNH reduced by triosephosphate, als have α-specificity for DPN. Thus, there are three major paths of ana erobic sugar degradation, which lead, respectively, to lactate, ethanol and malate.[5] The first is important to muscle metabolism but plays minor role in higher plants, where the second and third paths appea to be of more importance (75). These paths differ primarily in th manner in which pyruvate is handled. In the lactate fermentation pyruvate is reduced directly; in alcohol fermentation, a decarboxylatior product of pyruvate is reduced, and in malate formation, a carboxyla tion product of pyruvate, oxalacetate, serves as the oxidant for the DPN reduced by triosephosphate. It may not be a coincidence that lactic alcohol, and malic dehydrogenase all show α-stereospecificity for hydro gen transfer to DPN, whereas triosephosphate dehydrogenase ha β-stereospecificity.

All of the enzymes which we have been discussing are freely soluble In the case of the insoluble enzymes associated with particulates, which are discussed in another chapter, the importance of structure for func tion is almost self-evident. An important problem which is receiving current attention is concerned with the nature of the arrangement o enzymes in organized structures such as plastids and mitochondria (see Chapter 1). The implications of the line of thought developed here are that the soluble components of the cytoplasm may also possess a more orderly functional arrangement than is apt to be assumed if we think only in terms of a bag of enzymes.

B. INACTIVE ENZYME PRECURSORS

Most enzymes obtained by extraction of plant or animal tissues are fully active from the start. It sometimes happens, however, that the enzyme activity of an extract or broken-cell preparation increases on standing. This may be due to the presence of a proenzyme in the orig inal extract. Proenzymes (or zymogens) are enzyme precursors which themselves have no enzyme function but which are converted into active enzymes by the action of other enzymes or by agents such as

[5] If aerobic conditions are required for malate formation, the implication is that an adequate supply of reduced DPN may not be formed by way of the triosephosphate dehydrogenase reaction.

hydrogen ions. The classical example is pepsinogen, the inactive precursor of pepsin, the proteolytic enzyme of the gastric juice (40, 85). Pepsinogen is converted to pepsin by exposure to low pH or by treatment with other proteolytic enzymes such as trypsin. Pepsin itself also converts pepsinogen to pepsin. The conversion has been studied in some detail and shown to consist of the splitting of a peptide fragment from the pepsinogen molecule. The proteolytic enzymes of the pancreatic juice, trypsin and chymotrypsin, are also secreted originally in the form of the inactive precursors, trypsinogen and chymotrypsinogen (40, 85).

One of the most interesting examples of the conversion of a proenzyme to an enzyme is that of phosphorylase. The Coris and their associates showed that this enzyme, which catalyzes the reversible formation of glycogen and phosphate from glucose-1-phosphate, exists in two forms, phosphorylase a and phosphorylase b. The latter is the predominant form in resting muscle and is inactive unless adenylic acid is added (22, 57). Since muscle contains insufficient adenylic acid to activate phosphorylase b, this form of the enzyme is presumed to be inactive *in situ* (22). Muscle extracts contain an activating enzyme which converts phosphorylase b to phosphorylase a in the presence of Ca^{++} or Mn^{++} ions and adenosine triphosphate (34). In addition, there is an inactivating enzyme in the extracts, which converts phosphorylase a to b (51). The activation reaction is a dimerization, in which two molecules of phosphorylase b are converted to one of phosphorylase a and the latter molecule acquires four phosphate groups from the four molecules of ATP which are required:

$$2 \text{ Phosphorylase b} + 4 \text{ ATP} \rightleftharpoons \text{phosphorylase a-P}_4 + 4 \text{ ADP}$$

The conversion of phosphorylase a to b involves a loss of the phosphate (58). A similar situation obtains in liver. The active and inactive forms of the liver enzyme have rather different properties from those of the muscle enzyme, but their general relationship is similar. Though phosphorylase is widespread in plant tissues, the plant phosphorylases have not been investigated as intensively as those of animal tissues. Sumner *et al.* (114) have achieved 1000-fold purification of phosphorylase from jack beans and have found flavin adenine dinucleotide associated with the purified protein, but it is not clear whether the flavin derivative has a necessary relationship to the phosphorylase, and it also appears to be an open question whether a precursor-active enzyme relationship can be demonstrated in plants.

There are probably few enzymologists who have not, at one time or

other, examined the effect of a hormone on an enzyme reaction in th
hope of finding some clue to the chemical mechanism whereby th
hormone exerts its dramatic effects *in vivo*. With a limited number o
exceptions, such experiments have been almost uniformly unsuccessfu
Thus repeated efforts have failed to reveal a specific *in vitro* effect c
a plant hormone such as indoleacetic acid on any purified enzyme. Th
usual failure of this type of experimentation suggests that most hor
mones exert their effect on enzyme systems only indirectly, perhaps b
controlling membrane permeability or by affecting the synthesis o
breakdown of enzymes. The problem of the chemical mechanism o
hormone action is one of the most pressing of our largely unsolved prob
lems. It is therefore of particular interest that the formation of activ
phosphorylase in animal tissues has been shown to be controlled b
the hormone epinephrine (adrenaline). Injection of epinephrine int
the intact animal causes a striking increase in the amount of phosphor
ylase a formed from phosphorylase b in the presence of the kinase
activating enzyme, in both liver and muscle (22, 116). This effect o
epinephrine can be demonstrated in homogenates as well as in slice
(116). It is one of the few instances in which the action of a hormon
has been pinpointed on a particular enzyme.

C. SPECIES DIFFERENCES AND GENETIC CONTROL

Another fascinating and urgent problem relating to enzymes is con
cerned with the mechanism whereby these catalysts are formed. Suc
a problem has vast ramifications, reaching into the area of genetic con
trol of enzyme synthesis (134). Attacks on this problem are being mad
from several sides. The question of the chemical mechanism of protei
synthesis is under direct and intensive investigation (103). Increasin
insight is also coming from studies of adaptive enzyme formation an
from the more genetic attack, which has led to the suggestion that ther
is a fairly direct gene-enzyme relationship, perhaps of the sort wherei
a particular gene exerts its effect by controlling the synthesis of on
particular enzyme (10). The details of these studies are described else
where, but it seems pertinent to outline here some of the rapidly ac
cumulating facts which relate genetic differences to enzyme-protei
structure.

It has long been known that in order to designate what particula
enzyme may be under discussion, the biological source of the enzym
must be indicated, since enzymes with the same catalytic effect, bu
prepared from different sources, may be different in their properties
This would be expected from the well-known fact that every specie
produces its own species-specific proteins. Since most of the protein

have enzyme activity, it follows that the enzymes show species specificity also. This can be demonstrated by immunological techniques. An enzyme injected into the blood stream of an animal of another species often elicits the formation of antibodies, and these antibodies react specifically with the antigen used to induce them. An enzyme with the same catalytic action, but prepared from a different species, apparently shows no more cross reactions with antibody to the homologous enzyme than would normally be expected for any other proteins of the two species. Combination of the enzyme with a specific antibody usually results in inhibition of the catalytic activity of the enzyme.

It is not always necessary to use immunological tests to detect differences between homologous enzymes from different species. The difference in properties may be sufficiently striking to be detected by relatively simple methods. As an example, we may cite studies of homologous enzymes for carbohydrate breakdown (e.g., triosephosphate dehydrogenase) prepared from rabbit muscle on the one hand, and from yeast on the other (128). Structural studies of insulin prepared from different species have given the interesting result that, for five different species examined, the molecules are identical except for the amino acids in positions 8, 9, and 10 within the intrachain disulfide bridge of chain *A* (Fig. 1). The differences between insulin of cattle, pig, sheep, horse, and whale are shown in Table VIII (41).

TABLE VIII
AMINO ACIDS OF POSITIONS 8, 9 AND 10 OF INSULIN FROM VARIOUS ANIMALS[a]

Animal	Residue number		
	8	9	10
Cattle	Ala	Ser	Val
Pig	Thr	Ser	Ileu
Sheep	Ala	Gly	Val
Horse	Thr	Gly	Ileu
Whale	Thr	Ser	Ileu

[a] Data from Harris *et al.* (41).

Similar studies of other biologically active proteins are in progress. Thus, investigation of the structure of the peptide fragment adjacent to the prosthetic group of cytochrome c have been extended by Tuppy and Paléus (124) to cytochromes from beef, salmon, and chicken. The chain of ten amino acids containing the heme linked to two cysteine residues is identical for salmon and beef cytochrome, but chicken cytochrome contains serine instead of alanine at the residue position immediately following the first residue of cysteine (page 157). Can it be significant, as Theorell (121) has suggested, that this difference also occurs between two cysteine residues?

Of particular current interest are the studies of Ingram on the structure of normal human and sickle-cell anemia hemoglobin. The condition of sickle-cell anemia is associated with the formation of hemoglobin S. Pauling and his associates had shown previously that hemoglobin S has a higher positive charge than normal hemoglobin, and a lower solubility in the reduced state (88, 91). Ingram (49) used tryptic hydrolysis to split the two kinds of hemoglobin into about 30 different peptides. All but one of these fragments appeared identical, whether derived from normal hemoglobin or from hemoglobin S. The one hemoglobin S fragment that was different had a more positive charge than the corresponding fragment from normal hemoglobin and was shown to contain valine instead of glutamic acid (49a). This work is particularly interesting because the production of hemoglobin S has been associated with one mutation of one gene (81). The implication is that one mutation may affect one amino acid.

Additional information of this sort is necessary before one can generalize, but whatever the outcome, it seems clear that the *structural* study of genetic differences among proteins may do much to clarify the relationship between gene and enzyme.

In preparing this chapter, the author has attempted to remove some of the mystery which is attached to the concept of an enzyme, particularly in the minds of those whose immersion in other specialties has not permitted them to follow the extraordinarily rapid development of the fascinating field of enzymology. Though it has been quite impossible to cite the numerous instances where we have quite specific (though always incomplete) knowledge of the mechanism of a particular enzyme reaction, an attempt has been made to show why enzyme chemistry per se can be regarded simply as a special aspect of the chemistry of proteins. It is the high and very specialized reactivity of proteins which is responsible for the phenomenon known as enzyme action. As the methods of purifying and studying enzymes are improved and acquire greater precision it seems not unlikely that the study of their mode of action will be relegated to a special area of physical organic chemistry, leaving the more biological aspects of the problem for the efforts of the biochemists proper.

The book of Dixon and Webb (24b), which was not available until after this chapter was completed, is recommended for anyone wishing to delve further into the subject of enzymology.

REFERENCES

1. Alberty, R. A. Enzyme kinetics. *Advances in Enzymology* **17,** 1–64 (1956).
2. Alberty, R. A. Enzyme kinetics. *In* "Currents in Biochemical Research" (D. E. Green, ed.), pp. 560–584. Interscience, New York, 1956.
3. Alberty, R. A. Kinetic effects of the ionization of groups in the enzyme molecule. *J. Cellular Comp. Physiol.* **47,** Suppl. 1, 245–281 (1956).
4. Ambe, K. S., and Sohonie, K. Trypsin inhibitor in Indian foods. III. Trypsin inhibitor in germinating double bean and field bean and their growing plants. *J. Sci. Ind. Research (India)* **15C,** 136–140 (1956); from *Chem. Abstr.* **51,** 1391 (1957).

4a. Anderson, L., and Jolles, G. R. A study of the linkage of phosphorus to protein in phosphoglucomutase. *Arch. Biochem. Biophys.* **70,** 121–128 (1957).

5. Anfinsen, C. B., and Redfield, R. R. Protein structure in relation to function and biosynthesis. *Advances in Protein Chem.* **11,** 1–100 (1956).
6. Astbury, W. T. X-Rays and the stoichiometry of the proteins. *Advances in Enzymol.* **3,** 63–108 (1943).
7. Axelrod, B. Enzymatic phosphate transfer. *Advances in Enzymol.* **17,** 159–188 (1956).
8. Balls, A. K., and Jansen, E. F. Stoichiometric inhibition of chymotrypsin. *Advances in Enzymol.* **13,** 321–343 (1952).
9. Barron, E. S. G. Thiol groups of biological importance. *Advances in Enzymol.* **11,** 201–266 (1951).
10. Beadle, G. W. Genes and the chemistry of the organism. *Am. Scientist* **34,** 31–53, 76 (1946).
11. Bear, R. S. The structure of collagen fibrils. *Advances in Protein Chem.* **7,** 69–160 (1952).
12. Beinert, H. Evidence for an intermediate in the oxidation-reduction of flavoproteins. *J. Biol. Chem.* **225,** 465–478 (1957).
13. Brand, E., and Edsall, J. T. The chemistry of the proteins and amino acids. *Ann. Rev. Biochem.* **16,** 223–272 (1947).
14. Brohult, S., and Sandegren, E. Seed proteins. *In* "The Proteins" (H. Neurath and K. Bailey, eds.), Vol. II, Part A, pp. 487–512. Academic Press, New York, 1954.
15. Bull, H. B. Spread monolayers of protein. *Advances in Protein Chem.* **3,** 95–121 (1947).
16. Chance, B. Enzyme mechanisms in living cells. *In* "The Mechanism of Enzyme Action" (W. D. McElroy and B. Glass, eds.), pp. 399–460. Johns Hopkins Press, Baltimore, Maryland, 1954.
17. Chance, B. Enzyme-substrate compounds and electron transfer. *In* "Currents in Biochemical Research" (D. E. Green, ed.), pp. 308–337. Interscience, New York, 1956.
18. Chargaff, E. Lipoproteins. *Advances in Protein Chemistry* **1,** 1–24 (1944).
19. Cheesman, D. F., and Davies, J. T. Physico-chemical and biological aspects of proteins at interfaces. *Advances in Protein Chem.* **9,** 439–501 (1954).
20. Cohen, J. A., Oosterbaan, R. A., Warringa, M. G. P. J., and Jansz, H. S. The chemical structure of the reactive group of esterases. *Discussions Faraday Soc.* **No. 20,** 114–125 (1955).
21. Cori, C. F. Problems of cellular biochemistry. *In* "Currents in Biochemical Research" (D. E. Green, ed.), pp. 198–214. Interscience, New York, 1956.

22. Cori, C. F. Regulation of enzyme activity in muscle during work. *In* "Enzymes: Units of Biological Structure and Function" (O. H. Gaebler, ed.), pp. 573–583. Academic Press, New York, 1956.
23. Cori, C. F., Velick, S. F., and Cori, G. T. The combination of diphosphopyridine nucleotide with glyceraldehyde phosphate dehydrogenase. *Biochim. et Biophys. Acta* **4,** 160–169 (1950).
24. Danielli, J. F., and Davies, J. T. Reactions at interfaces in relation to biological problems. *Advances in Enzymol.* **11,** 35–59 (1951).
24a. Dixon, G. H., and Neurath, H. The reaction of DFP with trypsin. *Biochim. et Biophys. Acta* **20,** 572–574 (1956).
24b. Dixon, M., and Webb, E. C. "Enzymes." Academic Press, New York, 1958.
25. Doudoroff, M., Barker, H. A., and Hassid, W. Z. Studies with bacterial sucrose phosphorylase. 1. The mechanism of action of sucrose phosphorylase as a glucose-transferring enzyme. *J. Biol. Chem.* **168,** 725–732 (1947).
26. Edsall, J. T. The size, shape and hydration of protein molecules. *In* "The Proteins" (H. Neurath and K. Bailey, eds.), Vol. I, Part B, pp. 549–726. Academic Press, New York, 1953.
27. Edsall, J. T. Configurations of polypeptide chains and protein molecules. *J. Cellular Comp. Physiol.* **47,** Suppl. 1, 163–200 (1956).
28. Englard, S., and Colowick, S. P. On the mechanism of the aconitase and isocitric dehydrogenase reactions. *J. Biol. Chem.* **226,** 1047–1058 (1957).
29. Eyring, H., and Stearn, A. E. The application of the theory of absolute reaction rates to proteins. *Chem. Revs.* **24,** 253–270 (1939).
30. Ferry, J. D. Protein Gels. *Advances in Protein Chem.* **4,** 1–78 (1948).
31. Fevold, H. L. Egg proteins. *Advances in Protein Chem.* **6,** 187–252 (1951).
32. Finkle, B. J., and Smith, E. L. Sulfhydryl groups of crystalline papain. *Federation Proc.* **16,** 180 (1957); Crystalline papain: number and reactivity of thiol groups; chromatographic behavior. *J. Biol. Chem.* **230,** 669–690 (1958).
33. Fischer, E. Einfluss der Configuration auf die Wirkung der Enzyme. *Ber. deut. chem. Ges.* **27,** 2985–2993 (1894).
34. Fischer, E. H., and Krebs, E. G. Conversion of phosporylase *b* to phosphorylase *a* in muscle extracts. *J. Biol. Chem.* **216,** 121–132 (1955).
35. Fraenkel-Conrat, H., Harris, J. I., and Levy, A. L. Recent developments in the techniques for terminal and sequence studies on peptides and proteins. *In* "Methods of Biochemical Analysis" (D. Glick, ed.), Vol. II, pp. 359–425. Interscience, New York, 1955.
36. Fruton, J. S., and Simmonds, S. "General Biochemistry." Wiley, New York, 1958. See p. 216 for general reactions catalyzed by enzymes.
37. George, P. On the nature of hemoprotein reactions. *In* "Currents in Biochemical Research" (D. E. Green, ed.), pp. 338–377. Interscience, New York, 1956.
38. Graves, J. L., and Vennesland, B. The stereospecific hydrogen exchange in the dihydroorotic dehydrogenase reaction. *J. Biol. Chem.* **226,** 307–316 (1957).
39. Graves, J. L., Vennesland, B., Utter, M. F., and Pennington, R. J. The mechanism of the reversible carboxylation of phosphoenol pyruvate. *J. Biol. Chem.* **223,** 551–557 (1956).
40. Green, N. M., and Neurath, H. Proteolytic enzymes. *In* "The Proteins" (H. Neurath and K. Bailey, eds.), Vol. II, Part B, pp. 1057–1198. Academic Press, New York, 1954.
41. Harris, J. I., Sanger, F., and Naughton, M. A. Species differences in insulin. *Arch. Biochem. Biophys.* **65,** 427–438 (1956).

42. Hassid, W. Z., and Doudoroff, M. Synthesis of disaccharides with bacterial enzymes. *Advances in Enzymol.* **10,** 123–143 (1950).
43. Hirs, C. H. W., Stein, W. H., and Moore, S. The amino acid composition of ribonuclease. *J. Biol. Chem.* **211,** 941–950 (1954).
44. Hoffmann-Ostenhof, O. Suggestions for a more rational classification and nomenclature of enzymes. *Advances in Enzymol.* **14,** 219–260 (1953).
45. Hoffmann-Ostenhof, O. "Enzymologie." Springer, Vienna, 1954.
46. Holzer, H., Schultz, G., and Lynen, F. Bestimmung des Quotienten DPNH/DPN in lebenden Hefezellen durch Analyse stationärer Alkohol und Acetaldehyde-Konzentrationen. *Biochem. Z.* **328,** 252–263 (1956).
47. Huggins, C., Tapley, D. F., and Jensen, E. V. Sulphydryl-disulfide relationships in the induction of gels in proteins by urea. *Nature* **167,** 592–593 (1951).
48. Hughes, W. L. Interstitial proteins: the proteins of blood plasma and lymph. *In* "The Proteins" (H. Neurath and K. Bailey, eds.), Vol. II, Part B, pp. 663–754. Academic Press, New York, 1954.
49. Ingram, V. M. A specific chemical difference between the globins of normal human and sickle-cell anaemia haemoglobin. *Nature* **178,** 792–794 (1956).
49a. Ingram, V. M. Gene mutation in human haemoglobin: the chemical difference between normal and sickle-cell haemoglobin. *Nature* **180,** 326–328 (1957).
50. Kaplan, N. O., Colowick, S. P., and Neufeld, E. F. Pyridine nucleotide transhydrogenase. II. Direct evidence for and mechanism of the transhydrogenase reaction. *J. Biol. Chem.* **195,** 107–119 (1952).
50a. Keilin, D. Cytochrome and intracellular respiratory pigments. *Ergeb. Enzymforsch.* **2,** 239–271 (1933).
51. Keller, P. J., and Cori, G. T. Enzymic conversion of phosphorylase *a* to phosphorylase *b*. *Biochim, et Biophys. Acta.* **12,** 235–238 (1953).
52. Koshland, D. E., Jr. Group transfer as an enzymatic substitution mechanism. *In* "The Mechanism of Enzyme Action" (W. D. McElroy and B. Glass, eds.), pp. 608–641. Johns Hopkins Press, Baltimore, Maryland, 1954.
53. Koshland, D. E., Jr. Isotopic exchange criteria for enzyme mechanisms. *Discussions Faraday Soc.* **No. 20,** 142–148 (1955).
54. Koshland, D. E., Jr. Molecular geometry in enzyme action. *J. Cellular Comp. Physiol.* **47,** Suppl. 1, 217–234 (1956).
55. Koshland, D. E., Jr., and Erwin, M. J. Enzyme catalysis and enzyme specificity —combination of amino acids at the active site of phosphoglucomutase. *J. Am. Chem. Soc.* **79,** 2657–2658 (1957).
56. Koshland, D. E., Jr., and Kennedy, E. P. Properties of the phosphorylated active site of phosphoglucomutase. *J. Biol. Chem.* **228,** 419–431 (1957).
57. Krebs, E. G., and Fischer, E. H. Phosphorylase activity of skeletal muscle extracts. *J. Biol. Chem.* **216,** 113–120 (1955).
58. Krebs, E. G., Kent, A. B., and Fischer, E. H. Stoichiometry of the phosphorylase *b* to *a* reaction. *Federation Proc.* **16,** 206 (1957).
59. Krebs, E. G., Rafter, G. W., and Junge, J. M. Yeast glyceraldehyde-3-phosphate dehydrogenase II. Yeast protein 2. *J. Biol. Chem.* **200,** 479–492 (1953).
60. Langenbeck, W. Chemismus der organischen Katalyse. *Advances in Enzymol.* **14,** 163–192 (1953).
61. Laskowski, M., and Laskowski, M., Jr. Naturally occurring trypsin inhibitors. *Advances in Protein Chem.* **9,** 203–242 (1954).
62. Levy, H. R., and Vennesland, B. The stereospecificity of enzymatic hydrogen transfer from diphosphopyridine nucleotide. *J. Biol. Chem.* **228,** 85–96 (1957).

63. Lieben, F. "Geschichte der Physiologischen Chemie." Deuticke, Leipzig and Vienna, 1935.
64. Lineweaver, H. The energy of activation of enzyme reactions, and their velocity below 0°. *J. Am. Chem. Soc.* **61**, 403–408 (1939).
65. Lipmann, F. Metabolic generation and utilization of phosphate bond energy. *Advances in Enzymol.* **1**, 99–162 (1941).
66. Lipmann, F. Development of the acetylation problem, a personal account. *Science* **120**, 855–865 (1954).
67. Loewus, F. A., Levy, H. R., and Vennesland, B. The enzymatic transfer of hydrogen. VI. The reaction catalyzed by D-glyceraldehyde-3-phosphate dehydrogenase. *J. Biol. Chem.* **223**, 589–597 (1956).
68. Low, B. W. The structure and configuration of amino acids, peptides and proteins. *In* "The Proteins" (H. Neurath and K. Bailey, eds.), Vol. I, Part A, pp. 235–391. Academic Press, New York, 1953.
69. Low, B. W., and Edsall, J. T. Aspects of protein structure. *In* "Currents in Biochemical Research" (D. E. Green, ed.), pp. 378–433. Interscience, New York, 1956.
70. Lugg, J. W. H. Plant proteins. *Advances in Protein Chem.* **5**, 229–304 (1949).
71. Mahler, H. R. Nature and function of metalloflavoproteins. *Advances in Enzymol.* **17**, 233–291 (1956).
72. Mason, H. S. Mechanisms of oxygen metabolism. *Science* **125**, 1185–1188 (1957).
73. Mason, H. S. Comparative biochemistry of the phenolase complex. *Advances in Enzymol.* **16**, 105–184 (1955).
74. Mason, H. S., Fowlks, W. L., and Peterson, E. Oxygen transfer and electron transport by the phenolase complex. *J. Am. Chem. Soc.* **77**, 2914–2915 (1955).
75. Mazelis, M., and Vennesland, B. Carbon dioxide fixation into oxalacetate in higher plants. *Plant Physiol.* **32**, 591–600 (1958).
76. Mazia, D. SH and growth. *In* "Glutathione: A Symposium" (S. Colowick, A. Lazarow, E. Racker, D. R. Schwartz, E. Stadtman, and H. Waelsch, eds.), pp. 209–228. Academic Press, New York, 1954.
77. Metzler, D. E., Ikawa, M., and Snell, E. E. A general mechanism for vitamin B_6-catalyzed reactions. *J. Am. Chem. Soc.* **76**, 648–652 (1954).
78. Michaelis, L., and Schubert, M. P. The theory of reversible two-step oxidation involving free radicals. *Chem. Revs.* **22**, 437–470 (1938).
79. Morton, R. K. The group-transfer activity of certain hydrolytic enzymes. Discussions Faraday Soc. **No. 20**, 149–156 (1955).
80. Najjar, V. A., and Pullman, M. E. The occurrence of a group transfer involving enzyme (phosphoglucomutase) and substrate. *Science* **119**, 631–634 (1954).
81. Neel, J. V. The inheritance of sickle cell anemia. *Science* **110**, 64–66 (1949).
82. Neilands, J. B., and Stumpf, P. K. "Outlines of Enzyme Chemistry." Wiley, New York, 1955.
83. Nicholas, D. J. D. Role of metals in enzymes with specific reference to flavoproteins. *Nature* **179**, 800–804 (1957).
84. Northrop, J. H., Kunitz, M., and Herriott, R. M. "Crystalline Enzymes," 2nd ed. Columbia Univ. Press, New York, 1948.
85. Nygaard, A. P., and Rutter, W. J. Interaction of pyridine-nucleotide linked enzymes. *Acta Chem. Scand.* **10**, 37–48 (1956).
86. Pauling, L. The future of enzyme research. *In* "Enzymes: Units of Biological Structure and Function" (O. H. Gaebler, ed.), pp. 177–182. Academic Press, New York, 1956.

127. Vallee, B. L., Hoch, F. L., Adelstein, S. J., and Wacker, W. E. C. Pyridine nucleotide dependent metallodehydrogenases. *J. Am. Chem. Soc.* **78,** 5879–5883 (1956).

128. Velick, S. F. The alcohol and glyceraldehyde-3-phosphate dehydrogenases of yeast and mammals. *In* "The Mechanism of Enzyme Action" (W. D. McElroy and B. Glass, eds.), pp. 491–519. Johns Hopkins Press, Baltimore, Maryland, 1954.

129. Velick, S. F. Biological Oxidations. *Ann. Rev. Biochem.* **25,** 257–290 (1956).

130. Vennesland, B. Some applications of deuterium to the study of enzyme mechanisms. *Discussions Faraday Soc.* **No. 20,** 240–248 (1955).

131. Vennesland, B. Steric specificity of hydrogen transfer in pyridine nucleotide dehydrogenase reactions. *J. Cellular Comp. Physiol.* **47,** Suppl. 1, 201–216 (1956).

132. Vennesland, B., and Westheimer, F. H. Hydrogen transport and steric specificity in reactions catalyzed by pyridine nucleotide dehydrogenases. *In* "The Mechanism of Enzyme Action" (W. D. McElroy and B. Glass, eds.), pp. 357–379. Johns Hopkins Press, Baltimore, Maryland, 1954.

133. Virtanen, A. I., and DeLey, J. The enzyme activity and nitrogen content of bacterial cells. *Arch. Biochem.* **16,** 169–176 (1948).

134. Wagner, R. P., and Mitchell, H. K. "Genetics and Metabolism." Wiley, New York, 1955.

135. Wallenfels, K., and Sund, H. Über den Mechanismus der Wasserstoffübertragung mit Pyridinnucleotiden. *Biochem. Z.* **329,** 17–82 (1957). A series of six papers.

136. Wang, J. H. On the detailed mechanism of a new type of catalase-like action. *J. Am. Chem. Soc.* **77,** 4715–4719 (1955).

137. Warburg, O. "Schwermetalle als Wirkungsgruppen von Fermenten." Saenger, Berlin, 1946; "Heavy Metal Prosthetic Groups and Enzyme Action." Oxford Univ. Press, London and New York, 1949.

138. Warburg, O. "Wasserstoffübertragende Fermente." Editio Cantor, Freiburg im Breisgau, 1949.

139. Waugh, D. F. Protein-Protein interactions. *Advances in Protein Chem.* **9,** 325–436 (1954).

140. Westheimer, F. H. "One-electron" and "two-electron" oxidation-reduction reactions in inorganic and organic chemistry. *In* "The Mechanism of Enzyme Action" (W. D. McElroy and B. Glass, eds.), pp. 321–356. Johns Hopkins Press, Baltimore, Maryland, 1954.

141. Willstätter, R., and Stoll, A. Untersuchungen über Chlorophyll. *In* "Untersuchungen über Enzyme" (Willstätter, R., ed.), pp. 251–337. Springer, Berlin, 1928.

141a. Willstätter, R., and Stoll, A. Untersuchungen über Chlorophyll. XI. Über Chlorophyllase. *Ann.* **378,** 18–72 (1910).

141b. Willstätter, R., and Stoll, A. "Untersuchungen über Chlorophyll." Berlin, 1913. J. Springer.

142. Wilson, I. B. Promotion of acetylcholine-esterase activity by the anionic site. *Discussions Faraday Soc.* **No. 20,** 119–125 (1955).

143. Woolley, D. W. Biological antagonisms between structurally related compounds. *Advances in Enzymol.* **6,** 129–146 (1946).

144. Yates, R. A., and Pardee, A. B. Control by uracil of formation of enzymes required for orotate synthesis. *J. Biol. Chem.* **227,** 677–692 (1957).

PREAMBLE TO CHAPTER 3

Chapter 3 deals with the means by which the energy stored in cells, by methods to be described in Volume IB Chapters 4 and 5, may subsequently be released and so become available and harnessed to useful purposes. The arrangements by which this is accomplished at the cellular and subcellular level are among those properties that are most characteristic of organized living systems, properties which in short distinguish the quick from the dead! A variety of physiological processes require energy in usable form. These will be discussed in subsequent volumes, for cells function in many ways by using their respiratory energy to do work, and thus to maintain essentially none-equilibrium conditions (see e.g. Chapter 4 of Volume II). Later, however, the topics of photosynthesis and respiration which are dealt with in Volume I at the cellular and subcellular level, will need to be reconsidered from the somewhat different standpoint of the behavior of whole organs and organisms; this will be done as part of the treatment of nutrition (Volume III) and of metabolism (Volume IV).

CHAPTER THREE

Cellular Respiration

David R. Goddard and Walter D. Bonner

I. Introduction

The oxidation of organic compounds by molecular oxygen may be considered as cellular respiration. Essentially, the problem is one of the transfer of electrons from organic substances through a series of organic catalyses (enzymes and coenzymes) to molecular oxygen, with the reduction of the oxygen to water. The oxidation of the organic compounds is normally, but not necessarily, accompanied by the formation of carbon dioxide. Perhaps of even more fundamental interest is the recognition that cellular respiration is a mechanism for the release of potential energy of organic compounds in forms utilizable by the cell. Some of the released energy is in the form of heat, and is lost to useful work, and some is channeled into useful work by the very enzymatic mechanisms which catalyze the energy release. This later fraction is used to drive uphill (endergonic) reactions which store the energy in chemical compounds in forms immediately available in the life of the cell.

The definition of respiration given above is restrictive in several particulars. First, the oxidation of inorganic compounds, such as hydrogen sulfide, sulfur, hydrogen, carbon monoxide, ammonia, and methane, is probably not fundamentally different in kind from the oxidation of glucose or ethyl alcohol. However, this type of inorganic respiration is often considered as distinct (it has been historically known as chemosynthesis) and is treated in a chapter in Volume IB.

Many plant physiologists have considered the anaerobic degradation of carbohydrates to alcohol and carbon dioxide or to lactic acid as a form of respiration. This type of metabolism is often called anaerobic respiration or intramolecular respiration. Since in the anaerobic degradation of carbohydrate an organic compound is the electron acceptor, resulting in a compound more reduced than carbohydrate (i.e., alcohol) and one more oxidized (i.e., CO_2), we prefer to designate this metabolism as fermentation. However, many of the reactions of fermentation may also occur during respiration. Fermentative metabolism may, in certain organisms, occur under aerobic conditions, so that both aerobic and anaerobic fermentations are recognized; it is the failure to reduce oxygen to water, and not the presence or absence of the gas, which is determining.

The term fermentation, as well as respiration, has been used with a lack of precision. For example, the "citric acid fermentation" is an aerobic process which utilizes atmospheric oxygen. Similarly, the "acetic acid fermentation" is a respiratory process without formation of carbon dioxide:

$$2 \begin{array}{c} CH_3 \\ | \\ CH_2OH \end{array} + O_2 \rightarrow \begin{array}{c} CH_3 \\ | \\ COOH \end{array} + 2\, H_2O \qquad (1)$$

When this reaction is carried out by *Acetobacter pasteurianus* (*Bacterium pasteurianum*) under proper environmental conditions, carbon dioxide is not formed and acetic acid accumulates. The conversion of carbohydrates by succulent plants to citric, isocitric, and malic acids may occur in the dark and at normal night temperatures without an evolution of carbon dioxide, and often with an absorption of carbon dioxide. This chapter will consider these incomplete oxidations, involving the reduction of oxygen to water, as respiration.

Lastly, organic compounds may be oxidized with such inorganic compounds as nitrate, nitrite, or sulfate serving as electron acceptors. Though these reactions have been considered as typical of bacteria, and outside the scope of this chapter, it is possible that similar reactions occur in green plants. Most plant tissues reduce nitrate to ammonia (or the amino group) and sulfate to sulfhydryl, in the former case with an increased production of carbon dioxide and an elevated respiratory quotient (where R.Q. = vol. of CO_2 evolved/vol. of O_2 absorbed).

In vertebrate physiology, a distinction must be made between external respirations, such as the gaseous exchange which occurs in lungs and gills, blood transport of oxygen and carbon dioxide, and the utilization of oxygen by the cells, or cellular respiration. In plant physiology, respiration and cellular respiration are identical.

The amount of energy released in the oxidation of organic compounds in cellular respiration is rather large. Reference to Table I

TABLE I
HEATS OF COMBUSTION OF SOME ORGANIC COMPOUNDS

Substance	R.Q.	kcal/gm[a]	ΔH kcal/mole
Starch	1.0	4.2	680[b]
Cane sugar	1.0	3.96	1354
Dextrose	1.0	3.74	674
Lactic acid	1.0	3.62	284
Ethyl alcohol	0.667	7.08	326
Animal protein	0.85	5.65[c]	—

[a] From J. M. Carpenter, Tables, Factors and Formulas for Computing Respiratory Exchanges, Carnegie Inst. Wash., Washington, D.C., 1924.
[b] Calculated for $C_6H_{10}O_5$.
[c] For complete oxidation to CO_2, H_2O, and nitrate; if to urea, the value is 4.40.

shows the heat liberated upon the oxidation of 1.0 gm of certain metabolites, as well as the heat liberated (ΔH) per gram mole. Since the maximum possible work is proportional to the free-energy change (ΔF) rather than to the ΔH, the values of ΔF are also included, where they are known with reasonable accuracy.

If we examine the equation of glucose oxidation:

$$\text{Glucose} + 6\ O_2 \rightarrow 6\ CO_2 + 6\ H_2O \qquad (2)$$
$$\Delta F = -686 \text{ kcal per mole}$$

we must recognize that any such value is approximate, since the concentration of glucose in solution, as well as the partial pressures of oxygen and carbon dioxide, will affect the value. Further, if it is recognized that each molecule of oxygen reduced must accept 4 electrons, we see that the oxidation of a molecule of glucose to carbon dioxide and water involves the transfer of 24 electrons or $^{686}/_{24} = 26.6$ kcal per mole of electron. The relation between free energy and potential is given by:

$$\Delta F = -n\mathbf{F}\Delta E \qquad (3)$$

where ΔF = free-energy change in kcal per mole
ΔE = potential difference in volts
F = Faraday = 23.066 kcal per volt equivalent
n = number of electrons lost on oxidation

The substitution of the 26.6 kcal per electron in this equation shows that the average potential difference between glucose and oxygen is 1.15 volts. If we take the oxygen potential at pH 7.0 and 1 atmosphere as +0.815 volts and correct to 0.2 atmosphere, we get the potential of oxygen as +0.78 volts. The above results would give a mean potential for glucose of —0.37 volts, a little higher than the hydrogen potential of —0.412 at pH 7.0 and 25°C. The maximum possible work per electron moving from glucose to oxygen would then be 1.15 volts, or 26.6 kcal per mole (of electrons). However, this energy is not released in a single step but in a series of graded steps, and some of the energy is coupled with energy-storing reactions so that it may be used in the work of the cell. In later pages we will discuss some of the mechanisms of energy coupling and cellular work.

A. Respiratory Rates

The rate of oxygen utilization by plant tissues varies over a wide range. Dry seeds have extremely low rates, less than 0.1 μl O_2 per gram dry weight per hour, while meristems may have rates as high as 7500 μl O_2 per gram dry weight per hour. When comparing different tissues or organisms, the basis of calculation is not clear. In a dry seed, a good deal of inert storage material is included in weight determinations, and in woody stems a large amount of nonliving xylem is included; in some situations the water content of the tissue is highly variable. In part this difficulty may be avoided by referring respiratory rates to protein content or respiration per cell.

The respiratory rates of plants vary widely, as is demonstrated in Table II,[1] where a few values for animals are included for comparative purposes. Figures 1 and 2 illustrate the respiratory rates of a primary root of corn (*Zea mays*), in relation to the distance from the apex. In Fig. 1, the respiratory rates are referred to wet and dry weights. Here there is an apparent peak rate at the region of maximal rates of cell division (0.5–2.2 mm behind the apex), and in Fig. 2 are

[1] In this chapter references in the text are cited in the manner adopted in this treatise. However, to each table which refers to experimental data, there is also appended a list of references to the authorities for the data in question.

TABLE II
RESPIRATORY RATES OF VARIOUS ORGANISMS

Organism	Temp. (°C)	Remarks	$\mu l\ O_2$/gm wet wt × hr	$\mu l\ O_2$/gm dry wt × hr	Ref.
Azotobacter chroöcoccum	22			2,000,000	1
Escherichia coli	40	20-Hr culture		200,000	2, p. 315
Micrococcus luteus	35			15,000	2, p. 315
Anabaena variabilis	25	Endogenous	1700–8400		2, p. 316
Chlorella pyrenoidosa	25	Endogenous		350–1500	2, p. 316
Chlorella pyrenoidosa	25	Glucose		20,000	2, p. 316
Ulva lactuca	25			810	2, p. 317
Fucus vesiculosus	18	Thallus	200		2, p. 318
Fucus vesiculosus	18	Antherozoids	2550		2, p. 318
Fucus vesiculosus	18	Eggs	540–1000		2, p. 318
Neurospora tetrasperma	25	Spores—dormant	90	250–590	3
Neurospora tetrasperma	25	Spores—germinating	7000	1000–20,000	3
Neurospora crassa	30	Mycelium		24,000–43,000	4
Baker's yeast	28	Endogenous		400–800	5
Baker's yeast		+ Glucose		40,000–80,000	5
Myrothecium verrucaria	30	Conidia—endogenous		2900–5600	2, p. 317
Myrothecium verrucaria	30	Conidia and sucrose; germinating		65,000–75,000	2, p. 317
Myrothecium verrucaria	30	Mycelia; pellets and sugar		58,000–65,000	2, p. 339
Barley (*Hordeum vulgare*)	22	Grain—dry	0.06	0.05	6
Barley (*Hordeum vulgare*)	22	Germinating	108		6
Barley (*Hordeum vulgare*)	20	Roots	960–1480	4840–7400	2, p. 365
Barley (*Hordeum vulgare*)	23	Leaves	266		2, p. 353
Carrot (*Daucus carota* var. *sativa*)	25	Root	25–30		7
Carrot (*Daucus carota* var. *sativa*)		Leaves—young	1133		8
Carrot (*Daucus carota* var. *sativa*)		Leaves—mature	439		8
Rye (*Secale cereale*) roots	25	Roots	2500		9
Opuntia monacantha	26	Shoot	41–96		2, p. 357
Arum maculatum	30	Spadix		15,600–31,800	2, p. 374
Lilium auratum	25	Pollen		10,600	2, p. 375
Citrus sinensis	21	Fruit	20–35		2, p. 378
Malus sylvestris (*Pyrus malus*)	22	Fruit	20–35		2, p. 380
Anopheles quadrimaculatus	26	Mosquito	2840		2, p. 280
Apis mellifera (hive bee)	42		17,466		2, p. 280
Musca sp.	20	House fly	3200		2, p. 280
Rana esculenta	20	Winter	85		2, p. 281
Rana esculenta	20	Summer	437		2, p. 281
Alligator lucius	25		64		2, p. 282

TABLE II (*Continued*)

Organism	Temp. (°C)	Remarks	μl O_2/gm wet wt × hr	μl O_2/gm dry wt × hr	Ref.
Python molurus	16		6.2	—	2, p. 282
Chicken	39		497	—	2, p. 282
Hummingbird		At midnight	1000	—	2, p. 282
Hummingbird		At noon	17,000	—	2, p. 339
Mouse		At rest	2500	—	2, p. 284
Mouse		Running	20,000	—	2, p. 284
Man	37	At rest	220	—	2, p. 285
Man	37	Max. work	4000	—	2, p. 285
Elephant	37	Standing at rest	148	—	10

References

1. Williams, A. M., and P. W. Wilson, *J. Bacteriol.* **67**, 353 (1954).
2. National Research Council, "Handbook of Respiration," Saunders, Philadelphia (1958).
3. Goddard, D. R., *Plant Physiol.* **13**, 241 (1938).
4. Cheng, S., *Plant Physiol.* **29**, 458 (1954).
5. Elvehjem, C. A., *J. Biol. Chem.* **90**, 111 (1931).
6. Merry, J. D., and D. R. Goddard, *Proc. Rochester Acad. Sci.* **8**, 28 (1941).
7. Turner, I. J., *Australian J. Exptl. Biol. Med.* **18**, 273 (1940).
8. Marsh, P. B., and D. R. Goddard, *Am. J. Botany* **26**, 724 (1939).
9. Goddard, D. R., unpublished data.
10. Bendict, F., Physiology of the Elephant, Carnegie Inst. Wash. (1936).

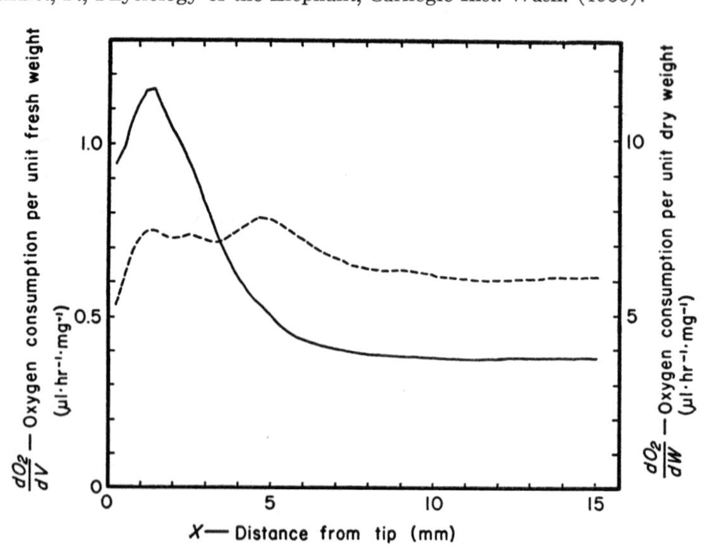

FIG. 1. The oxygen consumption of primary corn (*Zea mays*) roots in reference to distance from the tip. Solid curve in reference to fresh weight, broken curve related to dry weight. Unpublished experiments of Goddard.

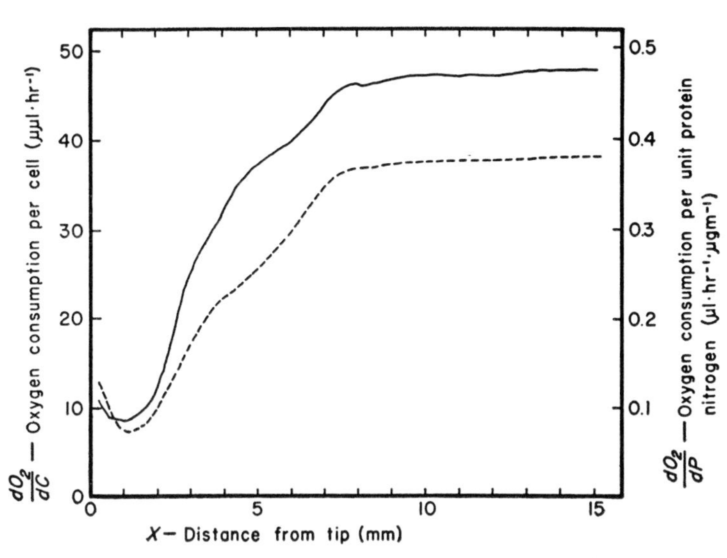

FIG. 2. The same data as in Fig. 1, plotted in reference to cell number (solid curve) and to protein N (broken curve). Mitosis occurs from 0.7 to 2.2 mm; elongation is maximal at 4–5 mm and ceases at 9.0 mm. Unpublished experiments of Goddard.

TABLE III
RESPIRATORY RATES ON A CELL BASIS[a]

Cell origin	Dry wt	Fresh wt (10^{-9} gm/cell)	N (10^{-9} gm/cell)	P (10^{-9} gm/cell)	O_2/hr (μμl)
Bean seed	2–123	11–250	0.08–4.4	0.01–0.05	12–78
Apple fruit	5–1300	30–6000	0.2–3.6	6.01–0.04	7–90
Corn roots	1–8	8–125	0.15–0.36	0.01–0.04	9–48
Pea roots	0.5–7	10–170	0.02–0.34	—	10–60
Onion root	—	—	0.05–0.30	—	6–50
Lily[b] microspores	—	390	0.221	—	712
Lily pollen	—	1060	0.73	—	1800

[a] Data from J. Lowenberg, *Plant Physiol.* **30,** 244–250 (1955) and unpublished Ph.D. Thesis of Dr. Maimon Nasatir, Univ. of Pennsylvania, 1958.

[b] Lily data: weights based on cell volume and an assumed density of 1.0; nitrogen data for lily are protein N.

the same respiratory data referred to protein nitrogen content, or per cell. Here, the region of rapid mitosis has a minimal rate of respiration, while a marked increase of rate is observed in the region of maximal cell elongation (2.2–7.0 mm behind the apex). The advantage of these respiratory data is that they may be correlated with rates of cell formation and elongation, as reported by Erickson and Goddard (38) and Erickson and Sax (39). In several cases respiratory rates per cell reveal

relationships otherwise obscured, and some selected data are reporte
in Table III.

1. *Measurement of Respiration*

The initial studies of de Saussure (30) published in 1804 were de
voted to the demonstration that plants consume oxygen and liberat
carbon dioxide. He made such measurements by enclosing plants in
container and by gas analysis determining the amount of oxygen use
and carbon dioxide liberated. Thus, he had also determined the re
spiratory quotient. This is still an acceptable method of study, but i
must be recognized that the atmosphere which surrounds the plan
material changes in composition during the period of the observation
and this may modify both the rate and the nature of the respiration.

Ideally, any quantitative measurements of respiration should give u
the data on all of the initial and final products; i.e., the substrate dis
appearing, the oxygen used, the carbon dioxide, water and heat formed
In practice this ideal is not attained. For example, in a growing system
or one where oxidative synthesis is occurring, two-thirds to four-fifth
of the hexose which disappears may be converted to higher molecula
weight compounds. However, it is usually desirable to determine bot
oxygen consumption and carbon dioxide production; then the respira
tory quotient is directly calculable. The R.Q. is of value, even thoug
it is not a certain indication of the nature of the substrate oxidized. Th
respiration of carbohydrate yields an R.Q. of 1.0, while protein an
fat yield values of 0.85 and 0.70. However, respiration dependent upo
several substrates is possible with intermediate values. Further, the con
version of carbohydrates to organic acids occurs with low R.Q. values
whereas the oxidation of malic acid to carbon dioxide and water yield
an R.Q. of 1.33. An R.Q. value above unity may represent either oxi
dation of organic acids or the simultaneous occurrence of respiratio
and fermentation due to partially anaerobic conditions. (The nature o
the substrate respired can be determined only by chemical analysis.)

The most widely used system of measurement of respiration in Eng
land and Europe has been the Pettenkofer method. Here a stream o
air is deprived of carbon dioxide by absorption towers, and the carbo
dioxide-free air is passed over the respiring plant parts; the respirator
carbon dioxide is then removed by absorption in NaOH, and the carbo
dioxide determined by titration. A large amount of respiratory data ha
been accumulated by this method. Respiration is here equated wit
carbon dioxide production, and if the conditions are such as to insur
an aerobic state for the cells, the results are valuable and reliable. Thi
method was highly developed in the laboratory of Blackman (10) a

Cambridge University. In his laboratory several tubes were set up in parallel, and the gas current was shifted from tube to tube by clockwork every 3 hours, so that continuous records were obtained. A physical limitation of this method was that the Pettenkofer tube did not allow a rapid gas stream with complete absorption of carbon dioxide; this difficulty may be avoided by the use of Reiset towers or sintered glass aerators.

A modification of this method is to absorb the carbon dioxide in 0.050 *N* NaOH in a tower which contains platinized platinum electrodes, and the decrease in conductivity that results from the conversion of NaOH to Na_2CO_3 is read on a 1000-cycle Wheatstone bridge. This method is well described by Newton (115), and calibration data have been published by Wolf *et al.* (167).

In the hands of critical workers either modification is an accurate determination of carbon dioxide production. Difficulties of interpretation occur if the carbon dioxide has its origin in two processes; this is frequently true if the tissues have their air spaces injected with water, and fermentative carbon dioxide is liberated, since the method cannot distinguish between the carbon dioxide of fermentation and that of respiration.

The gas stream methods have also been used for measuring fermentation; a stream of nitrogen or hydrogen, freed of carbon dioxide and oxygen, is passed over the tissue and the carbon dioxide of fermentation is absorbed (see Blackman, 10).

One difficulty caused by the evaluation of respiratory rates entirely in terms of carbon dioxide has been the confusion in theoretical understanding. There are plant organs where the rate of carbon dioxide evolution is the same under aerobic and anaerobic conditions. This has lead the unwary to the view "that respiration was identical under aerobic and anaerobic conditions." In many cases the anaerobic metabolism is alcoholic fermentation, and if we examine the two following equations we can see the magnitude of the error in this thinking:

$$C_6H_{12}O_6 + 6\ O_2 \rightarrow 6\ CO_2 + 6\ H_2O \qquad (4)$$
$$\Delta F = -686 \text{ kcal}$$

$$C_6H_{12}O_6 \rightarrow 2\ C_2H_5OH + 2\ CO_2 \qquad (5)$$
$$\Delta F = -54 \text{ kcal}$$

If the rate of carbon dioxide production is identical under the two situations, the rate of glucose decomposition is three times as great in nitrogen as in air, and the rate of energy liberation is 24% of the aerobic rate. The uncritical thinking may lead to an energy difference of 400% being considered an identity!

It is the use of carbon dioxide production as the sole measure of respiration that has maintained in areas of plant physiology the term anaerobic respiration. This term, which has much historical precedent has caused great confusion, as is illustrated in the above paragraph. It seems to these authors time to abandon this term, as well as that of intramolecular respiration, and to use fermentation in its place (45).

It is thus clear that if a single measure is to be made of respiration oxygen consumption is far more dependable than carbon dioxide production. However, it is desirable to measure both the oxygen used and the carbon dioxide released.

The oxygen consumption may be measured by the decrease in volume of the gas space, if the liberated carbon dioxide is chemically absorbed and there is no other gas changing in volume (either water vapor, ammonia, hydrogen, or nitrogen). Instruments depending on a changing volume are known as volumetric respirometers. Thunberg (146, 147) and later Fenn (41), among others, have designed volumetric microrespirometers. These instruments, if carefully used and with adequate controls, are sensitive to 0.5 μl of O_2 and will measure rates of 100 μl O_2 per hour with a reliability of $\pm 4.5\%$. More micro variants have been described by Cunningham and Kirk (27), and Tobias (149) has given a critical review of such instruments. Better known is the microrespirometer which functions at constant volume, and the decrease in pressure is measured on a water barometer. The Warburg apparatus and Barcroft differential microrespirometer are well known and have been described by Dixon (36) and Umbreit *et al.* (151). Such instruments are used successfully with cell suspensions and aquatic organisms. However, if aerial plants or plant parts are suspended in aqueous solutions, the tissues will inject with water and may become readily dependent upon the partial pressure of oxygen. In fact such tissues often become partially or completely anaerobic even though the liquid is saturated with oxygen at 0.2 atmosphere, as is demonstrated by complete reduction of the cytochrome systems. For oxygen uptake, the instruments are successfully used by having the plant part in the respiratory vessel in air saturated with water vapor. However, respiratory substrates and inhibitors cannot then be added in solution, nor is the indirect method of Warburg useful for determination of carbon dioxide.

McAlister (97) in 1937 measured the rate of carbon dioxide uptake in photosynthesis in a closed system, and the release of carbon dioxide in respiration by the tissue is followed by the specific absorption band of carbon dioxide in the infrared. Since commercial infrared carbon dioxide analyzers are now available, this is a practical method.

Brown *et al.* (15) have developed an elegant method of following oxygen uptake (or production) and also carbon dioxide uptake or production, using a mass spectrometer and heavy (stable) isotopes. If the cell suspension is in water of natural ratio of O^{16} and O^{18}, but the gas phase has a higher concentration of O^{18}, and a small sample of the gas is leaked into the recording mass spectrometer, the oxygen consumption will decrease the O^{18} concentration and evolution of oxygen will be at the expense of H_2O^{16}. Similarly, $C^{13}O_2$ may be used in the gas space, and carbon dioxide utilization will decrease the $C^{13}O_2$ concentration, while the respiratory carbon dioxide will increase the $C^{12}O_2$ as it is formed from the cell metabolites which will contain predominantly C^{12}.

For aquatic organisms and cell suspensions, carbon dioxide of respiration may be followed by the change in pH which occurs in a lightly buffered solution. Osterhout and Haas (121) in 1917 introduced this method, using indicators. Blinks and Skow (11) refined this method by the use of a recording glass electrode.

The above methods may be readily combined with the platinum electrode polarographic methods introduced by Davies and Brink (28). These methods have been used successfully by Brackett *et al.* (14) for photosynthesis and respiration of algal suspensions. These methods are successful with cell suspensions, mitochondrial suspensions, and aquatic organisms. They have not been readily adapted to the aerial parts of plants.

2. *Oxygen Tension*

It is clear that respiration, as defined in this chapter, is dependent upon the presence of molecular oxygen. It was early recognized in the period 1885–1891, by Pfeffer's students Wilson (166), Johannsen (65), and Stich (137), that plant respiration is unimpaired at 1–2% by volume of oxygen and that there is no oxygen reserve in the cell. The relation of respiratory rate to the percentage of oxygen in the surrounding atmosphere is illustrated in Figs. 3 and 4. It has often been assumed that the central regions of bulky plant tissues are anaerobic, though the French physiologist Devaux showed in 1890 (31–33) that this is not true. He demonstrated that in plant tissues gaseous diffusion occurs primarily through intercellular spaces. A simple demonstration is shown in Figs. 5 and 6 taken from Devaux. Further, by gas analysis, he found that the gas from the center of pumpkins (*Cucurbita pepo*) contained 18% oxygen and about 2% carbon dioxide. This same problem has been dealt with by Burton (see page 223 of this chapter).

Oxygen dissolves in water; however, the amount which dissolves

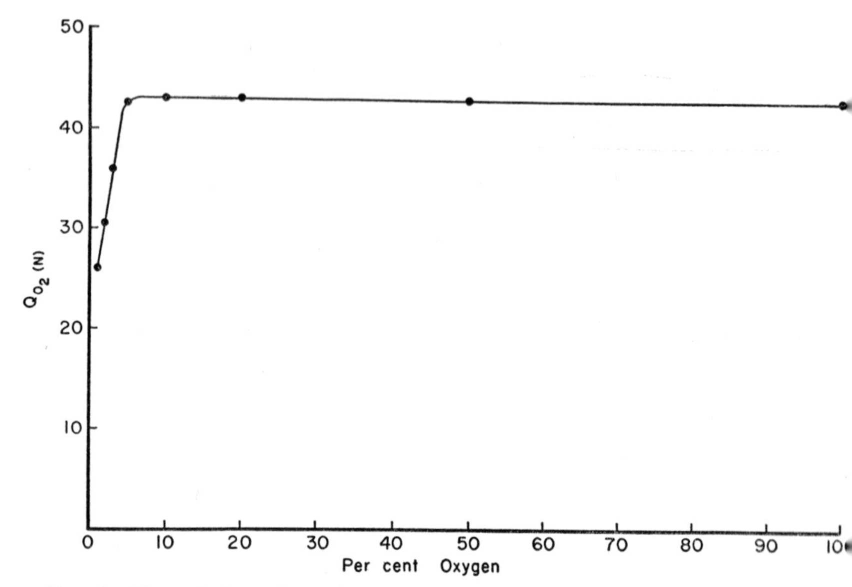

FIG. 3. The relation of respiratory rates to volume per cent oxygen; etiolated black valentine bean hypocotyls. Unpublished results of Susan Smith and W. D. Bonner, Jr.

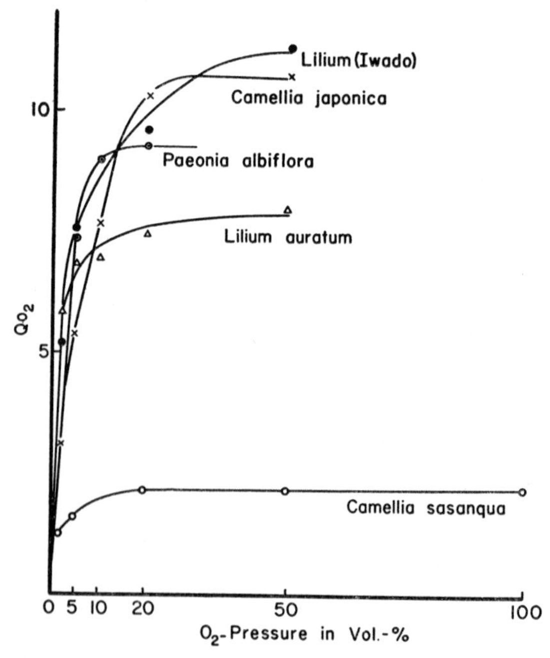

FIG. 4. The relation of respiratory rate of pollen to volume per cent oxygen. From Okunki, K. *Acta Phytochim.* (*Japan*) **11**, 34 (1939).

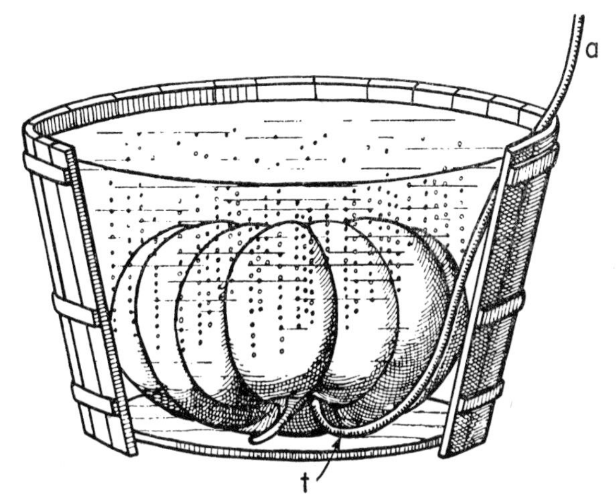

FIG. 5. A demonstration of gas channels from the central cavity of a pumpkin (*Cucurbita pepo*) through the outer fruit wall. From Devaux, H., *Rev. gen. botan.* 3, 49 (1891).

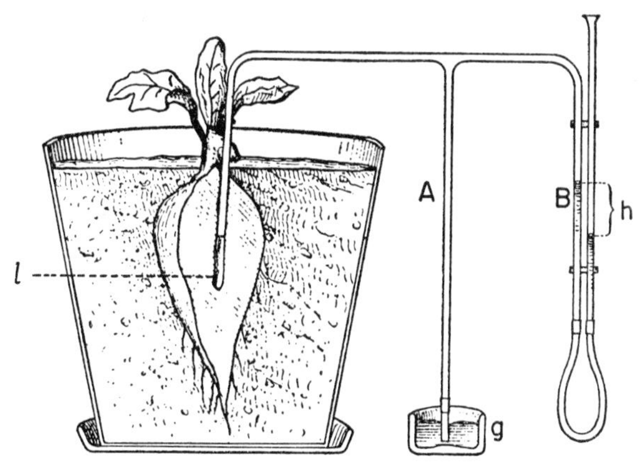

FIG. 6. Method of sampling gas from an artificial cavity of turnip (*Brassica rapa*). From Devaux, H., *Bull. soc. botan. France* **37**, 273 (1890).

depends upon the temperature, the pressure of oxygen, and the salt content of the liquid. The volume dissolved is defined by:

$$\text{Vol. of } O_2 = \frac{\alpha P}{760} \qquad (6)$$

where α = Bunsen's solubility coefficient = 0.0283 at 25°C; P = pressure of O_2 in millimeters of Hg. The solubility of oxygen in water is shown in Table IV. The diffusion constant of oxygen in air at 25°C is 0.205 ml/cm^2 $\times$ sec,* while in water the value is nearly 300,000

* This term has the dimensions of a velocity (cm/sec) for movement under a defined or unit pressure gradient. The physical diffusion coefficient of a substance has the dimensions cm^2/sec.

TABLE IV
SOLUBILITY OF OXYGEN IN WATER

Temperature (°C)	Bunsen's coefficient	ml O_2/liter
10	0.038	7.75
20	0.031	6.32
25	0.028	5.77

times smaller, 6.7×10^{-7} ml/cm^2 $\times$ sec. The diffusion constant through a living plant cell is not known, though it may well be lower than that for water.

For a respiring tissue, a steady state will result from oxygen diffusion and oxygen utilization.* Warburg (157) considered the situation for a sheet of tissue, with diffusion from both sides but ignoring the edges. He derived the equation:

$$C_x = C_0 - \frac{a}{2D}(Hx - x^2) \tag{7}$$

where $C_x = pO_2$ in atmospheres at x
$C_0 =$ external pO_2 in atmospheres
$D =$ diffusion constant; we will assume $D = 6.7 \times 10^{-7}$ ml/cm^2 $\times$ seconds
$a =$ respiratory rate in milliliters of O_2/ml of tissue $\times$ seconds
$H =$ thickness of tissue in centimeters
$x =$ distance from surface in centimeters

The distance x from the surface at which a defined pressure C_x, with a given external pressure of oxygen C_0, will obtain is defined by the relation:

$$x = \frac{H}{2} \pm \sqrt{\frac{H^2}{4} - \frac{2D}{a}(C_0 - C_x)} \tag{8}$$

If we take x as equal $H/2$, that is the tension at the center of the sheet, then:

$$H = \sqrt{\frac{8D}{a}(C_0 - C_x)} \tag{9}$$

If we apply equation (7) to a sheet of tissue without intercellular gas spaces with H taken as 0.05 cm, $C_0 = 0.208$ atmos., and $a = 2.77 \times 10^{-5}$ ml O_2 per sec, then C_x at the center of the tissue is 0.186 atmos. If the respiratory rate were ten times as high, then

* Reference may be made to W. O. James ("Plant Respiration," p. 143, Oxford Press, 1953) and the use of the term "invasion coefficient" noted. This relates to the diffusive advance of oxygen into bulky organs.

the pO_2 at the center of the tissue would be 0.068 atmos., a value that will maintain a maximum respiratory rate and suppress fermentation.

With the same respiratory rate, 100 μl O_2 per gram wet weight times hours, from equation (9), the limiting thickness at which pO_2 just falls to zero at the center of the section is 0.507 cm. If the respiratory rate were ten times as great, the limiting thickness would be 0.16 cm.

Similar equations have been derived for cylinders by Fenn (40) and for spheres by Gerard (42). They are given below.

For cylinders:

$$C_r = C_0 - \frac{a}{4D}(R^2 - r^2) \quad \textbf{(10)}$$

where $R =$ radius, and $r =$ radial distance from the center at which C_r obtains. When $r = 0$, and pO_2 just falls to zero at the center, the equation showing the critical pressure of C_0 to supply the cylinder is:

$$C_0 = \frac{aR^2}{4D} \quad (11)$$

or the limiting radius, for a given external pressure of oxygen with pO_2 reaching zero at the center, is:

$$R = \sqrt{\frac{4DC_0}{a}} \quad (12)$$

The corresponding equations for spheres are:

$$C_0 = C_r - \frac{a}{6D}(R^2 - r^2) \quad (13)$$

$$C_0 = \frac{aR^2}{6D} \quad (14)$$

and

$$R = \sqrt{\frac{6DC_0}{a}} \quad (15)$$

All of the above equations assume that the cyclosis of the cytoplasm does not contribute to gas transport and that there is no circulation of water through the tissue and no gas diffusion path, except through water (or cells). If, however, the tissue contains air spaces, the situation is markedly changed. Burton (16), for example, examined the situation for a potato (*Solanum tuberosum*) tuber. The respiratory rate is low, about 10^{-4} μl O_2 per minute per milliliter of tissue. He found that the air spaces in the tissue varied from 0.62 to 1.34% of the tissue volume. Further, he found the diffusion constant of oxygen in tuber tissue to be 2.9×10^{-4} μl/cm^2 $\times$ sec, a value 430 times greater than through water. No other values of oxygen diffusion through plant tissues are known, but the volume of air spaces is frequently much greater. It is probably safe to assume that gaseous diffusion through air spaces, in spite of its longer path, is frequently 1000 times as great as through an equal distance of water. Spherical plant structures with respiratory rates similar to that of the potato could have diameters of 14 cm, with 2% oxygen at the center.

It is of interest that as early as 1890 the French physiologist Devaux (33) recognized that gaseous exchange occurred through the intercellular spaces and that large bulky tissues were not anaerobic. He sampled the gas from plant cavities, as is shown in Fig. 6. Though he found carbon dioxide values much higher than in air, such bulky tissues were not anaerobic (Table V). Devaux also recognized that one cannot

TABLE V
THE GAS COMPOSITION OF SOME BULKY TISSUES[a]

Organ	CO_2 (vol. %)	O_2 (vol. %)	N_2 (vol. %)
Potato tuber	4.74	14.88	80.38
Turnip root	1.83	16.63	81.54
Beet root	4.68	12.44	83.38
Cucurbita maxima fruit	2.52	18.29	79.17

[a] Results from Devaux (31, 32).

determine the gas composition of a tissue by acid extraction, since the large amount of bicarbonate vitiates the results.

The effect of carbon dioxide on plant respiration has not been carefully studied. The carbon dioxide concentration in tissues often appears to be quite high, but the distinction between pCO_2, or the concentration of carbon dioxide in solution, and total carbon dioxide (bicarbonates) has usually been ignored. The internal carbon dioxide of massive tissues, i.e., potato (*Solanum tuberosum*), beet (*Beta vulgaris*), or carrot (*Daucus carota* var. *sativa*), may vary from 2 to 7%, while in leaves one would expect a carbon dioxide content close to that of the air.

The practice of measuring respiration in carbon dioxide-free atmospheres may introduce somewhat unphysiological conditions. Since the reactions of carboxylation are reversible, at low pCO_2 the concentrations of organic acids may fall.

B. RESPIRATION AND FERMENTATION

Parts of many plants placed in an anaerobic environment carry out an alcoholic fermentation, frequently with a ratio of CO_2:alcohol of 1.0, in some cases with less alcohol than carbon dioxide and in a few cases with formation of lactic acid as well. The phenomenon is not universal; the alcoholic fermentation is most marked in moist seeds, seedlings, storage roots, and in embryonic tissue. Some leaves fail to ferment under anaerobic conditions (122).

If oxygen is admitted at low pressure (usually well below 5.0%) both fermentation and respiration may occur simultaneously with an elevation in the ratio of $CO_2:O_2$ (the R.Q.) above the value in air. Some results obtained by Stich in 1891 are shown in Table VI. If the

TABLE VI
RESPIRATION AND FERMENTATION IN PLANT TISSUES[a]

Tissue	Duration in hours	% O_2	R.Q.
Triticum aestivum seedlings	3	20.8	0.98
	3	9.0	0.94
	3	5.0	0.93
	3	3.0	3.34
	18	3.0	3.73
Zea mays seedlings	3	20.8	0.89
	3	9.0	0.96
	24	9.1	0.97
	3	3.6	1.37
Pisum sativum seedlings	3	20.8	0.83
	3	9.3	0.86
	15	3.5	2.31

[a] Results from Stich (137).

oxygen pressure is raised, a point is reached at which the R.Q. is equal to the air value; i.e., no fermentation occurs. This pressure of oxygen has been called the extinction point. The effect of oxygen gas in suppressing fermentation is known as the Pasteur effect, since Pasteur first observed the phenomenon with yeast.

If the ratio of the rate of alcoholic fermentation to respiration (F:R) is 1:3 or less, the alcohol of fermentation could all be removed by respiration. However, if the F:R is greater than 1:3 the aerobic processes would not occur rapidly enough to eliminate the alcohol produced. Further, when F:R = 1:3, the rate of carbohydrate breakdown is equal anaerobically and aerobically:

$$C_6H_{12}O_6 + 6\ O_2 \rightarrow 6\ CO_2 + 6\ H_2O \quad (16)$$

$$C_6H_{12}O_6 \rightarrow 2\ CO_2 + 2\ C_2H_5OH \quad (17)$$

If F:R exceeds 1:3, the rate of carbohydrate destruction would be greater under anaerobic than under aerobic conditions. The F:R ratio varies widely for various tissues, but for many embryonic tissues it is often above 1.0. The mechanism of oxygen inhibition of fermentation has received a variety of explanations. Meyerhof (108) and later Blackman (9) proposed that oxidation of a carbohydrate (or any compound short of a C_2 fragment) might result in part of the energy of the oxidation being used to resynthesize carbohydrates. This could be illustrated as follows:

$$\text{(a)}\ C_6H_{12}O_6 + 6\ O_2 \rightarrow 6\ CO_2 + 6\ H_2O + \text{energy} \quad (18)$$

$$\text{(b)}\ 8\ C_3H_6O_3 + \text{energy} \rightarrow 4\ C_6H_{12}O_6 \quad (19)$$

The important points here would be: (1) a conservation of carbohydrate, (2) the operation of the synthesis before carbon dioxide production in fermentation. The experimental results are consistent with the Meyerhof-Blackman theory, but they may have alternative explanations.

There are relatively few experiments with higher plants where the rate of carbohydrate disappearance in nitrogen and in air has been measured. Meeuse (104) has carried out such experiments with pea (*Pisum sativum*) seedlings (which have an alcoholic fermentation, with an alcohol:carbon dioxide ratio of 1.0) and found that in young seedlings there is a conservation of carbohydrate in air. In addition to a lower carbohydrate breakdown in air than in nitrogen, there is growth in air but not in nitrogen, and a good deal of the starch and sugar which disappear in air are not degraded but built into cell walls and used in other synthetic reactions.

The prevalence of carbon dioxide fixation, particularly by succulent plants in the dark, makes it essential for us to realize that net rate of carbon dioxide release in a partially aerobic system is not critical evidence of the rate of fermentation; consideration must be given to a possible simultaneous carboxylation and reduction of carbon dioxide.

As we shall see in more detail below, fermentation will stop at the level of glyceraldehyde-3-phosphate in the absence of inorganic phosphate. If, in aerobic metabolism the concentration of inorganic phosphate is very low, this could result in an inhibition of fermentation. Further, the conversion of 1,3-diphosphoglyceric acid to 3-phosphoglyceric acid is dependent upon the concentration of adenosine diphosphate (ADP). Respiration drives the reaction:

$$H_3PO_4 + ADP \rightarrow ATP + H_2O \quad (20)$$

where ATP = adenosine triphosphate, thus lowering not only the level of inorganic phosphate but also that of ADP. In a strongly respiring system the ratio of ATP:ADP = 1000. Either the ADP or inorganic phosphate concentration, or both, may serve to regulate the rate of degradation of carbohydrates. However, the presence of adenosinetriphosphatase as a regulator of the ATP:ADP and inorganic phosphate levels cannot be ignored. See Meyerhof (109).

C. THE NATURE OF OXIDATION

We may define oxidation as the addition of oxygen, the removal of hydrogen, or the removal of electrons. The addition of oxygen may be direct:

$$A + O_2 \rightarrow AO_2 \tag{21}$$

or it may be indirect, the addition of water followed by dehydrogenation:

$$A + H_2O \rightarrow A\begin{matrix} OH \\ OH \end{matrix} \tag{22}$$

$$A\begin{matrix} OH \\ OH \end{matrix} + B \rightarrow AO_2 + BH_2 \tag{23}$$

Since both types of reactions occur, it was difficult to distinguish them until the use of oxygen isotope O^{18} was introduced. Mason (103) has given an excellent review of this problem. If the oxidation of catechol by pyrocatechase of *Pseudomonas* is studied, reaction (24) is found:

$$\text{Catechol (OH, OH)} + O_2 \rightarrow \textit{cis,cis}\text{-Muconic acid (COOH, COOH)} \tag{24}$$

Catechol *cis,cis*-Muconic acid

This reaction has been studied with oxygen gas enriched with O^{18} and with H_2O^{18}. Only in the former case was the O^{18} incorporated into the muconic acid (see Table VII).

TABLE VII
ENZYMATIC CLEAVAGE OF CATECHOL TO MUCONIC ACID IN THE PRESENCE OF O^{18}_2 AND H_2O^{18} [a]

	Atom % O^{18} excess in muconic acid	
Medium	Experiment	Theory
$O_2 + H_2O^{18}$	0.000	0.701
	0.000	
$O^{18}_2 + H_2O$	1.217	1.343
	1.229	

[a] Data from Mason (103).

It is clear that here a direct addition of oxygen has occurred. Mason has designated enzymes catalyzing such reactions as oxygen transferases.

Oxidation by hydrogenation was first demonstrated by Wieland (161) in the oxidation of benzaldehyde catalyzed by colloidal platinum [reactions (25) and (26)].

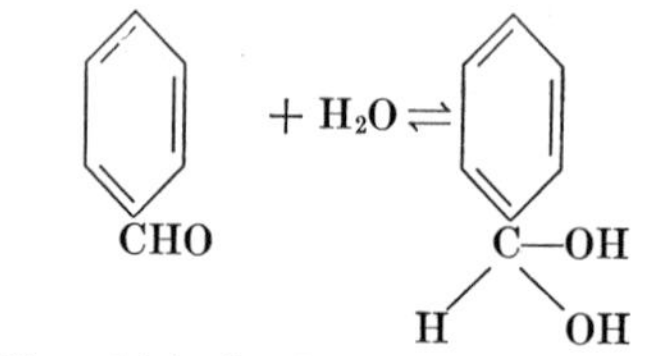

$$C_6H_5CHO + H_2O \rightleftharpoons C_6H_5C(H)(OH)OH \quad (25)$$

Benzaldehyde Hydrated benzaldehyde

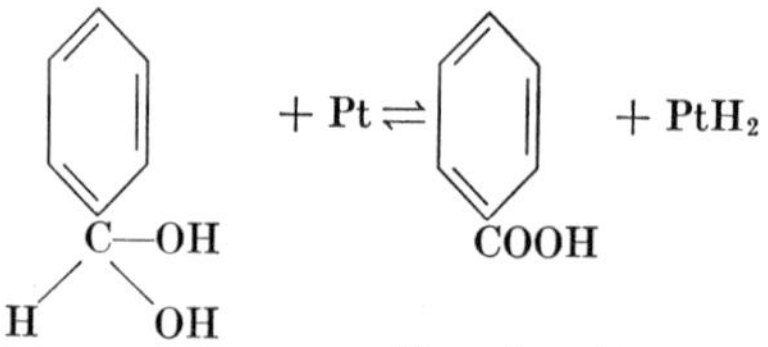

$$C_6H_5C(H)(OH)OH + Pt \rightleftharpoons C_6H_5COOH + PtH_2 \quad (26)$$

Benzoic acid

This reaction can be carried out in the complete absence of molecular oxygen, but not in the absence of water.

Wieland (162) and Thunberg (148) later showed that organisms, and extracts of seeds and muscles, can carry out similar reactions. For example, Thunberg showed that succinate may be oxidized to fumarate by an enzyme in muscle (and also in yeasts, bacteria, and higher plants). Methylene blue (Mb) was used as an artificial hydrogen acceptor [reaction (27)].

$$K^+{}^-OOC{-}CH_2{-}CH_2{-}COO^-K^+ + Mb \xrightleftharpoons{\text{enzyme}} K^+{}^-OOC{-}CH{=}CH{-}COO^-K^+ + MbH_2 \quad (27)$$

Succinate Fumarate

Such enzymes are known as dehydrogenases, and many specific dehydrogenases are known, each of which catalyzes the oxidation of a specific substrate.

Oxidation may also proceed by the mechanism of electron loss, such as the oxidation of ferrous ion to ferric ion:

$$Fe^{++} + A \rightleftharpoons Fe^{+++} + A^- \quad (28)$$

or

$$4\ Fe^{++} + O_2 \rightleftharpoons 4\ Fe^{+++} + 2\ O^{--} \quad (29)$$

The oxidation of the cytochromes by molecular oxygen are examples of such reactions. The O^{--} will have an extremely short half-life and will immediately be converted to water. Therefore, we may rewrite the equation:

$$4\ Fe^{++} + O_2 + 4\ H^+ \rightarrow 4\ Fe^{+++} + 2\ H_2O \qquad (30)$$

We consider that the usual oxidases of plant and animal cells function in such a manner. However, when the flavoproteins and several other enzymes react with oxygen, hydrogen peroxide is formed:

$$\text{Leucoflavoprotein} + O_2 \rightarrow \text{Flavoprotein} + H_2O_2 \qquad (31)$$

Oxidation by electron removal or by hydrogen removal ($2\ H^+ + 2\ e$) in organic compounds normally involves two electrons or two hydrogen atoms, as organic compounds normally have an even number of electrons. However, organic compounds with an odd number of electrons, such as triphenylmethyl, are known; such compounds are considered as free radicals. Michaelis and Schubert (111) recognized that in the oxidation of organic dyes one electron may be lost, resulting in an intermediate with an odd number of electrons; he called such an intermediate a semiquinone. For example, if duroquinone is oxidized, a semiquinone is produced. The semiquinone may be reduced to the hydroquinone or it may be oxidized to the quinone, or it may undergo dismutation, where two molecules of semiquinone react to form one of hydroquinone and one of quinone:

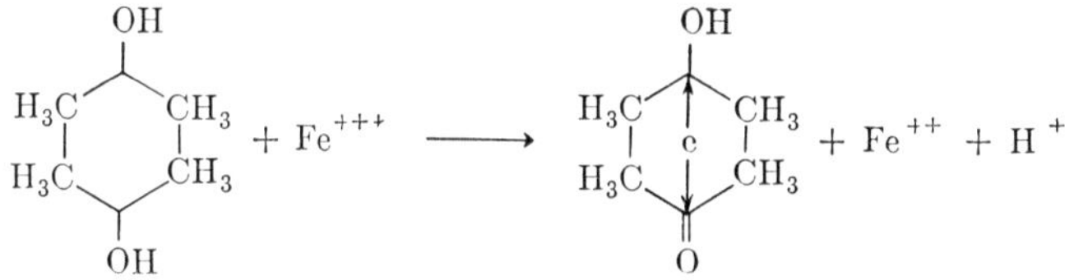

$$\text{Durohydroquinone (OH; } H_3C, CH_3, H_3C, CH_3\text{; OH)} + Fe^{+++} \longrightarrow \text{Semiquinone (OH; } H_3C, CH_3, e, H_3C, CH_3\text{; O)} + Fe^{++} + H^+ \qquad (32)$$

The interesting aspect of semiquinones is that in biological oxidations the substrate systems normally involve the loss of two electrons, the iron and copper enzymes one, while the flavoproteins, which may bridge such systems, may undergo either single or double electron oxidation-reductions. It is of interest that Haas (48) found that when flavoprotein is reduced in the presence of TPN (triphosphopyridine nucleotide), a red color indicating a semiquinone was formed. In 1958 Ehrenberg and Ludwig (37) confirmed Haas's observation and showed that in a mixture of TPNH and flavoprotein, 15–20% of the flavoprotein was probably present as a free radical. These observations were based upon paramagnetic resonance measurements. Whether the free radical is of significance in enzymatic catalysis is still uncertain.

As Mason (103) has pointed out, mixed reactions are possible where one atom of oxygen is incorporated into the compound and the other is reduced to water; this could be illustrated by the oxidation of a monophenol by mushroom phenol oxidase, as illustrated in Table VIII.

TABLE VIII

Entrance of O^{18} into the Benzene Ring by Oxidation of 3,4-Dimethylphenol by Mushroom Phenol Oxidase[a]

Medium	Per cent of theoretical possible O^{18} uptake
$O_2^{18} + H_2O$	89, 88, 95
$O_2 + H_2O^{18}$	0, 0.

[a] Data from Mason (103).

All of these mechanisms very probably play a role in cellular metabolism. In the appropriate places, we will consider the specific reactions.

II. Respiratory Substrates

We often speak of a plant respiring starch, sucrose, protein, or fat. It is true that, if one observes the germination of a seed in the dark, or the continued respiration of starving leaves, a marked decrease in one or more reserve foods may occur. These stored reserves are, therefore, in the final analysis the respiratory substrates.

However, it is clear that starch, protein, and fat are not directly oxidized and that the conversion of these compounds into respiratory metabolites must precede oxidation. Since this is a chapter on cellular respiration, most of the interconversions of these compounds will not be discussed here, but we will deal with some of the critical reactions. The proteins are hydrolyzed into amino acids and amides and, once these compounds have been deaminated by oxidative deamination (see page 252) or by transamination (see page 252), the α-keto acids are oxidized as organic acids. The oxidation of fatty acids and glycerol will be discussed separately on pages 250–252.

Of the many conversions of the carbohydrates, we will be concerned with those leading directly to respiratory substrates. Reserve carbohydrates, such as starches, glycogen, and other polysaccharides, may be hydrolyzed by specific enzymes to lower polysaccharides and then to disaccharides. The disaccharides then undergo hydrolysis by specific enzymes to form the corresponding hexose sugars. For example:

$$\text{Sucrose} + H_2O \xrightarrow{\text{invertase}} \text{glucose} + \text{fructose} \tag{33}$$

$$\text{Maltose} + H_2O \xrightarrow{\text{maltase}} 2 \text{ glucose} \quad (34)$$

The extent to which the degradation of the polysaccharides to simple sugars is hydrolytic in metabolizing, growing cells is by no means certain. The enzymes are widely distributed, and the equilibria lie far toward the side of the hexose sugars. It is possible that in germinating seeds and in the origin of transport sugars from reserve carbohydrates these hydrolytic reactions play a dominant role. However, it must be recognized that the enzymes so long considered as catalyzing the hydrolysis of the glucosidic bonds of sugars also catalyze transglucosidations, as illustrated by the action of *Leuconostoc mesenteroides* on sucrose to produce the polysaccharide dextran:

$$n \text{ Sucrose} \rightarrow n \text{ fructose} + (\text{glucose})n \quad (35)$$

The carbohydrates may then be broken down by one of three means:

(a) Hydrolysis of a glucosidic bond:

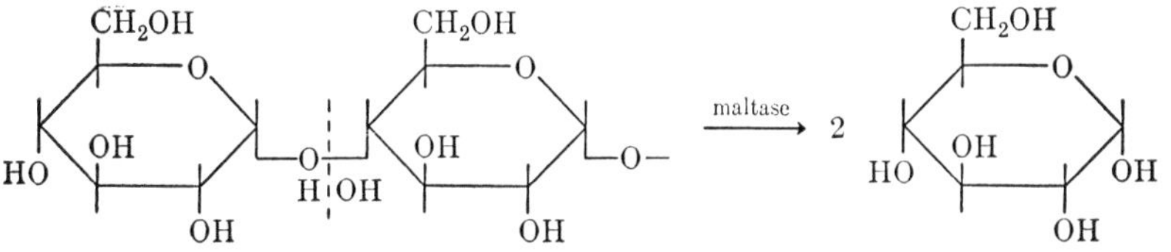

CH₂OH, O, OH, HO, OH — O — H OH — CH₂OH, O, OH, OH — O— $\xrightarrow{\text{maltase}}$ 2 CH₂OH, O, OH, HO, OH, OH (36)

Maltose

Glucose
(α-D-glucopyranose)

(b) Transglucosidation:

$$n \text{ Maltose} \xrightarrow{\text{maltase}} (\text{glucose})n + n \text{ glucose} \quad (37)$$

(c) Phosphorylation:

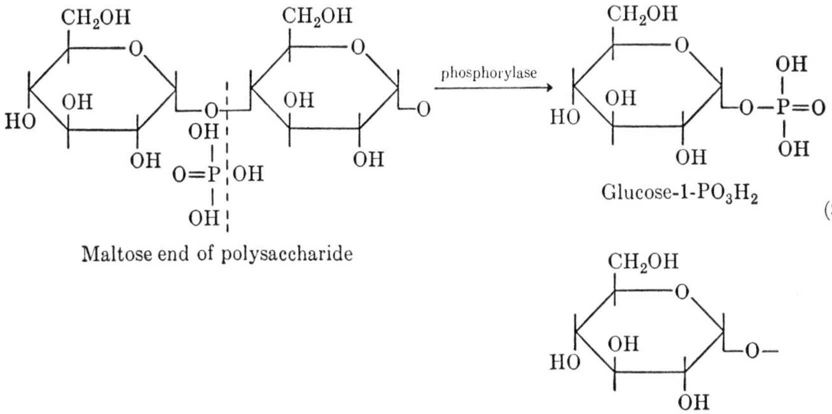

CH₂OH, O, OH, HO, OH — O — OH, O=P—OH, OH — CH₂OH, O, OH, OH — O $\xrightarrow{\text{phosphorylase}}$ CH₂OH, O, OH, HO, OH — O—P(=O)(OH)(OH)

Maltose end of polysaccharide

Glucose-1-PO_3H_2 (38)

CH₂OH, O, OH, HO, OH — O—

We will see that the carbohydrates enter the oxidation pathways only through a very small number of compounds.

Though glucose may be oxidized to gluconic acid by some fungi, we have no evidence that glucose is itself a normal respiratory substrate. In the pentose phosphate shunt described on page 240 *et seq.*, glucose-6-phosphate is the primary respiratory substrate. In the citric acid cycle, discussed on page 246, pyruvic acid appears as the substrate of respiration; and other organic acids of various metabolic origins can be similarly oxidized.

As we shall make clear, one of the major pathways of the oxidation of sugars has as its initial stages the same enzymatic mechanisms and intermediates as has fermentation. We may consider the steps from starch or glucose to pyruvic acid as a common pathway of fermentation and respiration.

A. FERMENTATIVE PATHWAY

In 1908 Harden and Young (53) discovered that in fermenting yeast juice inorganic phosphate was essential for the fermentation, and that a hexose diphosphate, later shown to be fructose-1,6-diphosphate, accumulated. From these experiments, evidence accumulated to show that free sugars, as such, are not fermented, but that the sugars are first esterified with inorganic phosphate. Harden and Young suggested that the following equation described the fermentation in yeast juice:

$$2\ C_6H_{12}O_6 + 2\ H_3PO_4 \rightarrow 2\ CO_2 + 2\ C_2H_5OH + C_6H_{10}O_6(PO_3H_2)_2 + 2\ H_2O \quad (39)$$

As we have seen above, glucose-1-phosphate may be formed from the phosphorolysis of glucosidic bonds of starch or glycogen under the catalysis of the enzyme phosphorylase. There is widely distributed in plants, microorganisms, and animals, an enzyme phosphoglucomutase, which converts glucose-1-phosphate into glucose-6-phosphate:

$$\underset{5.5\%}{\text{Glucose-1-phosphate}} \underset{\text{glucomutase}}{\overset{\text{phospho-}}{\rightleftharpoons}} \underset{94.5\%}{\text{glucose-6-phosphate}} \quad (40)$$

$$\Delta F = -1.7 \text{ kcal per mole (pH 7.5, 30°C)}$$

At equilibrium the approximate distribution of the products is shown above in per cent. This reaction is of great interest, as glucose-1,6-diphosphate is a coenzyme for this reaction. The reaction can be postulated to occur as follows:

$$\text{(a) Enzyme} - \text{phosphate} + \text{glucose-1-phosphate} \rightleftharpoons \text{glucose-1,6-diphosphate} + \text{enzyme} \quad (41)$$

$$\text{(b) Enzyme} + \text{glucose 1,6-diphosphate} \rightleftharpoons \text{glucose-6-phosphate} + \text{enzyme} - \text{phosphate} \quad (42)$$

This seems probable, as the phosphate of the sugars does not exchange with inorganic phosphate of the medium.

However, glucose-6-phosphate can have another origin, for though the direct esterification of a free sugar by phosphate is an endergonic reaction, with the equilibrium far on the side of free sugar, the energetics of a transphosphorylation are quite different. The nucleotide adenosine triphosphate (ATP) illustrated in (43) is able to donate a

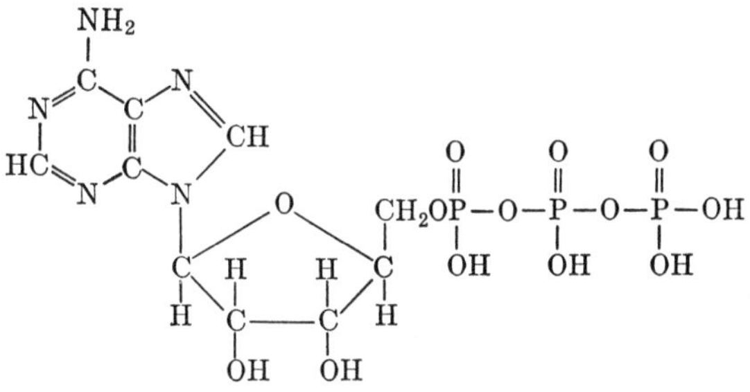

(43)

Adenosine triphosphate

phosphate group to glucose in the presence of the enzyme hexokinase and Mg ions:

$$\text{Glucose} + \text{ATP} \xrightleftharpoons{\text{hexokinase}} \text{glucose-6-}PO_3H_2 + \text{ADP} + H^+ \tag{44}$$
$$\Delta F = -6.7 \text{ kcal per mole (pH 7.5, 20°C)}$$

where ADP stands for adenosine diphosphate. The equilibrium lies far toward the sugar ester. The yeast enzyme transfers phosphate from ATP to mannose and fructose, forming the corresponding compounds esterified at position 6, while in higher plants a separate fructose kinase is known. Whether this means an additional mechanism in higher plants, or whether the glucose kinase is specific, is still unclear.

The structures of the sugars are shown in Fig. 7 and the interconversion of the sugars in Fig. 8.

The reaction between galactose and ATP in the presence of its kinase yields the galactose-1-PO_3H_2, not the 6-ester; the galactose-1-PO_3H_2 is in equilibrium with glucose-1-PO_3H_2 in the presence of specific enzymes and the coenzyme uridine diphosphate glucose (45).

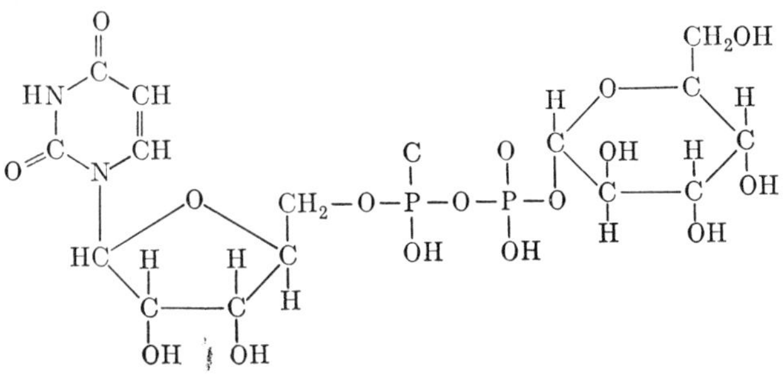

(45)

Uridine diphosphate glucose

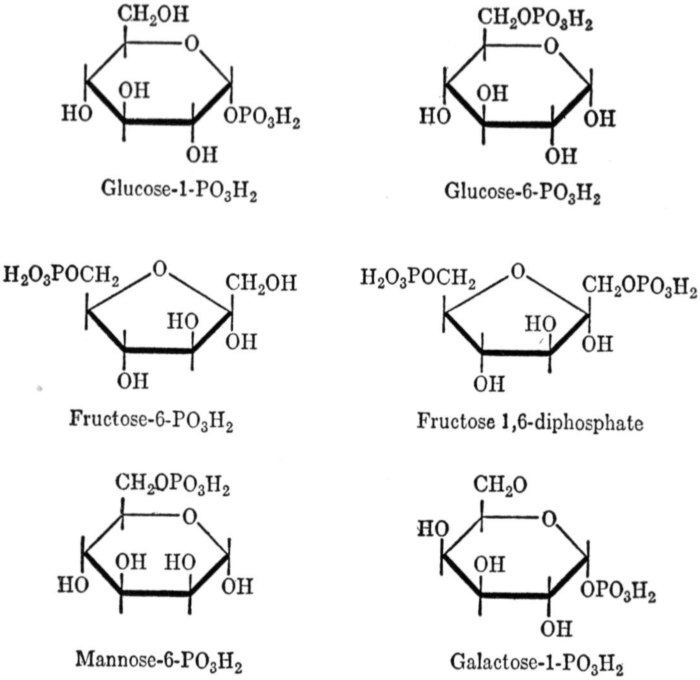

Glucose-1-PO$_3$H$_2$
Glucose-6-PO$_3$H$_2$
Fructose-6-PO$_3$H$_2$
Fructose 1,6-diphosphate
Mannose-6-PO$_3$H$_2$
Galactose-1-PO$_3$H$_2$

FIG. 7. Structure of sugars.

Galactose + ATP
Starch + H$_3$PO$_4$
Glucose-1-PO$_3$H$_2$
Galactose-1-PO$_3$H$_2$
Glucose + ATP
Glucose-6-PO$_3$H$_2$
?
Mannose-6-PO$_3$H$_2$
Mannose + ATP
Fructose + ATP
Fructose-6-PO$_3$H$_2$
Sucrose-PO$_3$H$_2$
+
UDP
UDPG
+ ATP
UDPG
Sucrose + UDP
Fructose-1,6-diphosphate

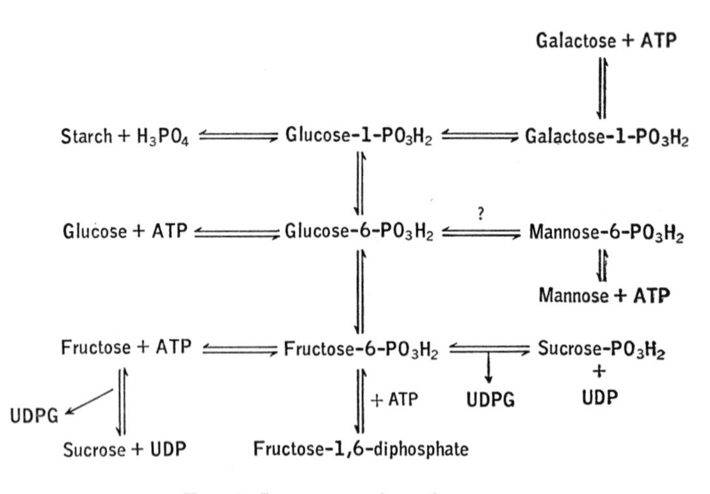

FIG. 8. Interconversion of sugars.

There are two known pathways (85, 152) for the conversion of galactose-1-PO_3H_2 to glucose-1-PO_3H_2. First, galactose phosphate reacts with uridine triphosphate (UTP):

$$\text{UTP} + \text{galactose-1-}PO_3H_2 \xrightarrow{\text{transuridylase}} \text{UDP-galactose} + \text{pyrophosphate} \quad (46)$$

Second, a reaction occurs between galactose phosphate and UDP glucose:

$$\text{UDP-glucose} + \text{galactose-1-}PO_3H_2 \rightarrow \text{UDP-galactose} + \text{glucose-1-}PO_3H_2 \quad (47)$$

This reaction is catalyzed by the enzyme galactose-1-P-uridyl transferase. The UDP-galactose formed by either mechanism may then react in the Lelior reaction:

$$\underset{75\%}{\text{UDP-glucose}} \rightleftharpoons \underset{25\%}{\text{UDP-galactose}} \quad (48)$$

This reaction is catalyzed by an enzyme known as UDP-galactose-4-epimerase or "galacto-waldenase."

One suspects that an enzyme will be found in plants, phosphomannose isomerase, which will convert the mannose phosphate to glucose-6-PO_3H_2.

For fermentation, and at least in part for respiration, the key compound is fructose-1,6-diphosphate. This compound has its origin from fructose-6-phosphate through a transphosphorylation from ATP:

$$\text{Fructose-6-}PO_3H_2 + \text{ATP} \xrightarrow[\text{fructokinase}]{\text{phospho-}} \text{fructose-1,6-diphosphate} + \text{ADP} + H^+ \quad (49)$$
$$\Delta F = -5.3 \text{ kcal}$$

Perhaps inosine triphosphate and uridine triphosphate may also serve as phosphate donors. Since galactose phosphate and mannose phosphate are converted to glucose-6-phosphate (even though indirectly), the conversion of glucose-6-phosphate to fructose-6-phosphate means that all of these sugars end up as fructose-1,6-diphosphate. The glucose phosphate conversion is illustrated below:

$$\underset{70\%}{\text{Glucose-6-}PO_3H_2} \underset{\text{glucoisomerase}}{\overset{\text{phospho-}}{\rightleftharpoons}} \underset{30\%}{\text{fructose-6-}PO_3H_2} \quad (50)$$

The fructose-1,6-diphosphate undergoes cleavage between carbon atoms 3 and 4 in the presence of the enzyme aldolase discovered in yeast and muscle by Meyerhof and Lohmann (110) and in higher plants by Tewfik and Stumpf (142). This gives two triose molecules, dihydroxyacetone phosphate and D-glyceraldehyde-3-phosphate (eq. 51). The enzyme is specific for dihydroxyacetone phosphate, but not for the aldehyde.

$$\underset{89\%}{\text{Fructose-1,6-diphosphate}} \overset{\text{aldolase}}{\rightleftharpoons} \underset{\substack{\text{D-3-Glyceraldehyde}\\ \text{phosphate}}}{\begin{matrix} CHO \\ | \\ CHOH \\ | \\ CH_2OPO_3H_2 \end{matrix}} + \underset{\substack{\text{Dihydroxyacetone}\\ \text{phosphate}}}{\begin{matrix} CH_2OH \\ | \\ C{=}O \\ | \\ CH_2OPO_3H_2 \end{matrix}} \quad (51)$$

11%

The aldo and keto trioses are in equilibrium with each other in the presence of the enzyme phosphoglyceroisomerase (or phosphotriose isomerase):

$$\underset{4\%}{\text{D-3-Glyceraldehyde phosphate}} \rightleftharpoons \underset{96\%}{\text{dihydroxyacetone phosphate}} \quad (52)$$

$$\Delta F = -1.8 \text{ kcal per mole (pH 8, 25°C)}$$

The glyceraldehyde-3-phosphate undergoes oxidation in an interesting coupled reaction sequence. The coenzyme diphosphopyridine nucleotide (DPN) oxidizes the aldehyde with simultaneous uptake of inorganic phosphate:

$$\text{Glyceraldehyde-3-}PO_3H_2 + DPN^+ + H_3PO_4 \rightarrow \text{1,3-diphosphoglyceric acid} + DPNH + H^+ \quad (53)$$

The enzyme is variously known as triosephosphate dehydrogenase or glyceraldehyde phosphate dehydrogenase. A similar enzyme has been shown in higher plants by Tewfik and Stumpf (143); and another with a different coenzyme by Arnon (1) and Gibbs (43).

The diphosphoglyceric acid now serves as a phosphate donor to ADP and 3-phosphoglyceric acid is formed, with the regeneration of ATP, catalyzed by the enzyme 3-phosphoglycerate kinase (or ATP-phosphoglyceric transphosphorylase) and Mg ions (eq. 54).

$$\underset{\text{1,3-Diphosphoglyceric acid}}{\begin{matrix} O \\ \| \\ C{-}OPO_3H_2 \\ | \\ CHOH \\ | \\ CH_2OPO_3H_2 \end{matrix}} + ADP \rightarrow \underset{\text{3-Phosphoglyceric acid}}{\begin{matrix} COOH \\ | \\ CHOH \\ | \\ CH_2OPO_3H_2 \end{matrix}} + ATP \quad (54)$$

$$\Delta F = -4.7 \text{ kcal}$$

The equilibrium lies far toward the right. It has been known for some years that 3-phosphoglyceric acid is an intermediate in fermentation and that it is readily fermented by yeast juice. In the presence of NaF, yeast juice does not produce alcohol or carbon dioxide, but does convert fructose-1,6-diphosphate into 3-phosphoglyceric acid, if some mechanism is available to maintain the oxidation of the DPN.

The 3-phosphoglyceric acid is converted to 2-phosphoglyceric acid by phosphoglyceromutase, and this in turn to phosphoenolpyruvic acid by the enzyme enolase:

$$\underset{\text{3-Phosphoglyceric acid}}{\begin{matrix} COOH \\ | \\ CHOH \\ | \\ CH_2OPO_3H_2 \end{matrix}} \xrightarrow[\text{glyceromutase}]{\text{phospho-}} \underset{\text{2-Phosphoglyceric acid}}{\begin{matrix} COOH \\ | \\ HCOPO_3H_2 \\ | \\ CH_2OH \end{matrix}} \xrightarrow{\text{enolase}} \underset{\text{Phosphoenolpyruvic acid}}{\begin{matrix} COOH \\ | \\ C{-}OPO_3H_2 \\ \| \\ CH_2 \end{matrix}} + H_2O \quad (55)$$

where at equilibrium, the ratio of the 3-phospho compound to the 2-phospho derivative is about 5, and the ratio of 2-phosphoglyceric acid to phosphoenolpyruvic is essentially 1. The intermediate for the conversion of the 3-phosphoglyceric acid is probably 2,3-diphosphoglyceric acid.

The phosphoenolpyruvic acid is now converted to pyruvic acid (eq. 56) with the simultaneous transfer of the phosphate to ADP in the presence of the enzyme pyruvic kinase (or ATP-phosphopyruvic transphosphorylase). The equilibrium is markedly toward the right.

$$\underset{\text{Phosphoenolpyruvic acid}}{\begin{matrix} COOH \\ | \\ COPO_3H_2 \\ \| \\ CH_2 \end{matrix}} + ADP + H_2O \xrightleftharpoons[\text{kinase}]{\text{pyruvic}} \underset{\text{Pyruvic acid}}{\begin{matrix} COOH \\ | \\ C{=}O \\ | \\ CH_3 \end{matrix}} + ATP \quad (56)$$

$$\Delta F = -4.7 \text{ kcal}$$

Now the pyruvic acid is a key substance, for it may undergo one of several reactions. It may be reduced to lactic acid; it may be decarboxylated to acetaldehyde on the way to alcohol; it may be aminated to form the amino acid alanine; or it may react with coenzyme A in the presence of cocarboxylase and other cofactors to form acetyl coenzyme A and serve as the starting point for the production of citric acid.

Anaerobically, we may expect the reduction of pyruvic acid by DPNH and lactic dehydrogenase:

$$\underset{\text{Pyruvic acid}}{\begin{matrix} CH_3 \\ | \\ C{=}O \\ | \\ COOH \end{matrix}} + DPNH + H^+ \xrightleftharpoons[\text{dehydrogenase}]{\text{lactic}} \underset{\text{Lactic acid}}{\begin{matrix} CH_3 \\ | \\ CHOH \\ | \\ COOH \end{matrix}} + DPN^+ \quad (57)$$

$$\Delta F = -5.3 \text{ kcal}$$

This reaction appears to be relatively rare in higher plants, though traces of lactic acid are found in potato fermentation as reported by

TABLE IX
ENZYMES OF THE EMBDEN-MEYERHOF-PARNAS SCHEME

Enzyme	Cofactors	Plant and tissue	Reference
Phosphorylase		Potatoes and peas	1
UDPG fructose transglycosylose			2
Phosphoglucomutase	Glucose-1,6-diphosphate	Leaves of potato; sugar beet; jack bean	3
Hexokinase		Cauliflower; potato tubers; mung bean	4
Fructokinase		Pea seeds	5
Phosphohexokinase		Pea leaves	6
Adenylic kinase (myokinase)			7
Glucose-1-phosphate kinase		?	
Phosphohexoisomerase		Pea seeds	8
Aldolase		Peas; potatoes; many plants	9
Phosphoglyceroisomerase		Pea seeds; pea plants	10
Triosephosphate dehydrogenase	DPN	Pea seedlings	11
3-Phosphoglycerate kinase	$Mg^{++} + K^{+}$ or NH_4^{+}	Wheat, cotton, corn seeds, pea leaves, etc.	12
Phosphoglyceromutase		?	
Enolase	Mg^{++}	Pea seeds	13
Pyruvic kinase	$Mg^{++} + K^{+}$ or NH_4^{+}	Wheat; corn seeds; leaves of tobacco, pea	14
α-Carboxylase	Diphosphothiamine	Wheat germ, seeds, roots Low or absent in leaves	15
Alcohol dehydrogenase	DPN or TPN	Wheat germ; peas	16

References

1. Hanes, C. S., *Proc. Roy. Soc.* **B128**, 421 (1939); **B129**, 174 (1940).
2. Buchanan, J. I. *et al. in* (W. D. McElroy and B. Glass, eds.), "Phosphorous Symposium II," p. 440 (1952).
3. Tanko, B., *Biochem. J.* **30**, 692 (1932); Cardini, C. E., *Enzymologia* **15**, 44 (1951); Sisahyan, N. M., and A. M. Kohyakava, *Biokhimiya* **16**, 292 (1951); Onodera, K., *J. Agr. Chem. Soc. Japan* **25**, 377 (1951–52).
4. Laties, G. G., *Plant Physiol.* **28**, 557 (1953); Saltman, P., *J. Biol. Chem.* **200**, 145 (1953); Bonner, J., and A. Millerd, *Arch. Biochem. Biophys.* **42**, 137 (1953); Katel'Mikova, A. V., *Biokhimiya* **17**, 462 (1952).
5. Medina, A., and A. Sols, *Biochim. et Biophys. Acta* **19**, 378 (1956).
6. Axelrod, B., P. Saltman, R. S. Bandurski, and R. S. Baker, *J. Biol. Chem.* **197**, 89 (1952).
7. Mazelis, M., *Plant Physiol.* **31**, 37 (1956).
8. Somers, F. G., and E. L. Crosby, *Arch. Biochem.* **6**, 295 (1945).
9. Tewfik, S., and P. K. Stumpf, *Am. J. Botany* **36**, 567 (1949); Cardini, C. E., *Enzymologia* **15**, 303 (1952).

Barker (3), and in wheat (*Triticum aestivum*) and rice (*Oryza sativa*) as shown by Phillips (122). In animal tissue and some bacteria such as *Streptococcus lactis*, this reaction accounts for a major part of carbohydrate disappearance under anaerobic conditions.

The decarboxylation of pyruvic acid to acetaldehyde is characteristic of yeast fermentation and is common in those higher plant tissues which have a typical alcoholic fermentation (embryonic tissues, the tissues of seedling peas and rice, carrot roots). Neuberg and co-workers discovered the enzyme carboxylase [this literature is reviewed by Harden (52)]

$$\underset{\text{Pyruvic acid}}{\begin{array}{c} CH_3 \\ | \\ C{=}O \\ | \\ COOH \end{array}} \xrightarrow[\text{diphosphothiamine}]{\text{carboxylase}} \underset{\text{Acetaldehyde}}{\begin{array}{c} CH_3 \\ | \\ CHO \end{array}} + CO_2 \qquad (58)$$

$$\Delta F = -6.2 \text{ kcal}$$

and Lohmann and Schuster (92) discovered that diphosphothiamine (DPT) is the coenzyme of carboxylase. Anaerobically, acetaldehyde undergoes reduction by DPNH in the presence of alcohol dehydrogenase to form ethanol:

$$\underset{\text{Acetaldehyde}}{\begin{array}{c} CH_3 \\ | \\ CHO \end{array}} + DPNH + H^+ \rightleftharpoons \underset{\text{Ethanol}}{\begin{array}{c} CH_3 \\ | \\ CH_2OH \end{array}} + DPN^+ \qquad (59)$$

$$\Delta F = -4.7 \text{ kcal}$$

The equilibrium is such that the ratio is clearly on the side of alcohol.

Reactions such as this one may be readily assayed in extracts by following the oxidation of DPNH on the spectrophotometer at 340 $m\mu$, a wavelength in the ultraviolet at which the reduced coenzyme absorbs strongly but the oxidized enzyme does not absorb. The reversal is equally followed.

The enzymes of the fermentation mechanisms are summarized in Table IX. A further summary is given in equations (60) and (61).

---

10. Stumpf, P. K., *J. Biol. Chem.* **182**, 261 (1950); Tewfik, S., and P. K. Stumpf, *J. Biol. Chem.* **192**, 519 (1951).
11. Gibbs, M., *Nature* **170**, 164 (1952); Arnon, D., *Science* **116**, 635 (1952).
12. Axelrod, B., and R. S. Bandurski, *J. Biol. Chem.* **204**, 939 (1953); Miller, G., and H. J. Evans, *Plant Physiol.* **32**, 346 (1957).
13. Miller, Gene W., *Plant Physiol.* **33**, 199 (1958).
14. Stumpf, P. K., *J. Biol. Chem.* **182**, 261 (1950).
15. Vennesland, B., and R. Z. Felsher, *Arch. Biochem.* **11**, 279 (1946); Clendenning, K. A., E. R. Waygood, and P. Weinberger, *Can. J. Botany* **30**, 395 (1952).
16. Stafford, H. A., and B. Vennesland, *Arch. Biochem. Biophys.* **44**, 404 (1953).

$$\text{Glucose} + 2\ \text{ADP} + 2\ \text{DPN}^+ + 2\ H_3PO_4 \rightarrow 2\ \text{pyruvic acid} + 2\ \text{ATP} + 2\ \text{DPNH} + 2\ H^+ + 2\ H_2O \quad (60)$$

Starting with glucose, one molecule of ATP is used in the hexokinase reaction, one in the phosphorylation of fructose-6-phosphate, and four are regenerated in later reactions for a net gain of two. If the reactions begin with glycogen or starch, only one molecule of ATP is used with a net gain of three molecules of ATP. In addition, two molecules of DPNH are produced per molecule of glucose; the DPNH is normally reoxidized anaerobically by the reduction of acetaldehyde to alcohol and aerobically over the cytochrome system.

The energetics of the fermentation system are worth examining:

$$\text{Glucose} \rightarrow 2\ C_2H_5OH + 2\ CO_2 \quad (61)$$
$$\Delta F_1 = -54\ \text{kcal}$$
$$2\ \text{ADP} + 2\ H_3PO_4 \rightarrow 2\ \text{ATP}$$
$$\Delta F_2 = \text{approx. } 16\ \text{kcal}$$
$$\text{Glucose} + 2\ \text{ADP} + 2\ H_3PO_4 \rightarrow 2\ \text{alcohol} + 2\ CO_2 + 2\ \text{ATP}$$
$$\Delta F_3 = F_1 + F_2 = -38\ \text{kcal}$$

Therefore, these reactions have stored in ATP approximately one-third of the energy liberated in fermentation. This ATP may later be used in synthetic reactions of the cell.

The wide occurrence of the Embden-Meyerhof-Parnas (E.M.P.) pathway of carbohydrate breakdown led to the uncritical acceptance of the view that this was the only important mechanism of carbohydrate degradation in all organisms, and under both aerobic and anaerobic conditions. At least one other pathway is of wide occurrence—this has been called the pentose phosphate shunt (Table X). We will see below that the relative amount of carbohydrate which undergoes metabolism over the E.M.P. or the pentose phosphate shunt may vary between organisms, or within the same organism at different developmental stages.

The dogmatic assertion of the universality of the Embden-Meyerhof-Parnas scheme is surprising in the light of the information available in the late 1930's. Warburg and Christian (160) found that glucose-6-PO_3H_2 could be oxidized by a glucose-6-phosphate dehydrogenase plus triphosphopyridine nucleotide (TPN) to 6-phosphogluconate.

$$\begin{array}{c} CHO \\ | \\ (CHOH)_4 \\ | \\ H_2COPO_3H_2 \\ \text{Glucose 6-}PO_3H_2 \end{array} + \text{TPN}^+ \underset{}{\overset{\text{dehydrogenase}}{\rightleftharpoons}} \begin{array}{c} COOH \\ | \\ (CHOH)_4 \\ | \\ H_2COPO_3H_2 \\ \text{6-Phosphogluconate} \end{array} + \text{TPNH} + H^+ \quad (62)$$

Further, in yeast extracts the 6-phosphogluconate is oxidized with the evolution of CO_2, and there were indications of pentose and triose

TABLE X
PENTOSE PHOSPHATE SHUNT

Enzyme	Cofactors	Tissue	Reference
Glucose-6-phosphate dehydrogenase	TPN	Wheat germ, pea leaves, spinach leaves, etc.	1,2,3,4
6-Phosphogluconate dehydrogenase	TPN	Pea, spinach, wheat germ	3,4,5
Phosphoriboisomerase		Alfalfa leaves, peas, spinach	3,6,7
Transketolase	Diphosphothiamine Mg^{++}	Spinach	8
Transaldolase		Spinach	9
Fructose diphosphatase		Spinach	10,11
Phosphoketopentoepimerase (epimerase)		Spinach	12

References

1. Mayer, A. M., A. Polyakoff-Mayber, and W. Appleman, *Physiol. Plantarum* **10,** 1 (1955).
2. Gibbs, N., and B. L. Horecker, *J. Biol. Chem.* **208,** 813 (1954).
3. Axelrod, B., R. S. Bandurski, C. M. Greiner, and R. Jang, *J. Biol. Chem.* **202,** 619 (1953).
4. Barnett, R. C., H. A. Stafford, E. E. Conn, and B. Vennesland, *Plant Physiol.* **28,** 115 (1953).
5. Anderson, D. G., H. A. Stafford, E. E. Conn, and B. Vennesland, *Plant Physiol.* **27,** 675 (1952).
6. Axelrod, B., and R. Jang, *J. Biol. Chem.* **209,** 847 (1954).
7. Tabachnick, M., P. A. Srere, J. Cooper, and F. Rocher, *Arch. Biochem. Biophys.* **74,** 315 (1958).
8. Horecker, B. L., and P. Z. Smyrniotis, and Klinow, H., *J. Biol. Chem.* **205,** 661 (1953).
9. Horecker, B. L., and P. Z. Smyrniotis, *J. Biol. Chem.* **212,** 811 (1955).
10. Racker, F., *Nature* **175,** 249 (1945).
11. Gibbs, M., and B. L. Horecker, *J. Biol. Chem.* **208,** 813 (1954).
12. Vishniac, W., B. L. Horecker, and S. Ochoa, *Advances in Enzymol.* **19,** 28 (1957).

among the products. Dickens (34) followed the oxidation of 6-phosphogluconate and obtained CO_2 and presumably pentose.

In 1948 Racker (123) started his studies of the enzymatic formation and breakdown of pentose phosphates; and in 1951 the problem was aggressively attacked in independent studies by Scott and Cohen (129), Horecker *et al.* (63), and Racker (123). It became clear that glucose-6-phosphate could be degraded to triose phosphates by a path which is independent of the E.M.P. pathway.

It was found that *Escherichia coli* could oxidize phosphogluconate, and ribose-5-phosphate was identified as a product; with a purified enzyme from yeast, ribulose-5-phosphate accumulated. Then it was found that phosphopentose isomerase equilibrated ribulose-5-phosphate and ribose-5-phosphate. Thus we may write:

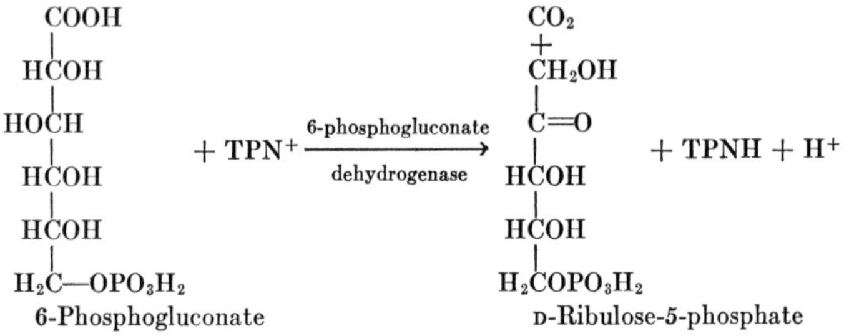

$$\begin{array}{l} COOH \\ | \\ HCOH \\ | \\ HOCH \\ | \\ HCOH \\ | \\ HCOH \\ | \\ H_2C{-}OPO_3H_2 \\ \text{6-Phosphogluconate} \end{array} + TPN^+ \xrightarrow[\text{dehydrogenase}]{\text{6-phosphogluconate}} \begin{array}{l} CO_2 \\ + \\ CH_2OH \\ | \\ C{=}O \\ | \\ HCOH \\ | \\ HCOH \\ | \\ H_2COPO_3H_2 \\ \text{D-Ribulose-5-phosphate} \end{array} + TPNH + H^+ \qquad (63)$$

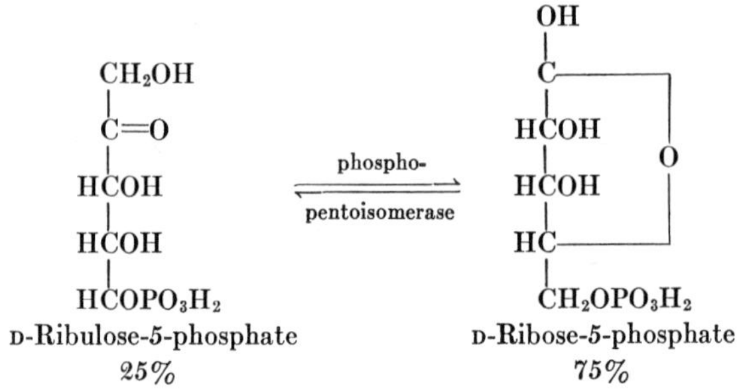

$$\begin{array}{l} CH_2OH \\ | \\ C{=}O \\ | \\ HCOH \\ | \\ HCOH \\ | \\ HCOPO_3H_2 \\ \text{D-Ribulose-5-phosphate} \\ 25\% \end{array} \underset{\text{pentoisomerase}}{\overset{\text{phospho-}}{\rightleftharpoons}} \begin{array}{l} OH \\ | \\ C{-}\!\!\!\!\quad\ \urcorner \\ | \qquad\quad | \\ HCOH \quad | \\ | \qquad\quad O \\ HCOH \quad | \\ | \qquad\quad | \\ HC{-}\!\!\!\!\quad\ \lrcorner \\ | \\ CH_2OPO_3H_2 \\ \text{D-Ribose-5-phosphate} \\ 75\% \end{array} \qquad (64)$$

It soon became apparent that bacteria, yeasts, liver, red cells, and higher plants could degrade ribulose and ribose phosphates to triose phosphates, but that no two-carbon residue could be identified.

Leaving the historical sequence, we may say that a new cycle of carbohydrate degradation has been discovered in which, following the oxidation of glucose-6-phosphate to 6-phosphogluconate and the oxidative decarboxylation of 6-phosphogluconate to ribulose-5-phosphate and carbon dioxide, two pentose sugars react, catalyzed by an enzyme transketolase to give a C_7 sugar sedoheptulose-7-phosphate and glyceraldehyde-3-phosphate.

This reaction is illustrated in equation (65).

Then, through the action of transaldolase, sedoheptulose-7-phosphate plus glyceraldehyde-3-phosphate react to form fructose-6-phosphate plus a C_4 sugar, D-erythrose-4-phosphate. The C_4 sugar ester now reacts as the aldehyde acceptor with xylulose-5-phosphate, catalyzed by transketolase to give another molecule of fructose-6-phosphate, plus glyceraldehyde-3-phosphate. Then two triose phosphate molecules can react with aldolase to form fructose-1,6-diphosphate. Fructose-6-phosphate and fructose diphosphate after hydrolysis can be converted to glucose-6-phosphate.

The enzyme transketolase has been crystallized from yeast and purified from spinach (*Spinacia oleracea*). It can be thought of as an enzyme that splits xylulose-5-phosphate to a triose phosphate plus "active

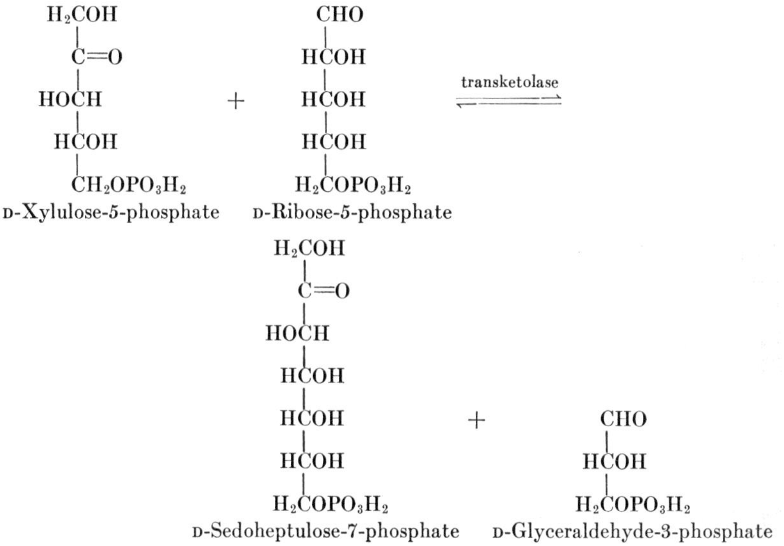

$$\begin{array}{c}H_2COH\\ |\\ C{=}O\\ |\\ HOCH\\ |\\ HCOH\\ |\\ CH_2OPO_3H_2\end{array} + \begin{array}{c}CHO\\ |\\ HCOH\\ |\\ HCOH\\ |\\ HCOH\\ |\\ H_2COPO_3H_2\end{array} \xrightleftharpoons{\text{transketolase}}$$

D-Xylulose-5-phosphate D-Ribose-5-phosphate

$$\begin{array}{c}H_2COH\\ |\\ C{=}O\\ |\\ HOCH\\ |\\ HCOH\\ |\\ HCOH\\ |\\ HCOH\\ |\\ H_2COPO_3H_2\end{array} + \begin{array}{c}CHO\\ |\\ HCOH\\ |\\ H_2COPO_3H_2\end{array} \qquad (65)$$

D-Sedoheptulose-7-phosphate D-Glyceraldehyde-3-phosphate

glycoaldehyde," a C_2 sugar not released from the enzyme and bound to DPT. The "active glycoaldehyde" can be combined with another aldehyde; if ribose phosphate is the aldehyde acceptor, then sedoheptulose-7-phosphate is formed.

Sedoheptulose had been identified many years earlier by Bennet-Clark (6) as a major constituent of the succulent plant *Sedum* sp.

The sedoheptulose then reacts with glyceraldehyde-3-phosphate in the presence of the enzyme transaldolase to form fructose-6-phosphate and erythrose-4-phosphate.

Then the erythrose-4-phosphate may react with xylose-5-phosphate to form fructose-6-phosphate and glyceraldehyde phosphate. Reversal of the aldolase reaction, and the equilibrium between glyceraldehyde phosphate and dihydroxyacetone phosphate, result in the formation of fructose-1,6-diphosphate. This diester may then be hydrolyzed by a specific phosphotase to fructose-6-phosphate.

The net result of the cycle is the oxidation of glucose-6-phosphate to 6 carbon dioxide and 6 water, if an enzyme is present to regenerate TPN^+ by reaction with molecular oxygen. We will see later that the cytochrome system is able to bring about this oxidation.

The scheme can be shown diagrammatically below:

(1) Oxidation of glucose-6-phosphate:

$$6 \text{ Glucose-6-phosphate} + 6 \text{ TPN} + 6 \text{ H}_2\text{O} \rightarrow 6 \text{ 6-phosphogluconate} + 6 \text{ TPNH} + 6 \text{ H}^+ \quad (66)$$

(2) Oxidation of phosphogluconate:

(a) $$6 \text{ 6-Phosphogluconate} + 6 \text{ TPN}^+ \rightarrow 6 \text{ ribulose-5-phosphate} + 6 \text{ CO}_2 + 6 \text{ TPNH} + 6 \text{ H}^+ \quad (67)$$

(b) $$\text{Ribulose-5-phosphate} \rightleftharpoons \text{ribose-5-phosphate}$$

(c) $$\text{Ribulose-5-phosphate} \rightleftharpoons \text{xylulose-5-phosphate}$$

(d) $$2 \text{ Xylulose-5-phosphate} + 2 \text{ ribose-5-phosphate} \xrightarrow{\text{transketolase}} 2 \text{ sedoheptulose-7-phosphate} + 2 \text{ glyceraldehyde-3-phosphate}$$

(e) $$2 \text{ Sedoheptulose-7-phosphate} + 2 \text{ glyceraldehyde-3-phosphate} \xrightarrow{\text{transaldolase}} 2 \text{ fructose-6-phosphate} + 2 \text{ erythrose-4-phosphate}$$

(f) $$2 \text{ Erythrose-4-phosphate} + 2 \text{ xylulose-5-phosphate} \xrightarrow{\text{transketolase}} 2 \text{ fructose-6-phosphate} + 2 \text{ glyceraldehyde-3-phosphate}$$

(g) $$2 \text{ Glyceraldehyde-3-phosphate} + \text{H}_2\text{O} \rightarrow \text{fructose-6-phosphate} + \text{H}_3\text{PO}_4$$

(3) Sum of (1) + (2)

$$\text{Glucose-6-phosphate} + 12 \text{ TPN}^+ + 7 \text{ H}_2\text{O} \rightarrow 6 \text{ CO}_2 + 12 \text{ TPNH} + 12 \text{ H}^+ \quad (68)$$

(4) $$12 \text{ TPNH} + 12 \text{ H}^+ + 6 \text{ O}_2 \xrightarrow[\text{system}]{\text{cytochrome}} 12 \text{ H}_2\text{O} + 12 \text{ TPN}^+ \quad (69)$$

(5) Sum of (3) and (4)

$$\text{Glucose-6-PO}_3\text{H}_2 + 6 \text{ O}_2 \rightarrow 6 \text{ CO}_2 + 5 \text{ H}_2\text{O} + \text{H}_3\text{PO}_4 \quad (70)$$

The very basic problem is the degree to which the phosphate shunt system accounts for the actual oxidation of carbohydrate in plants. This has been investigated by Gibbs and Beevers (44), using glucose labeled with C^{14} either in position 1 or 6. If the initial stages of the respiration of glucose pass through the Embden-Meyerhof-Parnas system, then the initial radioactive carbon dioxide should be the same with C^6- or C^1-labeled sugar, since at the C-3 stage there is an interconversion of dihydroxyacetone phosphate and glyceraldehyde-3-phosphate. Therefore, the $C^6:C^1$ ratio should be unity. If, however, part of the oxidation is over the shunt, the ratio of $C^6:C^1$ should be less than 1.0, and the ratio indicates the maximum metabolism over the E.M.P. pathway and $1 - C^6:C^1$ is an approximate estimate of the contribution of the shunt. The evidence indicates that in embryological parts of plants the E.M.P. pathway accounts for essentially all of the carbon dioxide, but as the tissues mature its contribution may fall to 50% or less, as is illustrated in Table XI.

However, there is still uncertainty as to the general validity of the pentose phosphate shunt. The shunt depends upon the velocity of oxi-

TABLE XI

THE RATIO OF $C^{14}O^{2}$ AND C^{1}-LABELED GLUCOSE IN AEROBIC METABOLISM[a]

Plant	Part	Stage or age	$C^6:C^1$
Castor bean	Root	0–1.0 cm from tip	0.98; 0.98
		1.0–2.0 cm from tip	0.77
		2.0–3.0 cm from tip	0.64
		3.0–4.0 cm from tip	0.50
Castor bean	Cotyledons	4 Days old	0.77
		5 Days old	0.81
		6 Days old	0.54
		7 Days old	0.56
Pea	Leaves	Immature	0.42; 0.56
		Mature	0.32; 0.39

[a] From Gibbs, M. and H. Beevers, *Plant Physiol.* **30**, 343 (1955).

lation of glucose-6-phosphate by its TPN-dependent dehydrogenase nd the rate of decarboxylation of phosphogluconic acid. It would appear that, in plant tissues, both reactions may be fast enough. This ystem will also be dependent upon the rapid reoxidation of TPNH, nd at present no satisfactory mechanism is known. As will be shown ater, isolated mitochondria do not oxidize TPNH. Perhaps TPNH may e reoxidized by DPN^+ with the formation of DPNH in the presence f the enzyme transhydrogenase. This problem needs clarification beore we can understand how the pentose phosphate shunt operates.

An alternate pathway is available for the interconversion of C_6 sugars and C_5 sugars. This pathway depends upon the activity of transketolase and transaldolase. It may be summarized as follows:

2 Fructose-6-phosphate + D-glyceraldehyde-3-phosphate ⇌
2 xylose-5-phosphate + ribose-5-phosphate (70a)

The equilibrium for this reaction is not far from unity.

This over-all reaction (70a) results from a series of reactions. First, reaction (67f) is followed by the following:

D-Erythrose-4-phosphate + fructose-6-phosphate ⇌
sedoheptulose-7-phosphate + D-glyceraldehyde-3-phosphate (70b)

This reaction is catalyzed by transaldolase. Then the sedoheptulose reacts as in equation (67d). The sum is equation (70a).

The extent of these reactions in plant respiration is unclear, bu their occurrence could cast doubt on the labeling experiments that hav been used in an attempt to determine the contribution of the pentos phosphate shunt.

B. THE CITRIC ACID CYCLE

Pyruvic acid may be produced aerobically or anaerobically fron glucose by the E.M.P. pathway. If the oxidation of carbohydrate is t be complete, the pyruvate must be itself metabolized. Though severa mechanisms are known for the oxidation of pyruvate by microorgan isms, it is largely due to the work of Krebs that we owe our under standing of oxidation of pyruvate in higher organisms. This subject i well reviewed by Ochoa (117) and by Krebs (79).

Krebs and Johnston (80) recognized that malonic acid poisoned th interconversions of succinate and fumarate, but that in pigeon breas muscle, if both pyruvate and fumarate were added, succinate ac cumulated. Further, the oxidation of pyruvate did not occur in th presence of malonate, unless there was a simultaneous addition o fumarate when one mole of fumarate brought about the oxidation o one mole of pyruvate. Thus, some new pathway was essential for th formation of succinate. Since Krebs found that in muscle poisone with arsenite the oxidation of fumarate (and pyruvate) stopped witl the accumulation of the 5-carbon acid, α-ketoglutarate, and it wa previously known that the oxidation of citrate is blocked at α-keto glutarate by arsenite, Krebs proposed that citrate was an intermediat in the oxidation of pyruvate.

In general, his scheme was as follows:

(1) Fumarate + $H_2O \rightarrow$ malate (71)
(2) Malate + ½ $O_2 \rightarrow$ oxaloacetate + H_2O
(3) Oxaloacetate + pyruvate + ½ $O_2 \rightarrow$ citrate + CO_2
(4) Citrate + ½ $O_2 \rightarrow$ α-ketoglutarate + CO_2 + H_2O
(5) α-Ketoglutarate + ½ $O_2 \rightarrow$ succinate + CO_2
(6) Succinate + ½ $O_2 \rightarrow$ fumarate + H_2O

Pyruvate + 2½ $O_2 \rightarrow$ 3 CO_2 + 2 H_2O

Thus, one turn of the cycle would bring about the complete oxidation of pyruvate. Krebs recognized that the scheme, as presented above, is diagrammatic and that intermediates, coenzymes, phosphates, and the electron-transporting system were missing.

Evidence soon accumulated that such a metabolic pathway seemed to be widely distributed. An important addition was the discovery of

oenzyme A by Lipmann (90). The structure of coenzyme A is illus-
rated in formula (72).

$$\text{(Adenine–ribose-3'-}O\text{-}PO_3H_2\text{)}\;CH_2\cdot O\cdot \underset{\underset{O}{\|}}{\overset{OH}{P}}\cdot O\cdot \underset{\underset{O}{\|}}{\overset{OH}{P}}\cdot O\cdot CH_2\cdot \underset{Me}{\overset{Me}{C}}\cdot \overset{OH}{CH}\cdot CO\cdot NH\cdot CH_2\cdot CH_2\cdot CO\cdot NH\cdot CH_2\cdot CH_2\cdot SH \qquad (72)$$

Lipmann first demonstrated that CoA was an acetyl acceptor in the
eaction with acetylphosphate and in the presence of an enzyme, phos-
hotransacetylase, which occurs in bacteria but seems to be absent
rom higher plants. Coenzyme A seems to be widely distributed and
was shown by Seifter (130) to be present in higher plants.

The oxidation of pyruvic acid is not simple; it appears to require several enzymes and coenzymes, which include diphosphothiamine (DPT or cocarboxylase), α-lipoic acid, coenzyme A, and DPN. Without attempting to identify the intermediates and reactions, we summarize the results in equation (73).

$$\underset{\text{Pyruvic acid}}{\begin{array}{c} CH_3 \\ | \\ C{=}O \\ | \\ COOH \end{array}} + CoA - SH + \tfrac{1}{2}\,O_2 \rightarrow \underset{\text{Acetyl-coenzyme A}}{\begin{array}{c} CH_3 \\ | \\ C{=}O \\ | \\ S \\ | \\ CoA \end{array}} + CO_2 + H_2O \qquad (73)$$

Ochoa *et al.* (118) discovered an enzyme which he called the condensing enzyme, which couples acetyl CoA and oxaloacetic acid to form citric acid (eq. 74).

$$\begin{array}{c} CH_3 \\ | \\ C{=}O \\ | \\ S \\ | \\ CoA \end{array} + \underset{\text{Oxaloacetic acid}}{\begin{array}{c} HO{-}C{-}COOH \\ \| \\ CH \\ | \\ COOH \end{array}} \xrightarrow{+H_2O} \underset{\text{Citric acid}}{\begin{array}{c} COOH \\ | \\ CH_2 \\ | \\ HO{-}C{-}COOH \\ | \\ CH_2 \\ | \\ COOH \end{array}} + CoA - SH \qquad (74)$$

$$\Delta F = -7\ \text{kcal}$$

The citric acid formed in this condensation is in equilibrium with *cis*-aconitic acid and with D-isocitric acid, catalyzed by the enzyme aconitase (eq. 75).

$$\begin{array}{ccccc} CH_2-COOH & & CH-COOH & & HO-CH-COOH \\ | & & \| & & | \\ HO-C-COOH & \rightleftharpoons & C-COOH & + H_2O \rightleftharpoons & CH-COOH \\ | & & | & & | \\ CH_2-COOH & & CH_2-COOH & & CH_2-COOH \\ 90.9\% & & 2.9\% & & 6.2\% \\ \text{Citric acid} & & \textit{cis}\text{-Aconitic acid} & & \text{D-Isocitric acid} \end{array} \quad (75)$$

The equilibrium values are for pH 7.4 and 25°C. There may be n free *cis*-aconitic acid in solution, as it may exist only bound to th enzyme.

Citric acid is widely distributed in higher plants and animals. In succulent plant, a species of *Kalanchoe* (*Bryophyllum*), Vickery (154a has shown that the isocitric acid may occur at concentrations of a least three times that of citric acid and appears not to equilibrate wit it.

Isocitric acid is readily oxidized by the isocitric dehydrogenase.

$$\text{D-Isocitrate} + DPN^+ \rightleftharpoons \alpha\text{-ketoglutarate} + DPNH + H^+ + CO_2 \quad (76)$$

This reaction appears to be readily reversible, but it probably is a step wise reaction that may involve oxalosuccinate as an intermediate.

The resulting α-ketoglutarate is oxidized by its dehydrogenase in th presence of DPN^+ and CoA. The reaction (77) is an interesting one, a the energy of the oxidation is partly conserved.

$$\begin{array}{c} COOH \\ | \\ CH_2 \\ | \\ CH_2 \\ | \\ C=O \\ | \\ COOH \end{array} + HS - CoA + DPN^+ \rightarrow \begin{array}{c} COOH \\ | \\ CH_2 \\ | \\ CH_2 \\ | \\ C=O \\ | \\ S \\ | \\ CoA \end{array} + DPNH + H^+ + CO_2 \quad (77)$$

α-Ketoglutarate Succinyl CoA

If succinyl CoA reacts with ADP + H_3PO_4, an esterification of ATP results. Again, ignoring mechanism and enzymes, one may write:

$$\text{Succinyl} - \text{S CoA} + ADP + H_3PO_4 \rightarrow ATP + \text{succinate} + \text{CoA} - SH \quad (78)$$

Thus, the energy released in the oxidation of α-ketoglutarate to succinate, is partially conserved in the esterification of ADP.

The cycle continues, by the conversion of 4-carbon acid, succinic acid to oxaloacetic acid, through the reactions with succinic dehydrogenase, fumarase, and malic dehydrogenase:

$$\text{Succinate} \rightleftharpoons \text{fumarate} + 2\,H + 2\,e \quad (79a)$$
$$\text{Fumarate} + H_2O \rightleftharpoons \text{malate} \quad (79b)$$
$$\text{Malate} + DPN^+ \rightleftharpoons \text{oxaloacetate} + DPNH + H^+ \quad (79c)$$

Thus, the cycle is complete, and for each turn of the cycle, one mole of pyruvate is oxidized to carbon dioxide and water. The cycle depends upon the presence of an active cytochrome system, to reoxidize the DPNH and the reduced succinic dehydrogenase. Most of the energy of cellular respiration is in fact released in the oxidation of pyruvate. Of the approximately 686 kcal released in the oxidation of glucose, approximately 590 kcal are released in the aerobic oxidation of two molecules of pyruvate.

The degree to which the citric acid cycle is the main pathway of pyruvate oxidation in higher plants is still uncertain. However, it has been shown by a series of workers (see 46, 50) that plant mitochondria can oxidize all of the acids in the citric acid cycle and that pyruvate is only oxidized provided that an additional acid is present, to give rise to oxaloacetate. There is not direct evidence that plant tissues have the condensing enzyme of Ochoa, but the indirect evidence and presence of acetyl-CoA are strong presumptive evidence for the presence of this enzyme.

The velocity of oxidation of isocitric acid and particularly α-ketoglutaric acid by plant mitochondria is very high, and this result has led many to believe that the major portion of carbohydrate metabolism passes over this cycle. This may be true; however, there is still no critical method of evaluating the extent of carbohydrate metabolized over this pathway in living tissues or organisms.

That the cycle is an important aspect of plant metabolism is apparent, for the α-keto acids, pyruvic, oxaloacetic, and α-ketoglutaric acids are connecting links between carbohydrate and amino acid metabolisms. The citric acid cycle furnishes a mechanism for the metabolism of any amino acid that may be converted directly, or through transamination, to one of these organic acids. In addition, the cycle may be important in synthetic metabolism as a source of these compounds for amino acid synthesis.

Furthermore, fat metabolism may be connected with the carbohydrate metabolism through such compounds as pyruvic acid and through acetyl-CoA and succinyl-CoA.

The citric acid cycle constitutes a nonphotosynthetic method of incorporation of carbon dioxide into organic compounds (18). Except for succulent plants, no net incorporation of carbon dioxide occurs by this means. There are several nonphotosynthetic carbon dioxide fixation reactions, of which we may show three:

$$\text{(a)}\ CO_2 + \alpha\text{-ketoglutaric acid} + TPNH + H^+ \xrightleftharpoons{\text{isocitric dehydrogenase}} \text{isocitrate} + TPN^+ \quad (80)$$

$$\text{(b)} \quad \text{Pyruvic acid} + CO_2 + TPNH + H^+ \underset{\text{enzyme}}{\overset{\text{malic}}{\rightleftharpoons}} \text{malate} + TPN^+ \quad (81)$$

$$\text{(c)} \quad \text{Phosphoenol pyruvate} + CO_2 + H_2O + H^+ \underset{\text{carboxylase}}{\overset{\text{phosphoenol pyruvate}}{\rightleftharpoons}} \text{oxaloacetic acid} + H_3PO_4 \quad (82)$$

Though Vennesland *et al.* (154) studied the α-ketoglutarate reaction with a soluble enzyme and TPNH, in mitochondrial preparations DPNH is the coenzyme. In the decarboxylation of α-keto acids the equilibrium lies far toward the side of free carbon dioxide. However in the above reactions, the reactions are driven by the reduced nucleotide, or by the energy released in the hydrolysis of the phosphate bond. At low pCO_2, the phosphoenol pyruvate reaction is of the greatest importance, as the equilibrium is favorable for fixation.

C. Oxidation of Fats

The fat content of many plant tissues, such as leaves, roots, stems, and floral parts, is low, usually considerably lower than in animal tissues. However, many seeds have a high fat content; one need only recall *Ricinus communis* seeds, soybeans (*Glycine max*), and such common plant fats as those derived from corn (*Zea mays*), flax (*Linum usitatissimum*), and the palm oils.

It has been known for a long time that when fat-containing seeds germinate an R.Q. of less than unity results; this has been evident since the work of Godlewski (47) in 1882, and it was proposed as early as 1874 by Liakowski (86) that fats are converted to sugars. Murlin and his colleagues (113) investigated by careful analytical means the disappearance of fats in germinating castor seeds. The low R.Q. values (as low as 0.34) were confirmed, and analytical results were given which demonstrated the conversion of fat to carbohydrate.

The expected R.Q. for the complete oxidation of fats is approximately 0.7, and is illustrated for a single fat, tripalmitin, below:

$$C_{51}H_{98}O_6 + 72.5\ O_2 = 51\ CO_2 + 49\ H_2O \quad (83)$$
$$\text{R.Q.} = 0.703$$

The mechanism of fat oxidation in higher plants is essentially unknown. It is assumed that the first stage is the hydrolysis of the fats by lipase to glycerol and free fatty acids. In general, it has long been thought that the fats were converted to carbohydrates (see Kostychev, 78) and then oxidized over the usual pathways. The recent work on animal tissues and bacteria indicates that fatty acids are degraded in a series of steps, with β-oxidation (Knoop, 77) until a two-carbon fragment, acetyl-CoA, is produced. The acetyl-CoA could then be oxidized over the Krebs cycle.

In animal tissues the fat-oxidizing systems are localized in the mitochondria and, though Stumpf and co-workers (63a, 138) have proposed that in plants the fat-metabolizing mechanism is in the microsomes, this seems improbable.

Following the studies on animals (114), one would propose that the fatty acid first reacts with ATP and coenzyme A; successive steps are independent of ATP. This reaction sequence may be diagrammed below:

$$R.CH_2.CH_2.COOH + ATP + CoA \underset{\text{synthetase}}{\overset{\text{fatty-acetyl-CoA}}{\rightleftharpoons}} R.CH_2.CH_2.CO.CoA + AMP + \text{pyrophosphate} \quad (84a)$$

$$R.CH_2.CH_2.CO.CoA + \tfrac{1}{2}\ O_2 \underset{\text{acetyl-CoA dehydrogenase + cytochrome system}}{\rightleftharpoons} R.CH{=}CH.CO.CoA + H_2O \quad (84b)$$

$$R.CH{=}CH.COCoA + H_2O \overset{\text{crotonase}}{\rightleftharpoons} RCHOH.CH_2.CO.CoA \quad (84c)$$

$$R.CHOH.CH_2.CO.CoA + DPN^+ \underset{\text{(L-}\beta\text{-Hydroxyacetyl-CoA dehydrogenase)}}{\rightleftharpoons} R.CO.CH_2.COCoA + DPNH + H^+ \quad (84d)$$

$$R.CO.CH_2.CO.CoA + CoA \underset{\text{acetyl-CoA transacylase}}{\rightleftharpoons} R.CO.CoA + CH_3.CO.CoA \quad (84e)$$

If one examines these reactions it becomes apparent that after coupling with CoA a dehydrogenation occurs between the α and β carbon atoms, followed by a hydration and a second dehydrogenation of β carbon atoms, and then by reaction with CoA, the shortening of the chain by two carbon atoms and the release of acetyl-CoA. Repetition of this reaction results in the degradation of the chain and the production of acetyl-CoA. Four hydrogens are produced and one molecule of oxygen is used for each acetyl-CoA produced; the energy released is presumably channeled through the cytochrome system with accompanying oxidative phosphorylation. The acetyl-CoA itself contains considerable energy, energy which would be released by oxidation through the citric acid cycle. Neilands and Stumpf (114) have calculated that the complete oxidation of palmitic acid ($C_{16}H_{32}O_2$) may result in the synthesis of 139 molecules of ATP, and if one corrects for the loss of two phosphate bonds in equation (84a) the net gain is 137, or about 70% of the energy released in the complete combustion.

In addition to the acetyl-CoA mechanism, various fatty acid oxidases have been described, such as lipoxidase. Here the fat becomes peroxidized (the addition of a molecule of O_2), but the role in cellular respiration is unknown.

The identification of the specific enzymes, the intermediates, and the site of action are still unsolved problems in the physiology of higher plants.

D. Oxidation of Proteins

In plant tissues, which are well supplied with available carbohydrates, the carbohydrates apparently spare the protein from appreciable oxidation. However, it has been known since the work of Schultze *et al.* (128) that in the germination of such seeds as those of *Lupinus* spp. protein is readily respired. Since nitrogen metabolism will be covered separately in this treatise (Volume III), the reader should refer to these chapters for detailed information.

Higher plants are known to contain proteolytic enzymes and polypeptidases (see, for literature, 8, 169). The liberated amino acids may participate in a series of possible reactions: oxidative deamination, hydrolytic deamination, decarboxylation, and transamination.

The oxidative deamination is well established for glutamic acid; it reacts as is shown in equation (85).

$$\underset{\text{Glutamic acid}}{\begin{matrix}COOH\\|\\(CH_2)_2\\|\\CHNH_2\\|\\COOH\end{matrix}} + DPN^+ + H_2O \underset{\text{dehydrogenase}}{\overset{\text{glutamic}}{\rightleftharpoons}} \underset{\alpha\text{-Ketoglutaric acid}}{\begin{matrix}COOH\\|\\(CH_2)_2\\|\\C{=}O\\|\\COOH\end{matrix}} + NH_3 + DPNH + H^+ \qquad (85)$$

The DPNH can then be oxidized by the cytochrome system, and the α-ketoglutarate can be metabolized by the citric acid cycle. Presumably, other amino acid dehydrogenases will be described.

Certain amino acids can enter the cycle by transamination with α-ketoglutarate, as is shown in equation (86).

$$\underset{\substack{\alpha\text{-Ketoglutaric}\\ \text{acid}}}{\begin{matrix}COOH\\|\\(CH_2)_2\\|\\C{=}O\\|\\COOH\end{matrix}} + \underset{\substack{\text{Aspartic}\\ \text{acid}}}{\begin{matrix}COOH\\|\\CH_2\\|\\CNH_2\\|\\COOH\end{matrix}} \underset{\text{transaminase}}{\overset{\text{glutamate-aspartate}}{\rightleftharpoons}} \underset{\substack{\text{Glutamic}\\ \text{acid}}}{\begin{matrix}COOH\\|\\(CH_2)_2\\|\\CHNH_2\\|\\COOH\end{matrix}} + \underset{\text{Oxaloacetate}}{\begin{matrix}COOH\\|\\CH_2\\|\\C{=}O\\|\\COOH\end{matrix}} \qquad (86)$$

Similarly, transaminases are known for a series of amino acids. The metabolism of some of the resulting acids is well known, for compounds such as pyruvic acid and oxaloacetate are respired by the citric acid cycle. In other cases, little is known about the pathway of degradation of the carbon skeleton. Thus it may be seen that α-ketoglutaric acid and glutamic acid, and to a lesser extent pyruvic acid and alanine and oxaloacetic acid and asparatic acid, may function catalytically in the oxidation of many individual amino acids. A few major pathways, through common branch points, may serve for the oxidation or for the synthesis of a wide variety of amino acids. The established transaminase reactions are shown in Table XII.

TABLE XII

TRANSAMINATION REACTIONS—THOSE ESTABLISHED IN HIGHER PLANTS[a]

Reactants	Products
(a) Glutamate plus:	
Aspartate[a]	Oxaloacetate + glutamic acid
1-Alanine[a]	Pyruvic acid + glutamic acid
1-Cysteine	Mercaptopyruvic acid + glutamic acid
Glycine[a]	Glyoxalate + glutamic acid
Leucine[a]	α-Ketoisocaproate + glutamic acid
(b) Oxaloacetic acid plus amino acids	Aspartic acid + α-keto acid
(c) Pyruvic acid[a] plus amino acids	Alanine + α-keto acid

[a] Data from M. Dixon and E. C. Webb, "Enzymes." Academic Press, New York, 1958.

Where the acid residue is a fatty acid, oxidation presumably occurs over the fat pathway and coenzyme A.

The transaminases depend upon the presence of phosphopyridoxal (87) as a coenzyme, and phosphopyridoxamine may also function but at somewhat lower velocity. The compounds are shown in equation (87).

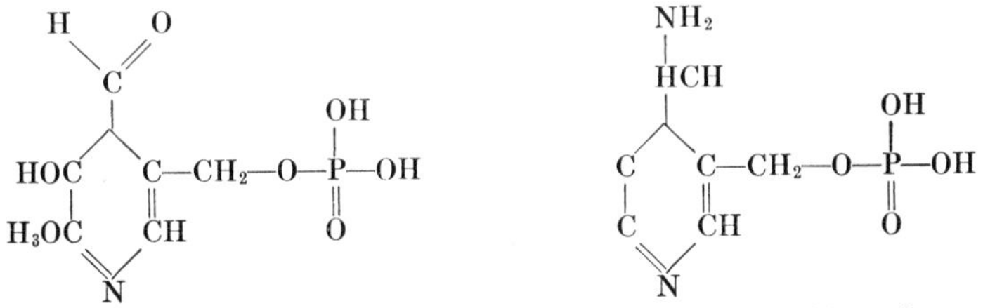

```
 H     O                                 NH2
  \   //                                  |
    C                                    HCH
    |              OH                     |                  OH
   / \              |                    / \                  |
HOC    C—CH2—O—P—OH                    C     C—CH2—O—P—OH        (87)
 |     ||           ||                 |     ||          ||
H3OC   CH           O                  C     CH          O
   \\  /                                 \\  /
     N                                     N
 Phosphopyridoxal                      Phosphopyridoxamine
```

Though the decarboxylation of amino acids is well known, whether such reactions participate in normal amino acid respiration is unknown.

III. The Enzymes of Oxidation-Reduction

A. THE ELECTRON TRANSPORT SYSTEM

Up to this point we have dealt with the manner in which carbohydrates, fats, and proteins, the respiratory substrates, are degraded into smaller molecules which themselves are substrates of respiration. It has been seen that many of these reactions are oxidations which have been accomplished by the removal of hydrogen atoms or of electrons. We will now turn to the transport of these hydrogen atoms and electrons to oxygen and the conservation of energy during such transport. The transport systems are the link between reduced substrates and oxygen and also contain the mechanism whereby the bulk of the energy of oxidation is conserved by cells. Such transport systems are extraordinarily complex, and it must be realized that their function is dependent on precise molecular geometry as well as cellular localization. We will discuss the localization of the respiratory enzymes in cells in as far as it is understood at the present time.

1. Oxidation-Reduction Potentials

Since the catalysis of the oxidation of cellular metabolites involves a series of enzymes and coenzymes that are themselves substances that undergo reversible oxidation-reduction reactions, and since the energy is released by a flow of electrons and hydrogen ions from substrates of low potential in a series of graded steps of ever-increasing potential, a discussion of oxidation-reduction potentials is in order. Recent and detailed treatments of oxidation-reduction potentials have been prepared by Hill (56) and by Slater (134).

If one mixes in a common solution two forms of a chemical substance, where the forms differ from each other in their level of oxidation (in the number of valence electrons), a potential difference will exist between two appropriate electrodes in contact with the solution. The electrodes in common use are bright platinum metal and a calomel electrode. Though a theoretical potential should exist for all substances that have two oxidation levels, in practice it is found that not all substances will donate or receive electrons from the metal—a requirement for an empirical potential.

Since the potential is a constant and theoretically meaningful only for equilibrium conditions, extraneous oxidizing substances such as oxygen gas and reducing substances must be rigidly excluded. If pure oxidant and reductant are available, they may be mixed in known ratios. Alternately, one may start with pure reductant and add known amounts of oxidant, thus obtaining an oxidation curve. Reciprocally, starting with pure oxidant, one may titrate with a reductant of known concentration. The potential difference between the electrodes at fixed pH is given by the Nernst equation:

$$E_h = E_0 + \frac{RT}{n\mathbf{F}} \ln \frac{(\mathrm{OX})}{(\mathrm{Red})} \qquad (88)$$

or converting to $\log_{10}$

$$E_h = E_0 + 2.303 \frac{RT}{n\text{F}} \log \frac{(\text{OX})}{(\text{Red})} \tag{89}$$

where E_h = observed potential difference between the two electrodes in volts

E_0 = the standard electrode potential, a constant specific for each substance under standard conditions, i.e., unit activities, 298A; pH = 0

R = gas constant = 8.314 joules per degree per mole

T = absolute temperature

n = number of valence electrons separating oxidant from reductant

F = Faraday = 96487 coulombs per mole

(OX) and (Red) refer to activities or, at low concentrations, molarities

Single electrode potentials cannot be measured, but only the difference in potential between two electrodes; but if one electrode has an assigned value all potentials between electrodes can be given numerical values in reference to the defined system. The convention adopted is to define the hydrogen electrode at one molar hydrogen ion concentration and one atmosphere hydrogen gas pressure as having zero potential. However, this convention does not fix the sign of the potential difference with other electrodes. In the United States of America, physical chemists consider any system more oxidizing than hydrogen as negative to it. So that the oxygen couple: $O_2 = 4e + 2O^{--}$ which differs from the hydrogen couple by 1.23 volts, is assigned a potential of −1.23 volts. The biochemists of all countries and the European physical chemists have adopted the inverse sign; so that any system that oxidizes hydrogen is considered positive, and the oxygen couple is assigned the value of +1.23 volts. In this chapter we will use the latter convention.

Hence, all potentials are referred to the standard hydrogen electrode. However, the hydrogen electrode potential itself varies with pH as follows:

$$E_h = -2.303 \frac{RT}{\text{F}} \text{pH} \tag{90}$$

and

$$2.303 \frac{RT}{\text{F}} \text{ at } 25°\text{C} = 0.0592$$

At pH 7.0 the hydrogen potential is −0.4137 volts.

In all that follows in this chapter, potentials will be given at pH 7.0. Since E_0 itself varies with pH, we will use E_0' as at pH of 7.0.

Inspection of equation (89) will show that when (OX) = (Red), $E_h = E_0'$; the experimental method of determination of E_0' is to measure the potential at half titration or with an equimolar mixture of oxidant and reductant. Theoretically, one would like to measure the potential between a hydrogen electrode at standard conditions and a bright platinum electrode in the oxidant-reductant mixture. In practice, one uses a saturated calomel electrode whose potential is known to be 0.2444 volts positive to the hydrogen electrode and makes the arithmetical correction.

TABLE XIII

OXIDATION-REDUCTION POTENTIALS OF SOME SELECTED RESPIRATORY SUBSTRATES, HYDROGEN ACCEPTORS, AND THE COMPONENTS OF THE ELECTRON TRANSPORT SYSTEM

Couple	E_0' (volts)	pH	T (°C)	Reference
α-Ketoglutarate/succinate	−0.68			2
Standard hydrogen electrode	−0.421	7.0	30	1
TPN^+/TPNH	−0.324	7.0		4
DPN^+/DPNH	−0.320	7.0		4
β-Hydroxybutyrate/acetoacetate	−0.293	7.0	38	3
Malate/oxaloacetate	−0.102	7.0	37	2,3
Flavoprotein/reduced flavoprotein	−0.063[a]	7.0	38	3
Succinate/fumarate	−0.015	7.0	30	1,3
Ferri-/ferro-cytochrome b	−0.04	7.4	30	5
Ferri-/ferro-cytochrome b	0.00			6
Methylene blue/leuco methylene blue	+0.011	7.0	30	1
2,6-Dichloroindophenol	+0.217	7.0	30	1
Ferri-/ferro-cytochrome c	+0.260	7.0	25	3,7
Ferri-/ferro-cytochrome a	+0.290	7.4	25	5,8
Ferri-/ferro-cytochrome a_3	?			
Standard oxygen electrode	+0.815	7.0	30	1

[a] Value uncertain, and may well vary with the specific protein.

References

1. W. S. Spector, ed., "Handbook of Biological Data," p. 4. Saunders, Philadelphia, 1956.
2. Slater, E. C. *in* "Handbuch der Pflanzenphysiologie," Vol. 12. Springer, Berlin. In press. Oxidation Reduction Potentials and Their Significance in Hydrogen Transfer.
3. Goddard, D. R. *in* "Physical Chemistry of Cells and Tissues" (R. Hober, ed.), p. 437. Blakiston, Philadelphia, 1946.
4. Burton, K., and Wilson, T. H., *Biochem. J.* **54**, 86 (1953).
5. Ball, E. G., *Biochem. Z.* **295**, 262 (1938).
6. Hill, R., *Nature* **174**, 501 (1954).
7. Davenport, H. E., and Hill, R., *Proc. Roy. Soc.* **B139**, 327 (1951).
8. Harburg, H. A., *J. Am. Chem. Soc.* **75**, 4625 (1953).

An oxidation-reduction potential depends on an equilibrium between reductant and oxidant and is meaningful only if measured under equilibrium conditions. Similarly, there must be a finite ratio of oxidant and reductant; a pure oxidant or reductant alone (if they could exist) would not have a defined potential.

Table XIII gives a list of E_0' values for a series of oxidation-reduction systems at pH 7. Any system of higher potential will oxidize any system below; but for some pairs of substances the time to reach equilibrium may be extraordinarily long. If one mixes two systems that react, they will reach equilibrium, where the potentials of the two systems must be identical; so one may write:

$$E_{h_1} = E_{0_1}' + 2.303 \frac{RT}{n\mathrm{F}} \log \frac{(\mathrm{OX})_1}{(\mathrm{Red})_1} = E_{h_2} = E_{0_2}' + 2.303 \frac{RT}{n\mathrm{F}} \log \frac{(\mathrm{OX})_2}{(\mathrm{Red})_2} \tag{91}$$

At equilibrium $E_{h_1} = E_{h_2}$, and evaluation of 2.303 RT/nF at 30° gives for $n = 1$, 0.060 volts and for $n = 2$, 0.030 volts. Substituting these values and rearranging terms gives:

for a one-electron system

$$E_{0_1}' - E_{0_2}' = 0.060 \log \frac{(\mathrm{OX})_2}{(\mathrm{Red})_2} - \log \frac{(\mathrm{OX})_1}{(\mathrm{Red})_1} \tag{92}$$

and for a two-electron system

$$E_{0_1}' - E_{0_2}' = 0.030 \log \frac{(\mathrm{OX})_2}{(\mathrm{Red})_2} - \log \frac{(\mathrm{OX})_1}{(\mathrm{Red})_1} \tag{93}$$

Inspection of the above will give the results shown in Table XIV.

The above examples are cases where a system of higher potential is oxidizing one of lower potential. However, a system of lower potential may partially oxidize a system above it, if the potential difference is

TABLE XIV

OXIDATION OF A SYSTEM OF LOWER POTENTIAL ($\mathrm{SPECIES}_2$) BY ONE OF HIGHER POTENTIAL ($\mathrm{SPECIES}_1$), AT 30°C

$E_{0_1}' - E_{0_2}'$ (volts)		
$n = 1$	$n = 2$	Per cent of $\mathrm{species}_2$ at equilibrium
0.06	0.03	90
0.12	0.06	99
0.18	0.09	99.9

not too large and an excess of the lower system is present. For example, substitution in equation (93), when $n = 2$, of a system where E_{0_2}' is 0.03 volts negative to E_{0_1}' will bring about 50% oxidation of the higher system if the lower system is present at tenfold higher concentration; but with the same concentration difference a difference of potentials of —0.06 and —0.09 volts, the per cents of oxidation would be 1% and 0.1%, respectively.

Oxidation-reduction potentials are of considerable theoretical interest in cellular metabolisms, for they allow us to make a serial order from molecular oxygen, through an intermediate series of enzymes and coenzymes, to the respiratory substrates. Further, the energy released between two stages may be directly calculated from the potential differences using the relationships given earlier (see eq. 3) since:

$$\Delta F = -n\mathbf{F}\Delta E$$

where ΔF = free-energy change in kcal per mole
ΔE = potential difference in volts
$\mathbf{F}$ = Faraday = 23.066 kcal per volt equivalent
n = number of electrons lost on oxidation

If one mole of A is oxidized to B with a loss of one electron, and the concentration of the reductant and oxidant were to remain unchanged, 23.026 kcal would be released. Cells are favorable systems for such calculations, as their oxidant is the atmosphere, upon which they draw, substrates are replaced from insoluble storage materials or the environment, and the concentrations of the intermediate oxidants do not change markedly in concentration. In other words, they are both open thermodynamic systems and steady state systems.

As a first approximation, one may use standard E_0' values, and determine the potential difference between two systems. For example, if one considers the step between DPN^+:DPNH and ferri:ferro cytochrome c, the voltage difference based on E_0' values is 0.58 volts, or the free energy per mole for two electrons is 26.8 kcal. Similarly, the energy between cytochrome c and O_2 at 0.2 atmosphere 23.94 kcal for 2 moles of cytochrome (corresponding to one of $DPNH + H^+$). However, we have assumed that the ratios of ferri:ferro cytochrome c and DPN^+:DPNH are unity. If, for example, the DPN^+:DPNH ratio were 0.1, and the ferricytochrome c:ferrocytochrome c ratio were 10, then instead of using E_0' values, the E_h values must be used, and these can be calculated from equation (89). The cytochrome potential would be raised (at 30°C) to 0.32 volt and the DPN potential lowered to —0.402, giving a potential difference of 0.722 volt, or a free-energy change 33.2 kcal in place of the previous value of 26.8.

There is, therefore, some real interest in determining the ratio of oxidized: reduced components of the respiratory chain. Fortunately, this can be done on the differential spectrometer for those enzyme components with appropriate spectral absorptions, under various steady state conditions, and is illustrated by the results of Chance and Williams (23).

The above considerations apply to equilibria (or steady states). Though the potentials allow one to calculate what the equilibria would be, they furnish no information as to the velocity of such reactions, or whether equilibrium will in fact occur within a finite time. For example, we know many compounds whose potentials indicate a large decrease in free energy if oxidized by oxygen, and yet no measurable reaction with oxygen gas has been detected, e.g., succinate is not oxidized by oxygen gas. If, however, there are suitable intermediate substances which undergo reversible oxidation-reduction, a catalyzed reaction of high velocity may result. As has been indicated, the respiratory enzymes are such intermediate reversible systems.

There have been at times discussions of oxidation-reduction potentials of cells or tissues. Such discussions are meaningless, since a living cell is not an equilibrium system, but one of many dynamic steady states. In a single cell, we may have simultaneously dissolved molecular oxygen, a finite ferricytochrome c: ferrocytochrome c ratio, and finite ratios of oxidized and reduced substrates, DPN^+: DPNH, etc. The potential differences existing in such a cell may exceed 1 volt, and the maintenance of these potential differences is essential for life, for it is the flow of electrons along this potential difference that makes possible the liberation of energy in forms useful for cellular work. If one ever finds a cell with a single oxidation-reduction potential, by definition one has a dead cell!

2. Hydrogen and Electron Transfer

We have already shown that the primary oxidations that occur during cellular respiration are catalyzed by dehydrogenases. In this discussion we will define dehydrogenases as those proteins that catalyze the reaction between substrate and hydrogen acceptor. Such reactions are of the general type:

$$H_2A + B \rightleftarrows A + H_2B \tag{94a}$$

The natural hydrogen acceptors, illustrated as substance B in the above equation, are DPN^+, flavoproteins, and, in certain rare instances, a specific cytochrome or TPN^+. An efficient mechanism, other than synthetic processes, for the oxidation of TPNH remains to be demonstrated. However, the enzyme pyridine nucleotide transhydrogenase

TABLE XV
DEHYDROGENASES[a]

Dehydrogenase and substrate	Reaction product	Acceptor	Reference
Glucose	Gluconate	DPN	24
Glucose-6-phosphate	6-Phosphogluconate	TPN	11
6-Phosphogluconate	Ribulose-5-phosphate	TPN	11
Mannitol-1-phosphate	Fructose-6-phosphate	DPN	28
Sorbitol	Fructose	DPN	27
Glycerol	Dihydroxyacetone	DPN	3
D-Glycerophosphate	Dihydroxyacetone phosphate	DPN	1
Glyceraldehyde-3-phosphate (+ phosphate)	1,3-Diphosphoglycerate	DPN	13,26
Glyceraldehyde-3-phosphate (+ phosphate)	1,3-Diphosphoglycerate	TPN	8
Alcohol (ethanol)	Acetaldehyde	DPN	19
Alcohol (ethanol)	Acetaldehyde	TPN	5,21
Aldehyde (acetaldehyde)	Acetate	DPN	18
Aldehyde (acetaldehyde)	Acetate	TPN	20
Butyryl coenzyme A	CH_3—CH=CH—CO CoA	?	14
Formic	CO_2	DPN	15
Hydroxymalonic	Ketomalonate	DPN	23
Isocitric	Oxalosuccinate	DPN	12
Isocitric	Oxalosuccinate	TPN	12
α-Ketoglutarate system	Succinyl-S-CoA	DPN	9
Lactic	Pyruvate	DPN	10
Lactic	Pyruvate	Cytochrome b_2	6
Malic	Oxaloacetate	DPN	16
Oxalic	CO_2	?	7
Quinic acid	5-Dehydroquinic acid	DPN	4
Succinic acid	Fumarate	Cytochrome b	2
Tartaric acid	End- or ketodihydroxy-fumarate	DPN	22
Betaine aldehyde	Betaine	DPN	17
Choline	Betaine aldehyde	?	17
Glutamic	α-Ketoglutarate, NH_4^+	DPN	25

[a] Some of the enzymes now classified as oxidases are probably dehydrogenases.

References

NOTE: Unless otherwise indicated, all references are to Volumes I and II of "Methods in Enzymology" (S. P. Colowick and O. Kaplan, eds.). Academic Press, New York, 1955.

1. Beisenhenz, G., T. Bücher, and K. H. Garbade, I, 391.
2. Bonner, W. D., Jr., I, 722.
3. Burton, R. M., I, 397.
4. Davis, B. D., C. Gilvorg, and S. Mitsuhashi, II, 307.
5. De Moss, R. D., I, 504.

(2) which catalyzes the reaction illustrated in equation (94b) may well be the link which provides direct TPNH oxidation.

$$\mathrm{TPNH + DPN^+ \rightarrow TPN^+ + DPNH} \tag{94b}$$

The fact that the removal and transfer of hydrogen is directly from substrate to acceptor has been elegantly demonstrated by Vennesland (153) by the use of deuterium-labeled substrates. These experiments show that the labeled hydrogen appears on the hydrogen acceptor; it does not appear in solution, a fact that clearly illustrates the reaction partners to consist of substrate-dehydrogenase-hydrogen acceptor. Though such a tri-complex is highly probable, a demonstration of one has not yet been accomplished.

The fact that there are very few hydrogen acceptors for a very large number of dehydrogenases (over forty) is one of the beautiful simplifying features of the transfer of hydrogen or electrons to oxygen. In the reactions they catalyze, the dehydrogenases exhibit an unusually high degree of specificity for substrate and a rather high degree of specificity for hydrogen acceptor. A list of dehydrogenases and their hydrogen acceptors is given in Table XV.

The DPNH, formed by the dehydrogenase-catalyzed oxidation of specific substrates, is reoxidized by hydrogen transport to a flavoprotein; flavoproteins in turn can transport electrons to a cytochrome.

---

6. Dixon, M., I, 444.
7. Franke, W., Schumann, F., and B. Bonerjee, *Z. Physiol. Chem.* **278,** 24 (1943).
8. Gibbs, M., I, 411.
9. Kaufman, S., I, 714.
10. Kornberg, A., I, 441.
11. Kornberg, A., and B. L. Horecker, I, 323.
12. Kornberg, A., I, 705, 707.
13. Krebs, E. G., I, 407.
14. Mahler, H. R., I, 553.
15. Nason, A., and H. N. Little, I, 536.
16. Ochoa, S., I, 735.
17. Quastel, J. H., I, 674.
18. Racker, E., I, 514.
19. Racker, E., I, 500.
20. Seegmiller, J. E., I, 511.
21. Stafford, H. A., and B. Vennesland, *Arch. Biochem. Biophys.* **44,** 404 (1953).
22. Stafford, H. A., *Plant Physiol.* **32,** 338 (1957.
23. Stafford, H. A., *Plant Physiol.* **31,** 135 (1956).
24. Strecker, H. J., I, 335.
25. Strecker, H. J., II, 220.
26. Velick, S. F., I, 401.
27. Wolff, J. B., I, 348.
28. Wolff, J. B., and N. O. Kaplan, I, 346.

Hence, the over-all result of cellular oxidations is the transport of hydrogen, or electrons, to an ultimate common pathway, the cytochrome or electron transport system. It is through the cytochrome system that the final act of cellular respiration is consummated, namely the transfer of electrons to oxygen, or in other words, the reaction of aerobic cells with oxygen. In addition to being the final common pathway of respiration, it is during the transport of electrons through the cytochrome system that the bulk of the energy of substrate oxidation is made available to the cell. Hence, a detailed consideration of the cytochromes is in order.

B. CYTOCHROMES

In 1886, MacMunn (98) presented carefully documented evidence showing that many tissues contained pigments related to, but not identical with, hemoglobin and myoglobin. He called these new pigments "histohaematins" and "myohaematins." Although the equipment used was crude, the deductions MacMunn made were remarkable and almost correct. He wrote: "Thus, from Echinoderms to man throughout the animal kingdom, we find in various tissues and organs a class of pigments whose spectra show a most remarkable resemblance to each other; . . . . ; their bands are intensified by alkalis and enfeebled by acids, intensified by reducing agents and enfeebled by oxidizing agents; they accordingly appear to be capable of oxidation and reduction and are therefore *respiratory*. If this view be correct, and I have every reason to believe that it is, we may consider that the histohaematins are of use in enabling the tissues in which they occur to take up oxygen from the circulating blood and *hold it* in the tissues, exchanging for it the carbon dioxide. Hence the histohaematins are concerned in the *internal respiration* of the tissues and organs of invertebrates and vertebrate animals."

The work of MacMunn was not accepted, and his notion of a new class of pigments was ridiculed. The view prevailed that "histohaematin" and "myohaematin" were decomposition products of hemoglobin and had no physiological function.

The work of MacMunn became buried in the literature and was not reconsidered until Keilin published his classical paper in 1925 (69, 70). In this paper, titled "On Cytochrome, a Respiratory Pigment Common to Animals, Yeast, and Higher Plants," Keilin not only described fully the behavior characteristics of these pigments, which he renamed cytochrome, but his work led him to believe that the cytochrome pigments were the link between dehydrogenases and oxygen, a view which proved to be correct.

Cytochromes are iron-porphyrin-proteins or hemoproteins. The prosthetic group, heme, varies according to the nature of the side-chain constituents. Hemes are, in general, rather unstable and easily oxidized substances, but the addition of a specific protein (a protein specific for each cytochrome) profoundly alters the ease of oxidation of the iron atom. Hemes characteristically have a three-banded absorption spectrum, two sharp bands in the visible spectrum and one in the blue

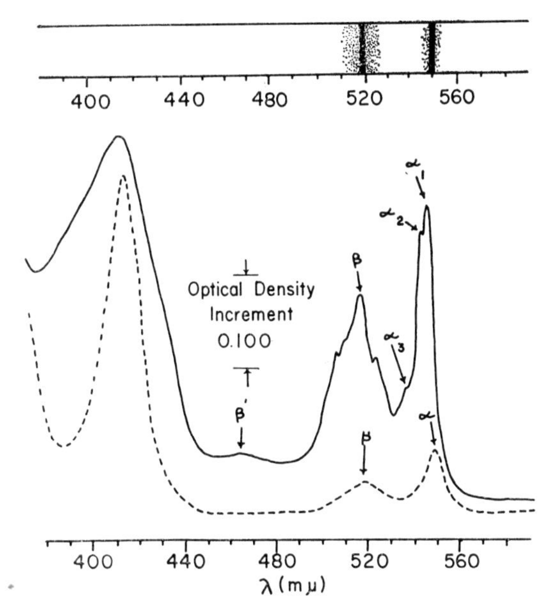

FIG. 9. Absolute absorption spectra of reduced cytochrome c. Above: as observed in a low-dispersion microspectroscope. Below: a comparison of the spectra, obtained through the use of a sensitive, split-beam recording spectrophotometer, at room temperature (broken curve) and at −170°C (solid curve). The γ-band (unmarked) at 415 mμ. It can be seen that at the low temperature there is a marked sharpening and intensification of the α- and β-bands and a shift of the maxima toward shorter wavelengths. Absorption spectra from Estabrook, R. W., *J. Biol. Chem.* 223, 781–794 (1956).

region. The bands are referred to from the longwave side as the alpha, beta, and gamma or (Soret) bands, respectively; these relationships are illustrated in Fig. 9. The positions of the absorption bands are modified according to the specific protein, the net result being that the absorption spectrum of each cytochrome is individual and characteristic.

Oxidation of hemes results in a change in valency of the iron. The oxidized form, ferriheme or parahematin (Fe^{+++}), has, in contrast to the reduced form, ferroheme (Fe^{++}), a poorly defined absorption in the visible spectrum. The dramatic change in the absorption, which depends on the oxidation state of the iron, gives an excellent means of

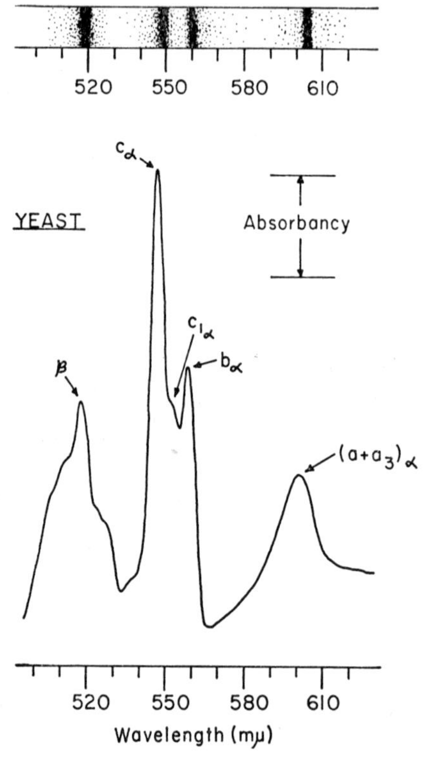

FIG. 10. The cytochrome spectrum of yeast cells. Above: the absorption spectrum of a suspension of anaerobic yeast cells, as observed in a low-dispersion microspectroscope. Below: the difference spectrum (at −190°C) of yeast cells. This spectrum represents the difference in absorption between a suspension of starved, aerobic cells and a suspension of yeast cells which has been reduced by the addition of substrate, glucose. Reduction represents an increase in the vertical axis.

studying the properties of cytochrome in intact tissues and in preparations derived from them, a fact which allowed Keilin to show that the oxidation state of the cytochrome was strongly dependent on the physiological state of the organism. Yeast cells placed in anaerobic conditions or in the presence of cyanide, azide, hydroxylamine, or sulfide, showed the characteristic sharp spectrum (Fig. 10); cells placed in aerobic conditions or treated with certain inhibitors showed the diffuse spectrum of oxidized cytochrome. It was from the interpretation of a wide variety of experiments such as these that Keilin deduced that the cytochromes linked dehydrogenases to oxygen.

So far, the term cytochrome has been used as a generic term. Reference to Fig. 10 shows the classical cytochrome spectrum as observed by Keilin, a spectrum consisting of the alpha bands of three well-defined components which were termed cytochromes a, b, and c, according to the positions of their alpha absorption bands. The fourth band at 520 mμ represents the fused beta bands of components b, c, and c_1.

The studies of Keilin were greatly strengthened by the preparation from minced heart muscle of a particulate suspension which was capable of carrying out the complete oxidation of succinate to fumarate by molecular oxygen (71). The "Keilin-Hartree heart-muscle preparation" has been used extensively to study the interactions between the cytochromes, between dehydrogenases, DPN^+, flavoprotein, and cytochrome, and the final reaction between cytochrome and oxygen. The work of Keilin was carried out parallel to the investigations of Warburg. In spite of a great deal of controversy between the two laboratories, modern interpretation of the respiratory process rests on the work of both Keilin and Warburg and is centered on their mutual interests in the reaction between respiring cells and oxygen.

In the third decade of the twentieth century there were two opposing views concerning the nature of cellular oxidation. There were those who supported Wieland's hypothesis which suggested that primary oxidations within the cells were mediated through hydrogen activation, a view that was greatly strengthened by Thunberg's discovery of dehydrogenases and, later, the demonstration of the link between dehydrogenases, cytochromes, and oxygen, as deduced by Keilin.

Warburg opposed the views as outlined above. Warburg had disproved the idea that cellular respiration consisted of the combustion of sugar directly to carbon dioxide and water and had shown that sugar was degraded during the respiratory process to smaller molecules—molecules which were common to all cells. Warburg believed that cellular oxidations were carried out through the direct participation of oxygen and that oxygen was made available through an "oxygen-transporting enzyme," an enzyme which he believed to be a hemoprotein. Warburg spent considerable effort in studying the catalytic effects of heavy metals on the oxidation of various organic molecules (158). Iron, in particular, in catalytic amounts, had a powerful effect on some oxidations, both in solution and on surfaces (charcoal). Such oxidations became models, in Warburg's mind, of cellular oxidation, a concept which was supported by Warburg's finding that cyanide similarly influenced cells and models.

The greatest contributions from Warburg's laboratory were his very elegant studies on the effects of carbon monoxide on cellular respiration, experiments for which he has received much and due credit. It was a well-known fact that carbon monoxide readily combines with the blood pigment hemoglobin, a reaction consisting of the displacement of oxygen by carbon monoxide in the hemoglobin molecule. Earlier (1897) Haldane had shown that this reaction proceeds only in the dark; light causes the dissociation of the hemoglobin carbon monoxide complex.

$$\text{Oxyhemoglobin} + \text{carbon monoxide} \underset{\text{light}}{\overset{\text{dark}}{\rightleftharpoons}} \text{carbon monoxide hemoglobin} + O_2 \quad (95)$$

$$\alpha\text{-band max.} = 576\text{–}578\ m\mu \qquad \alpha\text{-band max.} = 568\text{–}572\ m\mu$$

The relative affinities of carbon monoxide and oxygen for hemoglobin will result in an equilibrium, which is represented below:

$$K = \frac{[HbO_2][CO]}{[HbCO][O_2]} = 0.01 \quad (96)$$

To replace the oxygen of hemoglobin by carbon monoxide requires only a few tenths of a per cent of carbon monoxide, that is to say that carbon monoxide has a high affinity for hemoglobin compared to that for oxygen. On the assumption that the respiration of cells was mediated by a hemoprotein, Warburg deduced that respiration should be inhibited by carbon monoxide in the dark and that the inhibition should be relieved by light. Such is indeed the case, but, unlike hemoglobin, cells have a high affinity for oxygen compared to that of carbon monoxide, $K = 9\text{–}13$. Hence, high ratios of carbon monoxide to oxygen are required to inhibit the respiratory process.

In order to obtain further insight into the nature of the enzyme mediating respiration, Warburg studied the inhibitory action of carbon monoxide on yeast respiration as a function of the wavelength of light. In a beautiful series of experiments, the second quantitative action spectrum on record (158, 159), Warburg showed that the relative photochemical absorption spectrum (Fig. 11) corresponds to that of a hemoprotein.

In 1939, Keilin and Hartree (71) found that cytochrome a was actually composed of two components; a second component, cytochrome a_3, proved to be the component which reacts with oxygen and which had all the spectroscopic properties of Warburg's "oxygen-transporting enzyme." The name suggested by Keilin and Hartree for components a and a_3, cytochrome oxidase, has replaced Warburg's terminology.

The action spectrum for the photochemical release of carbon monoxide inhibition, as carried out by Warburg and his associates, was repeated by Melnick on yeast (106) and then extended to preparations of rat heart muscle (107). Castor and Chance (17), with their new and sensitive equipment, have produced elegant action spectra (Figs.

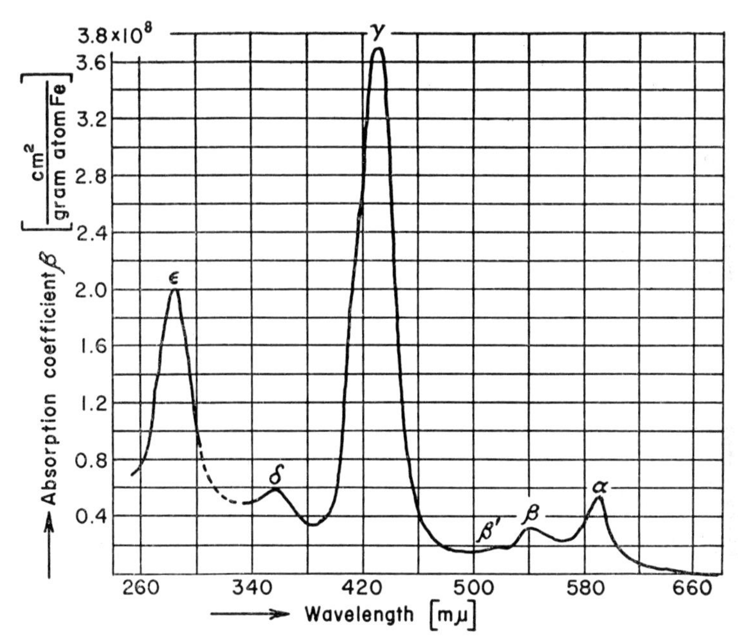

FIG. 11. The relative photochemical action spectrum of carbon monoxide-inhibited yeast respiration. From Warburg, O., "Heavy Metal Prosthetic Groups and Enzyme Action," p. 147, fig. 22. Oxford Univ. Press, London and New York, 1949.

12–14) and are able to distinguish between three oxygen-reacting hemoprotein respiratory enzymes. These respiratory enzymes are: (a) cytochrome a_3 (cytochrome oxidase), the most widely distributed of these oxidases; (b) cytochrome a_1, found in *Acetobacter pasteurianus;* (c) cytochrome o, found in *Acetobacter suboxydans* and *Staphylococcus aureus* (*Micrococcus pyogenes*). In Figs. 12 and 13, the action spectra for yeast and *A. pasteurianus* are similar to those earlier found by Kubowitz and Haas (82), in Warburg's laboratory and by methods more crude than those employed by Castor and Chance.

Cytochrome oxidase, then, is the final link to oxygen in the respira-

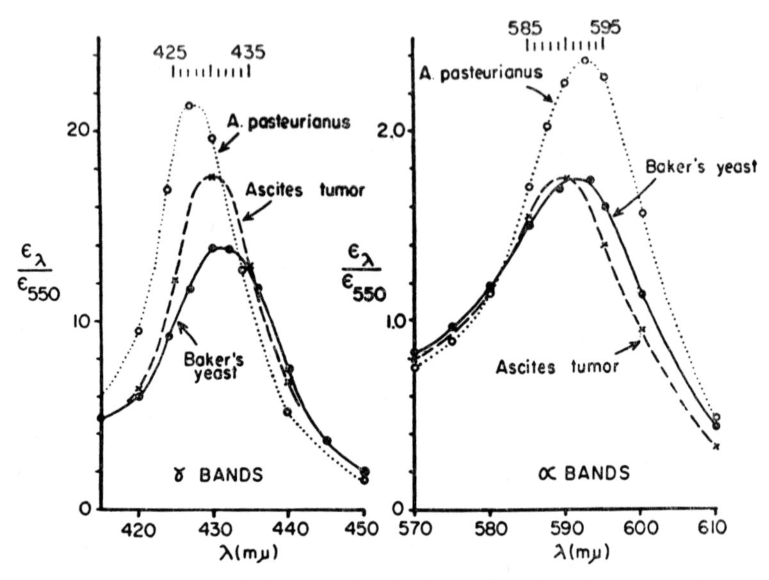

FIG. 12. A comparison of the γ- and α-bands of the photochemical action spectra of baker's yeast, ascites tumor cells (cytochrome a_3) and *Acetobacter pasteurianus* (cytochrome a_1). From Castor, L. N., and Chance, B. *J. Biol. Chem.* **217**, 453–465 **(1955).**

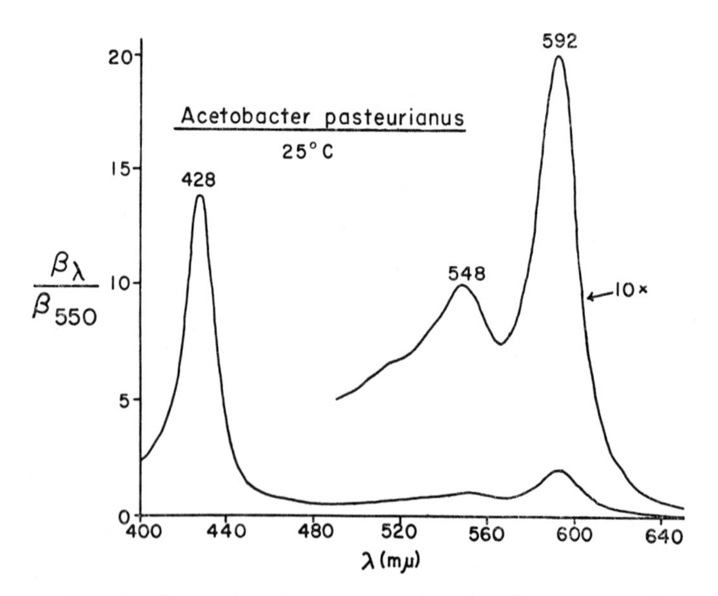

FIG. 13. The photochemical action spectrum for *Acetobacter pasteurianus* (cytochrome a_1). From Castor, L. N., and Chance, B., unpublished.

tory process of most tissues. It is unique in that it is one of only a very few cytochromes capable of rapid reaction with oxygen and in addition one that has an extraordinarily high affinity for oxygen. The oxygen affinity constant ($1/K_m$) of cytochrome oxidases in heart muscle is 4×10^7 (Longmuir, 93). It is interesting that there is considerable variation in the spectral characteristics of cytochrome oxidases from different sources (135). Regardless of this variation, cytochrome oxidases from different sources are alike in that they have a high affinity for oxygen, use cytochrome c as a substrate and do not

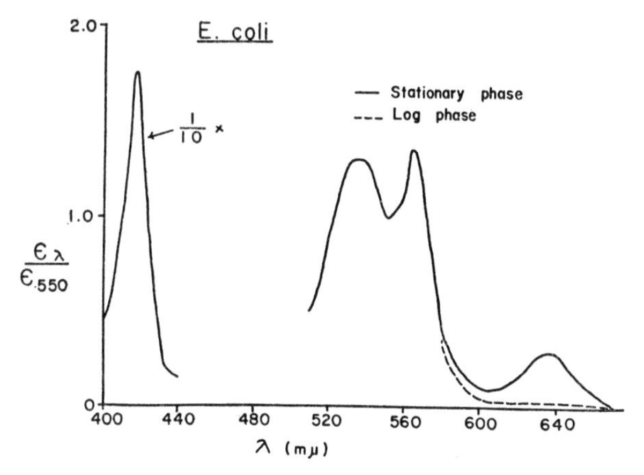

FIG. 14. The photochemical action spectra for *E. coli* in the log phase of growth (broken curve) where the respiration is mediated by cytochrome o. In the stationary phase of growth (unbroken curve) an additional peak at 637 mμ appears, a peak characteristic of cytochrome a_2. From Castor, L. N., and Chance, B. *J. Biol. Chem.*, in press.

possess the same protohematin structure which is common to the other cytochromes. As will be seen below, there may be instances where cytochromes other than cytochrome oxidase can react directly with oxygen.

The investigations of Warburg and of Keilin and his associates have been greatly extended in laboratories throughout the world. Today the student of respiration is presented with a great mass of information concerning the functioning of cytochromes and a bewildering number of different cytochromes from different organisms (see Table XVI). In spite of the large amount of information that is available concerning the nature and function of the cytochromes, there still remain many fundamental problems that the physiologist and biochemist must overcome before it can be said that electron transport through the cytochrome system is completely understood.

Much of our knowledge of cytochromes has been derived through the use of direct-vision, low-dispersion spectroscopes. The spectroscopic observation of whole tissues, homogenates, and cell-free preparations is made difficult by a large amount of light scattering. The use of a low-dispersion instrument enables the investigator to observe cytochrome absorption bands even though a great deal of light is lost by scattering. Such is not the case with instruments of a high degree of light dispersion. Indeed, had photoelectric spectrophotometers been in general use in 1925, Keilin might not have discovered the cytochromes.

Plant tissues present two immediate difficulties to the investigator: the cytochrome components are generally present in very low concentration and, in addition, plants characteristically contain chlorophyll and even nongreen tissues contain substances that absorb strongly in the blue, thus making observation difficult. However, in spite of these difficulties, much information on plant cytochromes has been gained through visual optical methods. Methodology as applied to plant tissues has been reviewed by Hartree (54).

In recent years the development of the divided-beam spectrophotometer by French and Chance and the double-beam spectrophotometer by Chance (22) has extended the range and precision of our observations. This latter instrument measures the difference in absorption between two closely spaced wavelengths and hence rejects changes in absorption that are independent of wavelength. The results obtained with these instruments on the kinetics of electron transport will be more fully illustrated below.

Useful information on the properties of each cytochrome would result from its extraction and preparation in a pure state; when preparations of several cytochromes have been made, their interactions can be studied by recombination. Unfortunately, the preparation of cytochromes in pure form has proved difficult, the pigments are firmly bound to cytoplasmic inclusions and, in addition, many are easily destroyed. It is only recently that some cytochromes have been extracted and purified. The first cytochrome prepared in pure form, cytochrome c, is a unique cytochrome and one that is generally present in relatively large concentrations. Cytochrome c is a very stable molecule. it will withstand acid, alkali, and heat; under physiological conditions it is not oxidized by molecular oxygen. Even though large amounts of very pure cytochrome c can be easily prepared, we do not know either the precise molecular configuration, the manner in which protein is linked to heme, or how this cytochrome really functions in electron

TABLE XVI

Optical Properties and Distribution of Cytochromes

Cytochrome	Occurrence	Absorption maxima of reduced cytochrome (mμ)			−191°C		Absorption maxima plus CO			Reference
		α	β	γ	α	E'_0	α	β	γ	
a	Widely distributed in aerobic cells	605	None[a]	Weak 450	600	+0.029		None		1a,b
a_1	*Acetobacter* and other bacteria	589	None[a]	435–440			590	540	427	2a,b
a_2	*Azotobacter*, *Escherichia coli*, and other bacteria[b]	630	None	—			636			2a,3,4
a_3	Widely distributed in aerobic cells	605	None[a]	445	600		590	540	430	1b
a_4	*Acetobacter peroxydans*	612								5
o	*Acetobacter suboxydans*, *Micrococcus pyogenes*	568[c]	535[c]	417[c]						6
b	Widely distributed	564	530	432		−0.04				1a,7
b_1	*Aerobacter aerogenes*, *E. coli*, other bacteria	560								4,8
b_2	Baker's yeast	557	530	420						9
b_3	Green leaves, cotyledons, potato tubers	559	529	—		+0.04				10
b_3	Plant microsomes	560	525	425						11
b_4[d]	Halotolerant bacteria	554	521	415						12
b_5	Microsomes of animal tissues, *Cecropia* pupae	556	526	423		+0.02				13
b_6	Plastids, *Arum* spadix microsomes	562 563				−0.06				14,15
b_7	*Arum* spadix microsomes	560	529			−0.03				15

TABLE XVI (*Continued*)

Cytochrome	Occurrence	Absorption maxima of reduced cytochrome (mμ)			−191°C	E'_0	Absorption maxima plus CO			Reference
		α	β	γ	α		α	β	γ	
c	Widely distributed					+0.26				1a,16
	Heart	550	521	415	547[e]					
	Plants	550	521	417	547[e]					
	Yeast	549.5	521	415	545[f]					
c_1	Mitochondria of animal tissues, yeast, higher plants?	553	524	418	551					17
c_2	Photosynthetic bacteria	550	521	415						18
c_3	Sulfur bacteria	553	525	419		−0.205				19
c_4	*Azotobacter vinelandii*	551	522	416		+0.30				20
c_5	*Azotobacter vinelandii*	555	526	420		+0.32				20
f	Plant chloroplasts	555	526	422		+0.365				10
h	*Helix pomatia*	556	526	422	556 550					21

[a] Photochemical action spectra of Castor and Chance suggest the presence of a beta band.
[b] Usually occurs with cytochrome a_1.
[c] From photochemical action spectrum of Castor and Chance.
[d] Probably a cytochrome of the type.
[e] Plus satellite.
[f] No satellite.

References for Table XVI

1a. Keilin, D., 1925. On cytochrome, a respiratory pigment common to animals, yeast and higher plants. *Proc. Roy. Soc.* **B98,** 312–339 (1925).
1b. Keilin, D., and E. F. Hartree, Cytochrome and cytochrome oxidase. *Proc. Roy. Soc.* **B127,** 167 (1939).
2a. Fujita, A., and Kodama, T., Untersuchungen uber Atmung und Garung pathogener Bakterien. III. *Biochem. Z.* **273,** 186 (1934).
2b. Warburg, O., "Heavy Metal Prosthetic Groups," 230 pp. Oxford Univ. Press, London, 1949.
3. Negeliein, E., and W. Gerischer, 1934. Direkter spektroskopischer Nachweis des sauerstoffübertragenden Ferments in Azobakter. *Biochem. Z.* **268,** 1 (1934).
4. Smith, L., Bacterial cytochromes. *Bacteriol. Rev.* **18,** 106 (1954).
5. Chin, C. H., The cytochrome system of *Acetobacter peroxidans* with reference to other *Acetobacter* species. *2e Congr. Intern. Biochim.,* Paris *Abstr. Communs.* p. 277 (1952).
6. Chance, B., Personal communication. Castor, L. N., and B. Chance, Photochemical action spectra of CO-inhibited respiration. *J. Biol. Chem.* **217,** 453–465 (1955).
7. Sekuzu, I., and K. Okunuki, Purification and some properties of cytochrome b from ox heart muscle. *J. Biochem.* (*Tokyo*) **43,** 107–109 (1956).
8. Keilin, D., Cytochrome and the supposed direct spectroscopic observation of oxidase. *Nature* **133,** 290–291 (1934).
9. Bach, S. J., M. Dixon, and D. Keilin, A new soluble cytochrome component from yeast. *Nature* **149,** 21 (1942); Appleby, C. A., and R. K. Morton, Crystalline cytochrome b_2 and lactic dehydrogenase. *Nature* **123,** 749 (1954).
10. Hill, R., and R. Scarisbrick, The hematin compounds of leaves. *New Phytologist* **50,** 98 (1951).
11. Martin, E. M., and R. K. Morton, Cytochrome b_3 of microsomes from plant tissues. *Nature* **176,** 113–114 (1955); Heme pigments of cytoplasmic particles from non-photosynthetic plant tissues. *Biochem. J.* **65,** 404–413 (1957).
12. Egami, F., N. Itahashi, R. Sato, and T. Mori, A cytochrome from halotolerant bacteria. *J. Biochem.* (*Toyko*) **40,** 527 (1953).
13. Sanborn, R. C., and C. M. Williams, The cytochrome system in the *Cecropia* silkworm with special reference to the properties of a new compound. *J. Gen. Physiol.* **33,** 579 (1950); Strittmatter, C. F., and E. G. Ball, A hemochromogen component of liver microsomes. *Proc. Natl. Acad. Sci. U.S.* **38,** 108 (1952).
14. Hill, R., The cytochrome b component of chloroplasts. *Nature* **174,** 501 (1954). of *Arum maculatum. New Phytologist* **55,** 206–212 (1956).
15. Bendall, O. S., and R. Hill, Cytochrome components in the spadix of *Arum maculatum. New Phytologist* **55,** 206–212 (1956).
16. Goddard, D. R., Cytochrome c and cytochrome coridase from wheat germ. *Am. J. Botany* **31,** 270–276 (1944); Theorell, H., and A. Akeson, Studies on cytochrome c. II. The optical properties of pure cytochrome c and some of its derivatives. *J. Am. Chem. Soc.* **63,** 1812–1818 (1941); Nunnikhoven, R., Amino acid composition and some other properties of yeast cytochrome c in comparison with horse-heart cytochrome c. *Biochim. et Biophys. Acta* **28,** 108 (1958); Li, Wen-Chieh, and Chen-Lu Tsou, Preparation of pure yeast cytochrome c. *Scientia Sinica* **5,** 663–674 (1956).

transport. As with cytochrome oxidase, there is considerable variation in the spectral properties of cytochrome c, indeed there are several cytochromes c on record, but of these cytochrome c and c_1 appear to have the most general distribution.

The group of cytochromes known as cytochrome b is diverse and is numbered from b to b_7 (cf., Table XVI). The cytochromes b of plants have not as yet been fully characterized; many plants appear to contain more than one cytochrome of the b type. Unlike cytochrome c, the cytochromes of the b group are autoxidizable, at least to a limited extent. Hill has extracted cytochrome b_3 from the leaves of broad beans and has named cytochromes b_6 and b_7. The unsatisfactory nature of our present knowledge concerning the role of the cytochromes b in plant respiration will become evident below.

Most, if not all, plants contain cytochrome oxidase. There was a period when other oxidases of plant tissues were thought to play a major role in mediating the transfer of electrons to oxygen, but such claims are now uncertain. Many of the early investigations of plant respiration were carried out before the importance of cytochromes was generally recognized and before the difficulties of demonstrating cytochromes in plant tissues had been overcome. Further, many investigators of plant respiration did not take into account the high oxygen affinity of plant tissues. An oxidase mediating respiration must have the same or greater oxygen affinity than does the tissue itself. The apparent oxygen affinity constants of various tissues and organisms are shown in Table XVII where it can be seen that, in spite of technical difficulties of measurement and the fact that the values listed are minimal, the affinity is high. At the present time the almost universal distribution of cytochrome oxidase and the electron transport system in the tissues of higher plants is generally accepted. The cytochromes of plants are reviewed by Hartree (55) and by Smith and Chance (136).

---

17. Yakushiji, E., and K. Okunuki, Über eine neue Cytochromkomponents und ihre Funktion. *Proc. Imp. Acad. (Japan)* **16,** 299 (1940).
18. Elsden, S. R., M. D. Kamen, and L. P. Vernon. A new soluble cytochrome. *J. Am. Chem. Soc.* **75,** 6374 (1953); Kamen, M. D., and L. P. Vernon, Comparative studies on bacterial cytochrome. *Biochim. et Biophys. Acta* **17,** 10 (1955).
19. Postgate, J. R., Cytochrome c_3 a bifunctional hematohematin. *Biochim. et Biophys. Acta* **18,** 427 (1955).
20. Tissieres, A., and R. H. Burris, Purification and properties of cytochrome c_4 and c_5 from *Azotobacter vinelandii. Biochim. et Biophys. Acta* **20,** 436 (1956).
21. Keilin, J., Helicorubin and cytochrome h. *Biochem. J.* **64,** 663–676 (1956).

TABLE XVII
APPARENT MICHAELIS AND AFFINITY CONSTANTS OF VARIOUS TISSUES FOR OXYGEN[a]

Organism or tissue	K_m	$1/K_m$	Reference
Tetrahymena geleii	0 order to 4×10^{-6}	—	E. G. S. Baker and J. P. Baumberger, *J. Cellular Comp. Physiol.* **17,** 285 (1941)
Baker's yeast	3×10^{-6}	3×10^{5}	R. J. Winzler, *J. Cellular Comp. Physiol.* **17,** 263 (1941)
Barley seedlings			
Roots	1.6×10^{-5}		W. D. Bonner, Jr. and A. R. Lubell, Unpublished
Coleoptiles	2.0×10^{-5}		
Aerobacter aerogenes	4.0×10^{-8}	2.5×10^{7}	I. S. Longmuir, *Biochem. J.* **57,** 81 (1954)
Potato slices	3×10^{-6}	3×10^{5}	K. V. Thimann, C. S. Yocum, and D. P. Hackett, *Arch. Biochem. Biophys.* **53,** 239 (1954)
Peltandra virginica	3×10^{-6}	3×10^{5}	C. S. Yocum and D. P. Hackett, *Plant Physiol.* **32,** 186 (1957)
Pea internodes	4×10^{-5}	2.5×10^{4}	E. Eichenberger and K. V. Thimann, *Arch. Biochem. Biophys.* **67,** 466 (1957)

[a] The values for plant tissues are probably low, since the methodology involves apparatus gas-diffusion problems that are difficult to overcome. Such problems are not encountered in liquid systems which use a platinum electrode.

C. LOCALIZATION OF ENZYMES IN CELLS

The first chapter of this volume considers the structure of the cell. Reference to this chapter underlines the fact that cytoplasm contains the nucleus, various plastids, mitochondria, and small, less-well-characterized bodies—bodies far smaller than can be resolved by the light microscope and for which the nomenclature is not yet clear. The term microsome is used to describe these small particles, even though the meaning of this term has changed through the years. With increasing knowledge and improving techniques, the term microsome has referred progressively to smaller and smaller particles. Today, the term is used exclusively by biochemists and the occurrence of these bodies as such in the living cell remains undecided.

Very rapid progress in the understanding of cellular respiration has resulted from the study of the localization of specific enzymes, or enzyme systems, within the cell. The most direct study of enzyme localization would be a cytological one; unfortunately, the problems of a direct cytological approach to enzyme localization have not been overcome. The cytological studies are dependent on pigment formation following the addition of suitable substances, such substances frequently being ones that form or change color following an oxidation or reduction. As yet it has been impossible to find substances which are specific for a particular enzyme or enzyme system, and one which reacts at the site of enzyme action. Thus, the cytologist is faced with formidable problems in the study of this important aspect of cellular geography.

The investigations of many cytologists have shown a gradation in size of the different cytoplasmic components, a gradation ranging from the largest, the nucleus, to the much smaller mitochondrion. Cytologists have considered the possibility of separating cytoplasmic components by taking advantage of the fact that variation in size (volume) is accompanied by a direct variation in mass and hence the components should be separable, one from the other, in different centrifugal fields. Such a technique, differential centrifugation, was first successfully applied by Bensley and Hoerr (7), later and more extensively by Hogeboom (60). The general availability of high-speed centrifuges since 1945 has lent great impetus to the study of intracellular localization of enzymes. In general, these techniques have included homogenization of the tissue in an isotonic medium followed by subjecting the homogenate to different centrifugal forces for various lengths of time. In application such methods are drastic, but surprisingly the same important conclusions may be drawn from the application of differential centrifugation to homogenates of many diverse types of tissues. These conclusions are summarized below; more extensive discussion is given by Brachet (13), Hacket (50), and Goddard and Stafford (46).

(1) The application of low centrifugal forces (300–500 *g*) for short time intervals results in the separation of the bulk of the nuclei, starch grains, and wall material.

(2) Centrifugal forces of 1000–2000 *g* for short periods of time sediments the larger plastids.

(3) Centrifugal forces of approximately 6000–10,000 *g* results in sedimentation of particulate matter (predominantly mitochondria), and with this fraction is associated most of the respiratory activity of the original tissue.

(4) High centrifugal forces (100,000 *g*) for periods of 1 hour or more sediment a material which is poorly characterized cytologically and biochemically. This sediment is referred to as the microsome fraction, a fraction whose respiratory function is undefined.

(5) The supernatant fluid obtained from the 100,000 *g* treatment contains the enzymes of glycolysis, among others.

The results of extensive studies clearly demonstrate that the enzymes involved in the oxidation of pyruvate as well as the system, or systems, in which the bulk of the energy of carbohydrate oxidation is made available to the cell are associated with the mitochondrial fraction. This latter phenomenon, the conservation of energy by cells, is associated with electron or hydrogen transport and the reaction of the cell with oxygen.

D. THE PATH OF ELECTRON TRANSPORT

From detailed studies of intact tissues and of heart muscle preparations Keilin and Hartree (71) proposed that the following sequence of reactions between succinic acid and oxygen occur during the oxidation of succinate to fumarate by the cytochrome system (the arrows indicate the path of electron transport).

$$\text{Succinate} \rightarrow \text{succinic dehydrogenase} \rightarrow \text{cyt.b} \rightarrow \text{cyt.c} \rightarrow \text{cyt.a} \rightarrow \text{cyt.a}_3 \rightarrow O_2 \quad (97)$$

It should be recognized that this is a sequence of reversible oxidation-reduction reactions. In the steady state the degree of oxidation or reduction of each component is determined by the relative concentration of each component, its velocity of oxidation and reduction, and the concentration of substrate and oxygen. In order that this sequence of reactions can act to transport electrons, there must be a gradient in potential from the substrate of oxidation to that of oxygen. That there is indeed such a gradient in oxidation-reduction potentials may be seen from Table XIII, where the oxidation-reduction potentials of various couples in the electron transport system are listed.

The study of the electron transport system can be carried out in a variety of ways; four such possible ways are mentioned, viz.: (a) the manometric or polarographic study of oxygen consumption of particulate preparations in the presence and absence of a variety of substrates and inhibitors; (b) observation of the absolute absorption spectra of tissues and preparations derived from them to determine the cytochrome components present, following treatment with specific substrates and inhibitors; (c) the use of difference spectra, such spectra being derived from the difference in absorption of tissues or tissue preparations under oxidizing and reducing conditions, and in the presence and absence of specific substrates and inhibitors; (d) by following the kinetics of the oxidation or reduction of a particular component of the system in relation to concentration of specific substrates or inhibitors. These points are better illustrated in Figs. 15–18.

Through the use of the double-beam spectrophotometer, it is possible to follow the kinetics of oxidation or reduction of a particular component of the system under prescribed conditions. Through the use of

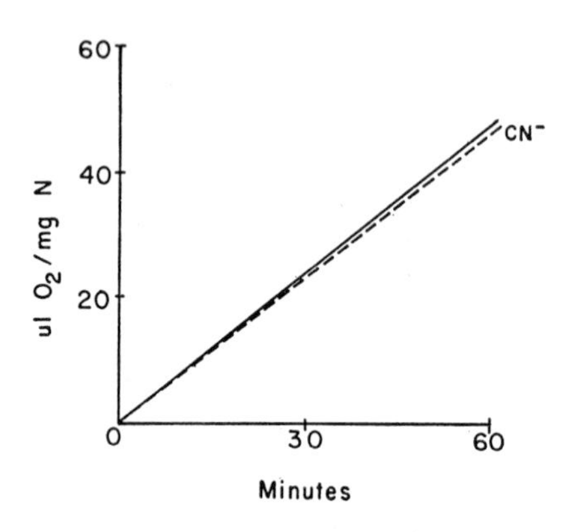

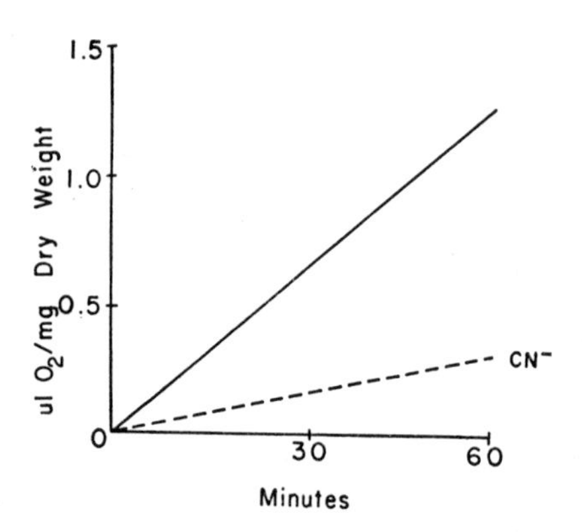

FIG. 15. Manometric estimation of the rate of oxygen utilization by plant tissues. Above: the time course of oxygen utilization of an aroid tissue, in air and in the presence of 2×10^{-4} *M* HCN. Below: similar data for carrot slices. The oxygen consumption of the aroid tissue is unaffected by HCN while that of carrot tissue is inhibited 73%. Data from Bonner, W. D., and Smith, S., unpublished.

manometric and optical techniques on a wide variety of tissue preparations and a wide variety of substrates and inhibitors, the original proposal of Keilin and Hartree has been modified. The electron transport system as now known is shown in Fig. 19. It should be emphasized that the transport system as illustrated remains tentative and will undergo modification in the future.

In plants the situation is more complex than that illustrated above. Keilin in 1925 pointed out that many plant tissues contain cytochrome but that there was a difference in the b component of the spectrum observed in yeast and muscle and that observed in higher plants. Table

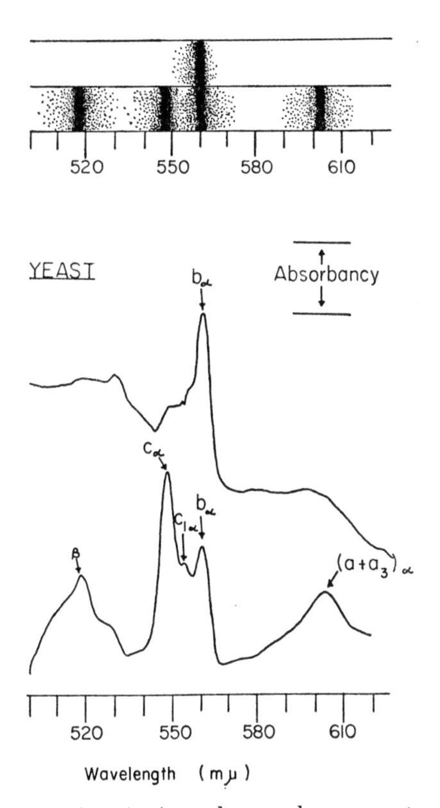

FIG. 16. The effect of antimycin A on the cytochrome spectrum of yeast cells. The line spectra show the absolute spectra as observed in a low-dispersion microspectroscope. The curves are difference spectra, the spectrum of starved, aerobic yeast cells minus that of yeast cells reduced with glucose in the presence and absence of antimycin A. The upper curve and the upper portion of the spectrum show the spectra of cells reduced with glucose in the presence of antimycin A; the lower curve and spectrum, glucose reduced yeast cells.

Inspection of the figure shows that the only component remaining in cells, reduced with substrate in the presence of antimycin A, is component b, hence antimycin A must inhibit electron transport between cytochromes b and c.

XVI shows the relative positions of the alpha bands of various components that have been described up to the present time. Many of these components have not been demonstrated in the tissues of plants; similarly, many of the components listed have not been shown to be present in animal tissues. At least two of the components listed in the table as occurring in plants are presumably not involved in respiratory electron transport; for example, cytochrome f and b_6 are found only in green tissues and are associated with the chloroplasts. That plants con-

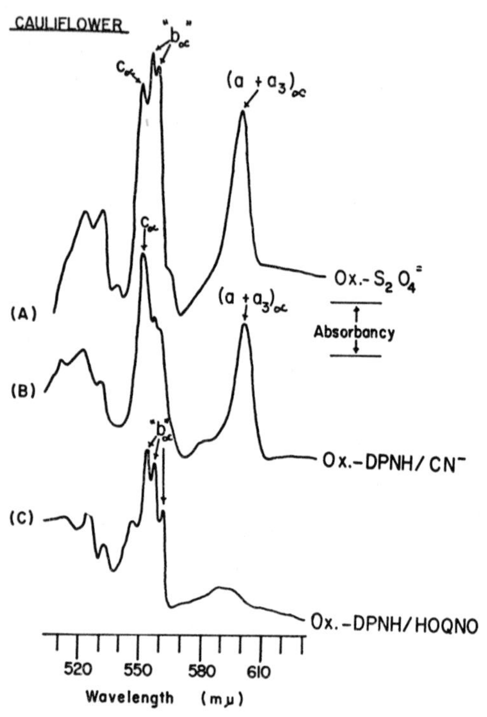

FIG. 17. Difference spectra of cauliflower-bud mitochondria.

(A) The difference in absorption between an aerobic suspension of mitochondria and a suspension reduced with sodium hydrosulfite.

(B) The difference in absorption between an aerobic suspension of mitochondria and a suspension reduced with DPNH in the presence of cyanide. Such a treatment keeps the $a + a_3$ and c components reduced while the b components tend to become oxidized.

(C) The difference in absorption between an aerobic suspension of mitochondria and a suspension reduced with DPNH in the presence of 8-hydroxy quinolin. Such a treatment, by interrupting electron transport between components b and c, keeps the b components reduced while the c becomes oxidized.

All spectra recorded at —190°C.

tain the components a, b, and c and that the transport of electrons during succinate oxidation proceeds as shown in Fig. 19 has been demonstrated. Okunuki (119) and Hill and Bhagvat (57, 58) were the first to demonstrate succinate oxidation by cell-free plant preparations; their demonstration has been confirmed by a wide variety of workers since

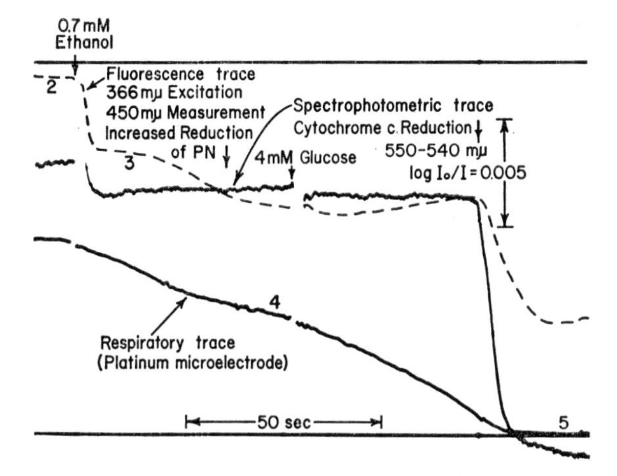

FIG. 18. An illustration of simultaneously following oxygen consumption (platinum microelectrode), cytochrome c reduction (double-beam spectrophotometer), and fluorescence of reduced pyridine nucleotide (oxidized pyridine nucleotide does not fluoresce) in a suspension of yeast cells. It may be seen that the addition of ethanol to the yeast cell suspension caused the immediate appearance of reduced pyridine nucleotide which was closely followed by a change in the steady-state reduction level of cytochrome c. Both of these events were accompanied by an increased rate of oxygen utilization. Further, when the oxygen concentration reached zero and the cells became anaerobic, cytochrome c became fully reduced, a reduction closely followed by pyridine nucleotide reduction. Unpublished data of Britton Chance (PN = pyridine nucleotide, i.e., DPNH).

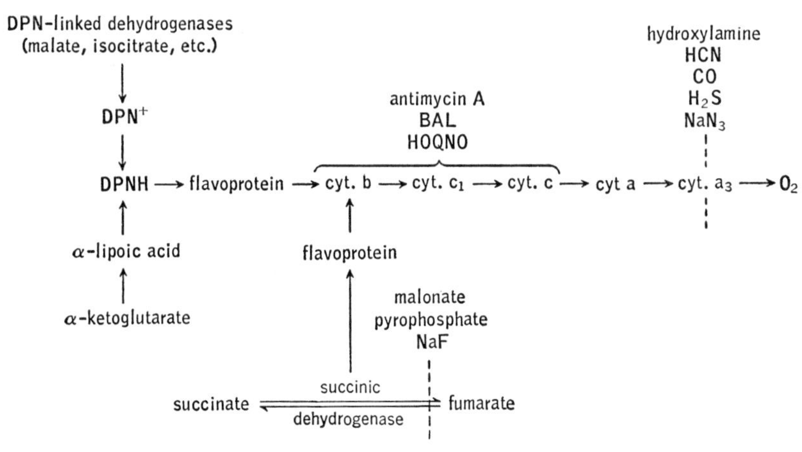

FIG. 19. The respiratory chain.

then. Oxidations by cell-free preparations from many plant sources exhibit photoreversible carbon monoxide inhibition, as well as cyanide and azide sensitivity. From these facts one must deduce that the electron transport system functions in plants as illustrated.

Many investigators have depended upon the photoreversible inhibition of respiration by carbon monoxide as evidence for the mediation of respiration by cytochrome oxidase and the cytochrome system. Failure to obtain the result has been interpreted as absence of cytochrome oxidase. Further, with some tissues the respiration is entirely insensitive to carbon monoxide and nearly so to cyanide. Bacterial cytochrome oxidases are known, as reviewed by Smith (135), which are inhibited by carbon monoxide without light reversal of the inhibition. Cytochrome oxidase is presumably a generic term, and considerable differences may exist between various oxidases.

The spadices of aroids (*Araceae*) are of particular interest because they have a very high respiration which is insensitive to cyanide and carbon monoxide, and yet the difference spectra show the typical bands of cytochrome a and a_3; and the oxidation of these reduced pigments by oxygen is blocked by carbon monoxide and cyanide. Further, these organs have a high affinity for oxygen in the presence of these inhibitors, so some other catalyst, perhaps a cytochrome b, is mediating election transport in the presence of inhibitor. Hackett and Haas (51) have found a decrease in oxidative phosphorylation in the presence of azide. It is thus clear that one cannot use the absence of photoreversible carbon monoxide inhibition or insensitivity to cyanide to draw conclusions concerning the absence of a particular cytochrome component.

Figure 20 shows the absolute absorption spectrum of particles derived from the spadices of skunk cabbage (*Symplocarpus foetidus*) before and after aeration in the presence of sodium azide. This, as well as other data derived from similar experiments, provides evidence that in many plants the reaction with oxygen can proceed via a pathway alternate to cytochromes a and a_3.

From the above discussion it will be realized that although many plants have electron transport systems seemingly like those of yeast, muscle, and bacteria, there still remain many cytochrome components whose role is unexplained, and basic problems remain in the understanding of the electron transport system.

Plants contain a large amount of heme in addition to the heme of cytochromes (59). In many tissues one of the major sources of such heme is found in the enzyme peroxidase, an enzyme discovered by Schönbein (127) and named by Linossier (88). Willstätter (163–165), was the first to purify the enzyme, but he did not realize that it con-

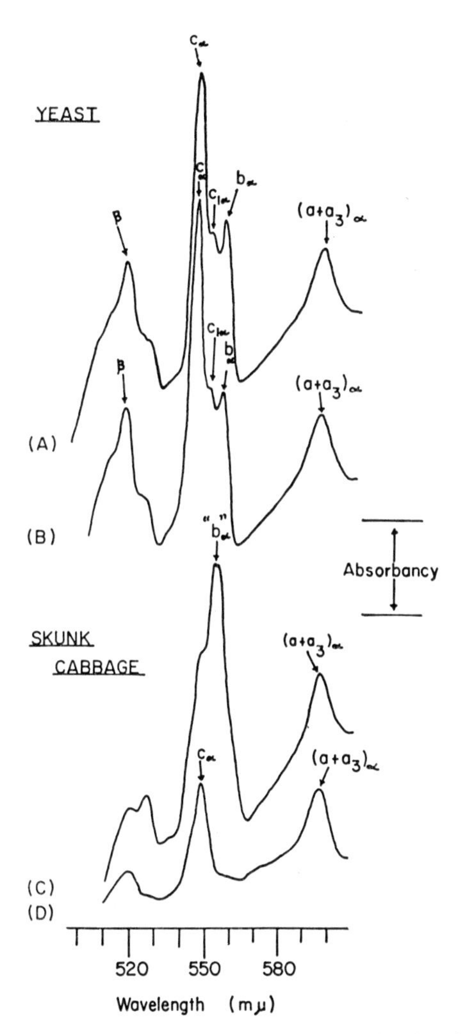

FIG. 20. The effect of cyanide on yeast cells and on skunk cabbage mitochondria. All spectra are difference spectra; the spectrum of oxidized cells or mitochondria minus substrate-reduced cells or mitochondria in the presence and absence of KCN. (A) Yeast cells reduced with glucose. (B) Yeast cells reduced with glucose in the presence of KCN. (C) Skunk cabbage mitochondria reduced with succinate. (D) Skunk cabbage mitochondria reduced with succinate in the presence of KCN.

tained heme. Kuhn and his associates (83) were the first to deduce that peroxidase was a hemoprotein, a fact that was confirmed by Sumner and Howell (140) and, in a definitive paper, by Keilin and Mann (73). Theorell (144, 145) isolated and crystallized peroxidase and then showed that the activity and characteristic absorption spectrum of the enzyme were lost by splitting the heme from the protein; recovery of both the activity and the spectrum were regained by recombination of the heme and protein.

Peroxidase in the presence of hydrogen peroxide catalyses the oxidation of phenolic substances and certain amines. The mechanism of reaction has been studied in detail by Keilin and Hartree, Chance and his associates, and by George. All of these investigations have been reviewed by Chance (20). The unusual feature of peroxidative reactions is that no complex between peroxidase and the substance being peroxidized has yet been described—rather hydrogen peroxide itself is the substrate for the enzyme. Hydrogen peroxide forms three distinct complexes with peroxidase. The first such complex has a life of very short duration and undergoes rearrangement to form complex II, the complex which is active in catalyzing peroxidation. Complex II decomposes in the presence of excess hydrogen peroxide forming a third, but inactive, peroxidase-hydrogen peroxide complex. These relationships are illustrated in equation (98). Fe^{+++} = peroxidase, H_2A = hydrogen donor; figures represent α-band absorption maxima.

$$\underset{645,583}{Fe^{+++}} + H_2O_2 \rightarrow \underset{658}{Fe^{+++}.H_2O_2I} \rightarrow \underset{561}{Fe^{+++}.H_2O_2II} + H_2A \rightarrow Fe^{+++} + 2\ H_2O + A;$$

$$\underset{583}{Fe^{+++}.H_2O_2III} \qquad (98)$$

Peroxidase, in addition to catalyzing reactions of the general nature outlined above, is capable of catalyzing the direct decomposition of hydrogen peroxide, an action like that of catalase and referred to as the catalactic action of peroxidase. The velocity of the later reaction is lower than that of catalase. Though peroxidase is found in a great variety of higher plants, the role of peroxidase in tissue respiration is not understood. Most investigations of peroxidase have been carried out with a purified enzyme from horse-radish (*Armoracia lapathifolia*) root and have been devoted to the mechanism of action and the properties of the intermediates. Chance (19) has shown that peroxidase can catalyze the oxidation of reduced cytochrome c, a reaction similar to that catalyzed by cytochrome c peroxidase, an enzyme found in yeast and several bacteria. The peroxidase-catalyzed reaction of reduced cytochrome c could provide a link between substrate and oxygen, but such a link has yet to be demonstrated.

Kenten and Mann (76) have demonstrated the presence of a peroxidase-catalyzed oxidation of Mn^{++} to Mn^{+++}; the H_2O_2 of the system they studied was provided by an amine oxidase which had been purified from pea seedlings. Using the peroxidase-H_2O_2-manganese system,

Kenten and Mann have demonstrated the oxidation of some dicarboxylic acids, although at a slow rate. The proposal that manganese could function in electron transport is by no means a new one, but there is as yet insufficient evidence to evaluate the significance of this proposal.

Another heme enzyme is catalase, an enzyme closely related to peroxidase. Raudnitz (125) and Loew (91) were the first to distinguish between the two catalysts peroxidase and catalase. Catalase was named by Loew in 1901 and first prepared in crystalline form by Sumner and Dounce in 1937 (139). Whether the crystalline catalase has the identical properties of the native enzyme is still uncertain.

Both catalase and peroxidase react with the same substrate H_2O_2 and form reasonably similar addition compounds with hydrogen peroxide, but catalase, unlike peroxidase, can use hydrogen peroxide both as electron donor and acceptor at the same time, the net result being the well-known decomposition:

$$2\ H_2O_2 \rightarrow O_2 + 2\ H_2O \quad (99)$$

At low hydrogen peroxide concentrations (approximately 10^{-9} *M*) catalase can also function as a peroxidase; this was first demonstrated by Keilin and Hartree (72). In their experiments, hydrogen peroxide was generated by a flavoprotein, oxidizing xanthine, and the H_2O_2 produced in this reaction was used with catalase to oxidize aldehyde or alcohol. It is now generally believed that the main function of catalase is as a peroxidase. Catalase is not widely distributed in higher plants but does occur in high concentration in yeast, bacteria, and animal tissues. When catalase is found in higher plants the concentration is low. Many of the reports of catalase in higher plants are doubtless due to peroxidase present in relatively high concentrations acting catalactically.

The cytochromes, peroxidase, and catalase have in common their protohematin character, but there is more protohematin in plant tissues than can be accounted for by the above-named substances. The nature of the additional heme, which in some cases can be a considerable portion of the total heme, is unknown. Hemoglobin is found in the nodules of legumes, but only in nodules actively fixing nitrogen (75). Hemoglobin has also been found in *Neurospora,* and there is a possibility that it may be more widespread than we realize. Since cytochromes have been suspected of playing a role in photosynthesis and since some cytochromes are capable of photoreduction, there may remain some as yet undiscovered cytochromes in this unknown heme fraction which could play a role in the varied physiological responses of higher plants to light.

TABLE XVIII
THE COPPER PROTEINS

Enzyme	Discovered by	Absorption maxima (mμ)	Molecular weight	Copper content (%)	Atoms copper per mole protein	Activity Q_{O_2}	E_0' (volts at pH 7.0)	Substrates for oxidation	Sensitivity to: CN^- N_3^- S^-	Sensitivity to: CO	Affinity constant ($1/K_m$)	References
Laccase	Yoshida 1883	615 280 Deep blue color	120,000	0.22	4	8000 Hydroquinone	+.415	Laccol, Urushiol, Hydroquinone, *p*-Phenylenediamine, Ascorbic acid	Inhibited	Not inhibited		6,9,13, 14,15
Phenol oxidase	Borquelot and Bertrand 1895	Colorless	100,000	0.25	4	1.5×10^6 Catechol	?	*o*-Diphenols (pure), O-di- and monophenols (crude)	Inhibited	Inhibited; not light-reversible	3×10^4 7×10^4 (apparent)	1,2,3,5, 7,8,10
Ascorbic acid oxidase	Szent-Györgyi 1931	605 288 Blue-green	150,000	0.25	6	1.5×10^6	?	Ascorbic acid	Inhibited	Not inhibited	3×10^3 (apparent)	2,3,4, 11,12

E. COPPER PROTEINS

The copper proteins, laccase and phenol oxidase, were among the earliest-known enzymes. These two enzymes, which are found in a large number of higher and lower plants, have the ability to react directly with oxygen and, by the classical definition, are, therefore, oxidases. A third copper protein, ascorbic acid oxidase, is also widely distributed in higher plants.

As far as is known, the oxygen affinity of the copper protein oxidases is low, in fact lower than the oxygen affinity of the tissues from which copper proteins are extracted. Many efforts have been made to involve the copper proteins in cellular respiration as the catalyst mediating the reaction to oxygen; such efforts have as yet been unsuccessful.

There has been a great deal of effort devoted to the study of the copper proteins, and, consequently, a voluminous literature has developed. In contrast to the majority of the cytochromes, the three copper protein oxidases are readily brought into solution and hence to a high degree of purity. In spite of this fact the present state of knowledge concerning the fundamental properties of the copper proteins is woefully inadequate. There are also indications that the properties of these enzymes as studied in homogenates and particulate preparations are quite different from the properties of the highly purified enzyme. In Table XVIII are tabulated the properties of the three copper protein

---

References for Table XVIII

1. Bourquelot, E., and Bertrand, S., *Compt. rend. soc. biol.* **121,** 783 (1895).
2. Dawson, C. R., and Tarpley, W. B., *in* "The Enzymes" (J. B. Sumner and K. Myrbäck, eds.), Vol. II, Part I, p. 492. Academic Press, New York, 1951.
3. Dawson, C. R., and Magee, R. J., *in* "Methods in Enzymology" (S. P. Colowick and N. O. Kaplan, eds.), Vol. II, pp. 817 and 837. Academic Press, New York, 1955.
4. Dunn, F. J., and Dawson, C. R., *J. Biol. Chem.* **189,** 485 (1951).
5. Keilin, D., and Mann, T., *Proc. Roy. Soc.* **B125,** 187 (1938).
6. Keilin, D., and Mann, T., *Nature* **143,** 23 (1939); **145,** 304 (1940).
7. Kubowitz, F., *Biochem. Z.* **292,** 221 (1937); **299,** 32 (1938).
8. Mallette, M. F., and Dawson, C. R., *Arch. Biochem.* **23,** 29 (1949).
9. Nakamura, T., *Biochim. et Biophys. Acta* **30,** 44 (1958); **30,** 538 (1958); **30,** 640 (1958).
10. Sisler, E. C., and Evans, H. J., *Plant Physiol.* **34,** 81 (1959).
11. Szent-Györgyi, A., *J. Biol. Chem.* **90,** 385 (1931).
12. Thimann, K. V., Yocum, C. S., and Hackett, D. P., *Arch. Biochem. Biophys.* **53,** 239 (1954).
13. Tissières, A., *Nature* **162,** 340 (1948).
14. Yakushiji, E., *Acta Phytochim.* (*Japan*) **12,** 22 (1941).
15. Yoshida, H., *J. Chem. Soc.* **43,** 472 (1883).

oxidases in so far as they are known at the present time. Some of the properties of each of these copper proteins will be discussed briefly. The copper proteins are reviewed by Bonner (12).

1. Laccase

Historically, laccase is one of the oldest-known catalysts. Although first described by Yoshida in 1883 and named by Bertrand in 1894, the enzyme has been used for centuries in the manufacture of the beautiful and durable lacquer wares of the Far East, especially of Japan. Laccase is found in abundance in the latex produced by plants of the genus *Rhus* and will, in the presence of air, oxidize either or both of the two phenolic substances, urushiol and laccol, also present in the latex.

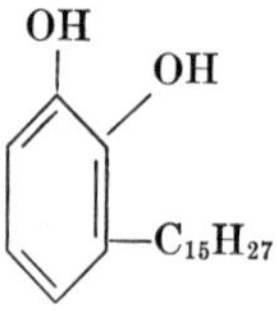

OH OH —$C_{15}H_{27}$

Urushiol

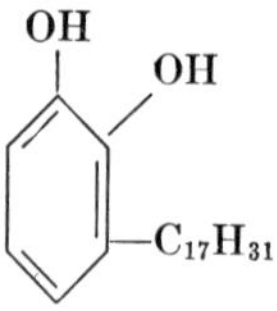

OH OH —$C_{17}H_{31}$

Laccol

These two substances characteristically produce irritations on the skin, as do similar compounds found in poison ivy (*Rhus radicans*), poison oak (*R. toxicodendron*), etc. The first quantitative work on the enzyme was carried out by Keilin and Mann (for references, see Table XVIII), who established the fact that it was a blue copper protein. The color may be inferred from the report that it was comparable to a 7% copper sulfate solution. The fact that the activity of laccase was dependent on copper was quantitatively confirmed by Tissières, who removed the copper from a purified laccase preparation by dialysis against cyanide. The resulting inactive protein could be reactivated only by the addition of cupric ions. No other metal ion could substitute for copper. More recently Nakamura has considerably extended our knowledge concerning the properties of purified laccase. Nakamura is the first to demonstrate the fact that a plant copper protein oxidase acts, as an oxidase, by virtue of a reversible valence change of the enzyme copper. Such a reversible valence change had been assumed to occur in copper protein oxidases but had never before been demonstrated. At the present time the physiological role of laccase is unknown.

2. Phenol Oxidase

The enzymatic oxidation of phenolic substances has been the subject of great interest for many years, an interest initiated by the often dramatic color changes that take place following the injury of various plant tissues. The first detailed study of such reactions was made by Schönbein (1856), just following his discovery of ozone. Schönbein's observations, in the form of a letter to Faraday, were published by Faraday; this brief paper (126) is probably the first demonstration of the catalytic effectiveness of living tissues on a chemical reaction.

The investigations of Bertrand, Kubowitz, Keilin, and Mann, and Dawson and co-workers have revealed many of the properties of phenol oxidase (Table XVIII). A curious feature of phenol oxidase is the ability of crude preparations to catalyze the oxidation of monophenols and *o*-diphenols while highly purified enzyme preparations can use only *o*-diphenols as substrates. The substrate specificity of crude and purified enzyme preparations has been studied in detail by

(a) OH + $\frac{1}{2}O_2$ ⟶ OH, OH

(b) OH, OH + $\frac{1}{2}O_2$ ⟶ O, O + H_2O

(c) O, O + H_2O ⟶ OH, OH, OH

(d) OH, OH, OH + O, O ⟶ OH, OH + O, O, OH ⟶ [O, O, OH]$_n$

(100)

(e) OH, OH + $\frac{1}{2}O_2$ ⟶ O, O + H_2O

(f) Sum:

OH + $1\frac{1}{2}O_2$ ⟶ O, O, OH + H_2O

numerous investigators, but the problem of substrate specificity is still unsettled. When phenol oxidase acts on mono- and diphenols, the end products are characteristically highly colored or black. However, in most higher plants, such colored compounds are produced in the tissues only after an injury or during senescence. The sequence of chemical events that has been proposed (100) for the enzymatic oxidation of phenol or catechol is given in equation (100).

An unexplained feature of the above reaction sequence is the rapid inactivation of the enzyme during *o*-diphenol oxidation while the oxidation of monophenols remains linear for long periods of time.

Reaction *a* (eq. 100) is an enzymatically catalyzed hydroxylation of an aromatic nucleus, a reaction first studied by Raper (124), who showed that the enzymatic oxidation of tyrosine resulted in the production of dihydroxyphenylalanine as an intermediate. More recently Mason *et al.* (102) have shown the following reaction to be catalyzed by phenol oxidase:

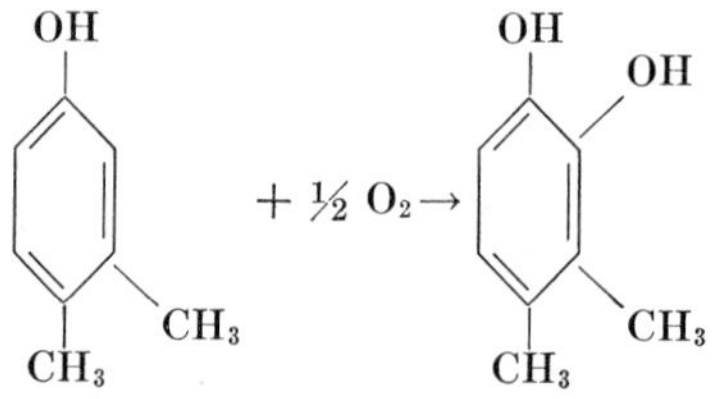

$$\text{OH, CH}_3\text{, CH}_3 \text{ (ring)} + \tfrac{1}{2}\,O_2 \rightarrow \text{OH, OH, CH}_3\text{, CH}_3 \text{ (ring)} \qquad (101)$$

The hydroxylation was followed using O^{18}; the oxygen of the *o*-hydroxyl group was not derived from water, only from oxygen. Hence, such a hydroxylation reaction is an aerobic reaction, even though, owing to the low apparent oxygen affinity, the reaction rate is limited by oxygen concentration.

While the two sequences of reactions outlined above may provide the link between phenolic compounds and some of the colored substances found in plants, such reactions probably do not play any direct role in the respiratory processes of plant tissues.

Kubowitz (81) deduced that phenol oxidase transferred electrons through a valence change of the copper; he further suggested that the important reaction in this electron transfer was the reversible oxidation of a diphenol to a quinone. Further, in the presence of a suitable reducing agent and a limited amount of *o*-diphenol, the *o*-diphenol-quinone reaction would function as an electron transport pair, the net result being oxidation of the reducing agent. Suitable reducing agents are ascorbic acid, reduced pyridine nucleotides, etc. Such a system can be described in the following series of equations, here designated equation (102).

$$
\begin{array}{lll}
\text{(a) DPNH} + H^+ + \text{quinone} & \rightarrow & DPN^+ + \text{catechol} \\
\text{(b) Catechol} + 2\ Cu^{++} & \rightarrow & \text{quinone} + 2\ Cu^+ + 2\ H^+ \\
\text{(c) } 2\ Cu^+ + 2\ H^+ + \frac{1}{2}\ O_2 & \rightarrow & 2\ Cu^{++} + H_2O \\
\hline
\text{(d) DPNH} + H^+ + \frac{1}{2}\ O_2 & \rightarrow & DPN^+ + H_2O
\end{array}
\qquad (102)
$$

It must be pointed out that reactions *b* and *c*, although very reasonable reactions, have never been subjected to experimental proof. Nevertheless, the above sequence of reactions has played a central role in the arguments that have been presented in support of the hypothesis that phenol oxidase plays the role of an oxidase, linking cellular oxidations to oxygen.

All efforts to demonstrate that phenol oxidase catalyzes the transfer of electrons to oxygen in tissue respiration have failed to consider two essential points, viz.: (a) the low affinity of phenol oxidase for oxygen as compared to that of the tissues themselves, and (b) the available evidence that plants do indeed contain cytochromes.

The view that phenol oxidase played a fundamental role in plant respiration obtained its impetus from Bach and Chodat and was nurtured by Onslow, Boswell, and Whiting and many others. The early work is summarized by Onslow (120). However, modern work has not lent support to these views. The group of enzymes of unknown physiological role, to which phenol oxidase belongs, presents an exciting challenge to future investigators in this field.

3. *Ascorbic Acid Oxidase*

Ascorbic acid oxidase is another copper protein for which a large and detailed literature has accumulated (see review of Dawson and Tarpley, 29). This enzyme has been prepared in a highly purified state and many of its physical properties are known (Table XVIII). Unlike phenol oxidase, ascorbic acid oxidase is very substrate specific, the reaction proceeding as follows:

```
       O                              O
       ‖                              ‖
       C─────────┐                    C─────────┐
       |         |                    |         |
   H─C─OH        |                   C=O        |
       |         O + O₂ →             |         O + H₂O₂        (103)
   H─C─OH        |                   C=O        |
       |         |                    |         |
   H─C───────────┘               H─C────────────┘
       |                              |
  HO─C─H                        HO─C─H
       |                              |
     CH₂OH                          CH₂OH
  Ascorbic acid                Dehydroascorbic acid
```

In the pure state ascorbic acid oxidase is blue-green in color; the color fades to yellow during the aerobic oxidation of ascorbic acid. The essentiality of copper for catalytic activity of the enzyme is provided by the sensitivity to cyanide, sulfide, etc., and by the demonstration that removal of copper by dialysis of the enzyme against cyanide inactivates the enzyme; activity can be restored only by the addition of copper. As in the case of phenol oxidase, evidence for a valence change in copper during catalysis is lacking.

The suggestion that ascorbic acid oxidase could function as an oxidase in plants, a suggestion first made by Szent-Györgyi (141), has received considerable support from studies on plants in which respiration is stable to carbon monoxide. Again, there has been no cognizance of the relation between the oxygen affinities of the enzyme and the tissue in question. Reference to Table XVIII shows that at the oxygen tension of air, ascorbic acid oxidase activity is more than 50% inhibited. This fact, coupled with the high oxygen affinity of plant tissues is sufficient evidence to preclude any major role for ascorbic acid oxidase in transferring electrons to oxygen. As may be the case with the other copper proteins, ascorbic acid oxidase might be an oxidase by virtue of cell rupture; in intact tissue it could act in electron transport to an acceptor other than oxygen.

Like the other copper protein oxidases, it is possible to establish an artificial system which can carry out the oxidation of reduced pyridine nucleotides, a system which can then be coupled to dehydrogenases and their substrates. The evidence which provides the basis of an artificial ascorbic acid oxidase system accumulated for twenty years. Following Szent-Györgyi's discovery of ascorbic acid oxidase in 1931 came the finding of Crook and Hopkins in 1938 (26) of dehydroascorbic acid reductase.

In 1951, Mapson and Goddard (101) and Conn and Vennesland (25) simultaneously announced the finding of the TPNH-specific enzyme glutathione reductase, an enzyme which reduces the disulfide dimer of glutathione to glutathione. With this latter discovery the following sequence of reactions (eq. 104) could be demonstrated:

$$\begin{array}{l} \text{TPNH} + \text{H}^+ + \text{G—S—S—G} \rightarrow \text{TPN}^+ + \text{GSH} \\ 2\ \text{GSH} + \text{dehydroascorbic acid} \rightarrow \text{ascorbic acid} + \text{G—S—S—G} \\ \text{Ascorbic acid} + \text{O}_2 \rightarrow \text{dehydroascorbic acid} + \text{H}_2\text{O}_2 \\ \hline \text{TPNH} + \text{H}^+ + \text{O}_2 \rightarrow \text{TPN}^+ + \text{H}_2\text{O}_2 \end{array} \tag{104}$$

In the original experiments, the TPNH was provided by isocitric acid and its dehydrogenase or by glucose-6-phosphate and its dehydrogenase. In view of the conclusions that have been reached concerning the doubtful role that ascorbic acid oxidase plays as an oxidase, it seems that such a sequence of reactions must contribute almost nothing to cellular respiration. However, the above sequence of reactions does provide a mechanism for the oxidation of TPNH.

F. FLAVOPROTEINS

The cells of bacteria, plants, and animals contain a considerable amount of flavin pigments. The major portion of these pigments is bound to protein and is known as flavoprotein. The two abundant flavins which can serve as prosthetic groups are: riboflavin-5[1]-phosphate, also known as flavin mononucleotide (FMN), and flavin adenine dinucleotide (FAD). The isoalloxazine nucleus of the nucleotides may undergo reversible oxidation and reduction, as is illustrated in equation (105).

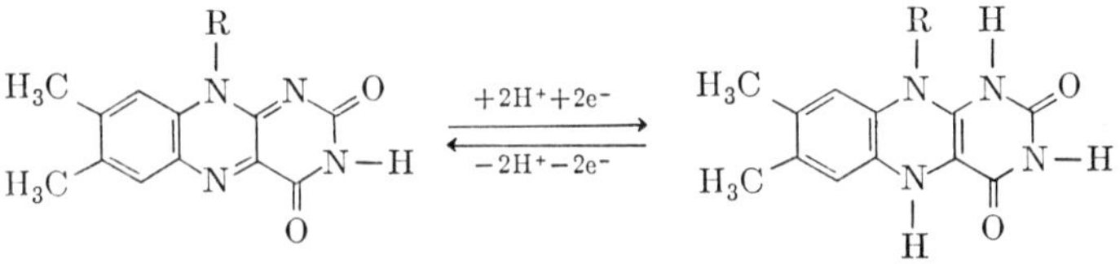

$$\text{Oxidized flavin (Leucoflavin)} \underset{-2H^+ - 2e^-}{\overset{+2H^+ + 2e^-}{\rightleftharpoons}} \text{Reduced flavin} \qquad (105)$$

Oxidized flavin
(Leucoflavin)

Reduced flavin

$$R = \text{Ribityl phosphate: } -CH_2-C(OH)(H)-C(OH)(H)-C(OH)(H)-CH_2OP(=O)(OH)OH$$

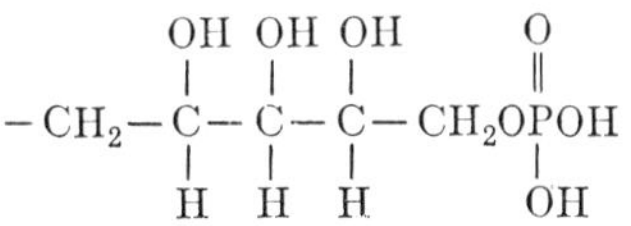

The leucoflavin is colorless, while the flavin is a yellow compound which absorbs blue light and, when excited by ultraviolet light, strongly fluoresces green light. Reviews dealing with the flavoproteins have been published by Theorell (144) and by Meeuse (105).

The flavins were first discovered by Warburg and Christian in 1932, who isolated a flavoprotein from yeast. The structure of the flavin, established by Kuhn, Györgyi and Wagner-Jauregg and Theorell (see review of Theorell), showed that flavoproteins could be separated into a specific protein and riboflavin phosphate.

Since flavoproteins were oxidized by molecular oxygen (though slowly) and the oxidation was strongly dependent upon oxygen pressure (even up to 1 atmosphere pressure), the view developed that they were cellular oxidases. It is possible that the respiration of the normally anaerobic bacteria *Streptococcus faecalis* and *Lactobacillus delbrueckii* is catalyzed by a flavoprotein. However, Theorell showed that the yellow enzyme of Warburg was oxidized by cytochrome c, and Haas and associates (49) showed that a flavoprotein isolated from yeast was oxidized 10^6 times faster with cytochrome c than with atmospheric O_2. In spite of many efforts to show that cyanide-resistant respiration is mediated by a flavoprotein functioning as an oxidase, overwhelming evidence is against this view.

Haas, Horecker and Hogness (see Haas, 48 and Horecker, 62) isolated a flavoprotein with a prosthetic group of flavin mononucleotide which was specifically reduced by TPNH and reoxidized by ferricytochrome c. This enzyme was called TPNH cytochrome c reductase. TPNH cytochrome c reductase is quite widely distributed; it can be used in model systems as follows:

$$\text{TPNH} + 2 \text{ ferricytochrome c} \rightleftarrows \text{TPN}^+ + 2 \text{ ferrocytochrome c} + \text{H}^+ \quad (106)$$

Such systems can be assayed by the marked change in spectral absorption at 340 mμ, since the reduced form of the pyridine nucleotide absorbs strongly while the oxidized form does not absorb at this wavelength. In spite of the high velocity of such reactions, the contribution of TPNH cytochrome c reductase to cellular respiration is obscure, as it does not occur in mitochondria, nor become reduced in anaerobic cells.

An analogous enzyme, DPNH cytochrome c reductase, has been isolated by Mahler and associates (99). This latter enzyme is presumably a flavoprotein which transfers electrons to cytochrome c, but the properties of the soluble enzyme are very different from those of the particulate bound enzyme. Over and above the evidence of Tsou and Wu (150, 168) it is clear that in the mitochondrial reactions leading from DPNH to oxygen the path of transport is from flavoprotein to cytochrome b. In the soluble "reductase" preparations the reaction is with cytochrome c. Clearly, these two situations are not analogous.

Succinic dehydrogenase is a metalloflavoprotein which contains nonhematin iron (131, 155, 156).

The term diaphorase has been used for flavoproteins that function in the transfer of hydrogen from dehydrogenase plus coenzyme to dyes such as methylene blue or 2,6-dichlorophenolindophenol. The physiological role of diaphorase is unknown.

Several other flavoproteins are known: the so-called D-amino acid oxidase, xanthine oxidase, and nitrate reductase. It is doubtful if any of these compounds directly transport electrons to oxygen. If they function in respiration their probable role is in electron transport at levels lower than oxygen. Only a small part of the total flavoprotein content of cells has been shown to undergo reduction when respiring cells become anaerobic. The role of the remaining flavoprotein remains uncertain.

IV. The Utilization of Energy

A. OXIDATIVE PHOSPHORYLATION

The heat of combustion of glucose is 674 kcal and the standard free-energy change is approximately 686 kcal. However, if the cell is to grow, accumulate substances against a concentration gradient, and synthesize large molecules from smaller ones, not all of this energy can be liberated as heat. The heat produced in respiration is lost to the cell in the sense that it cannot be used for work. Work can be performed only when there is a potential difference or gradient, and for the cell to function with an efficiency of 25% at 25°C there would have to be a temperature difference of 99°C maintained within the dimensions of a single cell, or perhaps within the dimensions of a single mitochondrion. No such temperature differences can occur in an aqueous environment. Another mechanism for producing cellular work must exist.

Cells are essentially molecular engines, conserving the energy within chemical bonds and using the energy released in the degradation of one bond to synthesize another. An example of this mechanism was given on the transglucosidation (page 231). Of even greater interest are the mechanisms whereby part of the energy released in oxidation reactions is stored in new chemical bonds.

The only mechanism that is well worked out is the coupling of the reactions of oxidation with the esterification of inorganic phosphate to form organically bound pyrophosphate. The acceptor of the inorganic phosphate is ADP, which is esterified with phosphate to form ATP, though other pyrimidine diphosphates may function in a similar manner; examples are uridine, guanine, and inosine diphosphates. The triphosphates of uridine, guanine, and inosine may also be synthesized in exchange reactions with ATP. For example, enzymes termed nucleoside diphosphokinases are known which catalyze to transphosphorylation:

$$\mathrm{ATP} + \begin{matrix}\mathrm{UDP}\\ \text{or}\\ \mathrm{GDP}\\ \text{or}\\ \mathrm{IDP}\end{matrix} \rightleftharpoons \mathrm{ADP} + \begin{matrix}\mathrm{UTP}\\ \text{or}\\ \mathrm{GTP}\\ \text{or}\\ \mathrm{ITP}\end{matrix} \qquad (107)$$

The energy stored in the pyrimidine triphosphates may later be used to drive synthetic reactions, reactions that, considered apart from the pyrimidine nucleotide, would have a free-energy increase.

Earlier in this chapter in describing intermediary reactions of fermentation we have described the coupled phosphorylation of ADP to

ATP which occurs upon the oxidation of phosphoglyceric aldehyde to phosphoglyceric acid by DPN. This type of phosphorylation is independent of aerobic oxidation. In the late 1930's Kalckar observed (67) that there was aerobic oxidation-dependent phosphorylation of inorganic phosphate. This fact was confirmed and shown to involve the conversion of ADP to ATP by Belitser and Tsybakova in Russia (4, 5) and by Needham and co-workers (113a) in England. In 1941 Colowick *et al.* (24) found that no less than ten molecules of phosphate were esterified for each molecule of glucose oxidized; Ochoa in 1941 (116) obtained evidence that even higer amounts of phosphate could be esterified. Most of these early studies were conducted with crude extracts and without correlation with the specific steps at which esterification occurred. It soon became apparent, however, that the oxidation of the various organic acids, normally considered components of the citric acid cycle, was part of the esterification mechanism. In spite of a wide variety of individual studies, reviewed by Hunter (64) and by Kaplan (68) the elucidation of the problem depended upon accumulating knowledge of mitochondria which had been isolated in a reasonably undamaged state. In 1948 and 1949 several workers (64), using preparations now known to be animal mitochondria, showed that the oxidation of DPNH or any one of a variety of organic acids led to the synthesis of ATP. The methodology may be of some interest, since the hydrolysis of the ATP formed, or other side reactions, would tend to lower the apparent ratio of phosphate atoms esterified to atoms of oxygen used (P:O ratio). The phosphate of the newly formed ATP was trapped as glucose-6-phosphate simply by the addition of purified hexokinase and glucose. In addition, possible hydrolysis of ATP was prevented by the addition of fluoride. In the last few years the P:O ratios of several oxidations have been shown to have limiting values: 1.8 for succinate, 2.8 for DPNH- and DPN-linked dehydrogenase systems, and 3.7 for α-ketoglutarate where an additional phosphate is esterified in the conversion of α-ketoglutarate to succinate. It was previously known that if mitochondria were harshly treated or allowed to age they could still transport electrons from substrate to oxygen but were unable to esterify ADP.

It was not until 1951 that Millerd *et al.* (112) first demonstrated that mitochondrial preparations from plants had the capacity for oxidative phosphorylation. Their preparations gave P:O ratios of approximately one. However, when Laties (84) carefully studied the conditions for the preparation and stabilization of mitochondria he obtained evidence that plant mitochondria were probably identical, as far as the mechanism of oxidative phosphorylation is concerned, to those of animals—a view that has been substantiated by many different workers.

The mechanism of the phosphorylation which is coupled with electron transport to oxygen is not understood. As stated above, the limiting P:O ratios vary according to the substrate being oxidized, a logical variation in view of the fact that it takes a potential difference of approximately 0.25 volt to synthesize ATP from ADP. Such potential differences are dependent on the point where the substrate of oxidation enters the respiratory chain. The relationship between the oxidation-reduction potential of substrate and the number of phosphorylating steps is illustrated in Table XIX.

TABLE XIX
RELATION BETWEEN OXIDATION-REDUCTION POTENTIAL AND NUMBER OF PHOSPHORYLATING STEPS

Substrate of oxidation	Oxidation-reduction potential (volts)	P:O ratio	Number of phosphorylating steps
α-Ketoglutarate	−0.68	3–4	4
DPNH	−0.320	2–3	3
Succinate	−0.015	1–2	2

The localization of the individual phosphorylation steps in the respiratory chain has proved to be difficult. There is as yet no completely satisfactory solution to this problem. Two approaches have been used extensively in the study of the phosphorylation sites: studies on isolated portions of the respiratory chain and studies of the steady state conditions that prevail between the components of the respiratory chain as determined in isolated mitochondria under a wide variety of conditions. From such studies it is thought that, apart from the formation of ATP between α-ketoglutarate and DPN (see equation 77), there are two phosphorylation sites between DPNH and cytochrome c, and one between cytochrome c and oxygen. These sites of phosphorylation are indicated in Fig. 21. Because of the many unusual complexities involved in the study of cellular energy conservation and because of the fluid state of our present knowledge, a detailed review of respiratory chain phosphorylation is out of order here. Present knowledge and the problems of study of respiratory chain phosphorylation are reviewed by Chance and Williams (23) and by Slater (132, 133). Unfortunately, at the present time there is little intimate knowledge of the respiratory chain and phosphorylation in plant tissues.

It is clear that oxidative phosphorylation, regardless of its mechanism, is a molecular reaction, and a reaction in which the energy is not transferred through the aqueous solution of the cell. Such a molecular energy transfer reaction will require something to accept the energy and accept it in such a form that the energy can be made available for the phosphorylation of ADP. Such an intermediate substance has been proposed by various investigators. Because of considerations arising from the effects of ADP and dinitrophenol (DNP) on phosphorylation and on respiratory rates (see below), it is proposed (Chance and Williams, 23) that the formation and utilization of the

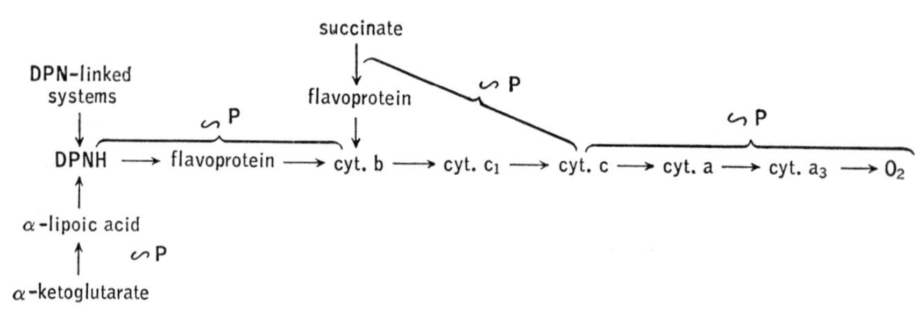

FIG. 21. Possible phosphorylative sites in the respiratory chain.

phosphorylation intermediate, $X \sim I$, is the rate-limiting step in the over-all system. The mechanism that has been proposed is shown below:

$$\begin{aligned} AH_2 + B + I &\rightleftharpoons A \sim I + BH_2 \\ A \sim I + X &\rightleftharpoons A + X \sim I \\ X \sim I + ADP + H_3PO_4 &\rightleftharpoons X + I + ATP \end{aligned} \tag{108}$$

Such a mechanism involves not only the hypothetical substances X and I but also suggests a direct combination of I with DPN or with the specific cytochrome involved. Undoubtedly, the above hypothesis will be revised with increasing knowledge of respiratory chain phosphorylation.

As stated earlier, the change in free energy for the oxidation of one mole of hexose, under standard conditions, is −686 kcal. The energy of formation of ATP and ADP is of the order of 8 to 14 kcal, but it must be remembered that this value depends on the molar concentrations of the reaction partners at any given time, the molar concentrations varying under different steady state conditions. Assuming an average value of 10 kcal for the reaction $ADP \rightleftharpoons ATP$ and remembering that it takes 12 atoms of oxygen for the oxidation of 1 mole of hexose and that the production of ATP per molecule of hexose varies from 1 (substrate level phosphorylation) to 4 (α-ketoglutarate oxidation), one can see that the production of ATP varies from 12 moles per mole hexose, an efficiency of $^{120}/_{686}$ (17.5%), to 40, an efficiency of $^{480}/_{686}$ (approximately 60%). From these simple calculations it is readily seen that during the process of cellular respiration it is indeed the final stages where most of the energy of hexose is conserved for cellular work.

B. RESPIRATORY CONTROL

One of the most fascinating aspects of cellular respiration, and one in which physiologists are just beginning to obtain insight, is the control of cellular respiration. It is obvious that in such a closely knit system as that described and in a system that is capable of very rapid reaction rates there must be some means of control of ATP production on the one hand and heat formation on the other. Students of animal physiology have known for a long time that feeding 2,4-dinitrophenol (DNP) to an animal results in high temperatures, loss of mobile activity, and death. DNP produces similar results in plants: loss of all metabolically mediated physiological activities and increased respiratory rates. Loomis and Lipmann in 1948 (94) found that the effect of DNP was to uncouple the process of ATP formation from that of electron transport. In other words, oxygen uptake, in the presence of DNP, is unaffected or even increased while the formation of ATP is markedly inhibited. From many experiments of this type we must deduce that the process of phosphorylation itself restricts the rate of electron transport through the system. The mechanism of this type of control will remain obscure until physiologists can understand more completely the nature of this type of phosphorylation.

Well-washed, freshly prepared and intact mitochondria have a low rate of endogenous respiration. On the addition of substrate to such fresh mitochondria the respiratory activity increases somewhat but not greatly. However, the addition of ADP immediately results in a dramatic increase in the rate of oxygen consumption. If the amount of added ADP is kept small, this increase is only temporary and in a short period of time the original rate as found in substrate alone is re-established. Studies of this kind (21, 23) have shown that the stimulated rate of oxidation decreases as the concentration of ADP falls off during its conversion to ATP. Here then is another major control of the rate of cellular respiration, the concentration of the phosphate acceptor relative to the concentration of the phosphorylated acceptor. Tissues that are not performing much cellular work will have a high phosphorylated acceptor concentration relative to the phosphate acceptor concentration and their rate of oxygen consumption will be at a minimum. When the tissue is called on to perform work, however, this situation is reversed and the rate of oxygen consumption will increase in response to the increased ADP level, resulting in additional ATP synthesis. Such considerations enable us to understand many observations which have been made in the past, for example the so-called "ground respiration" and "salt respiration."

A third type of respiratory control is the concentration of inorganic phosphate. Inorganic phosphate may control respiratory rates in two ways. First, the concentration of phosphate at any given site within a cell is governed by its rate of usage and its rate of replacement, the latter depending on the diffusion rate of phosphate through the cytoplasm to the point of usage. Secondly, there is considerable evidence that indicates the need for inorganic phosphate in maintaining the right spatial relationships of the electron transport components, that is to say, in providing free accessibility between the different components within the mitochondria, the correct physical geography.

It is seen by reference to Fig. 19 that a large portion of the electrons passing through the electron transport system arise from DPNH. Hence, the concentration of DPN within the cell must also exert a control on respiratory rates. Again, it is not the absolute concentration of DPN within the cell that is important, but the concentration of DPN at a given point within the cell, this latter concentration depending on the rate of diffusion and the diffusion path. It is probable that under ordinary conditions the absolute concentration of DPN is rarely limiting.

Another kind of respiratory control may be found in the concentration of oxygen or carbon dioxide within the cell. Little is known concerning the effects of carbon dioxide on respiratory rates, except that high concentrations of carbon dioxide retard this rate. Except for leaves, the concentration of carbon dioxide in the intracellular spaces is of the order of 1–5%, 33 to 165 times higher than in the air. Whether or not carbon dioxide influences respiratory rates it is noteworthy that one enzyme, PEP carboxylase, has a high affinity for carbon dioxide and the products of the reaction can greatly alter the steady state of the respiratory system by an alteration of substrate concentration.

Similarly, under ordinary conditions the pO_2 has little effect on the respiratory rate between 5 and 100% oxygen, an oxygen concentration well within the 15–20% oxygen that is present in the intracellular spaces. However, at very low oxygen pressures there is a marked inhibition of respiration and an acceleration in the rate of fermentation;

at zero oxygen pressure the rate of hexose utilization can be four times greater than in air, that is to say oxygen has a sparing effect on the rate of hexose utilization. This sparing effect was discovered by Pasteur and is known as the *Pasteur effect*. In spite of considerable investigation there has been, as yet, no completely satisfactory explanation of the Pasteur effect. The explanations that have been proposed may be grouped in three general categories, viz.:

(1) Competition between respiration and glycolysis for phosphate or for ADP and phosphate (61, 66, 95, 96).

(2) Inhibition of glycolysis by oxygen, or by an inhibitor formed in the presence of air (89).

(3) A hypothesis based on cell structure (35) which proposes that some of the energy of respiration may be used to separate structurally some of the enzymes from their substrates, thus controlling the rate of glycolysis. The exact mechanism and physiological significance of the Pasteur effect remain partially unsolved problems.

In addition to the above regulatory systems, the occurrence of photosynthesis in green plant tissues may well influence respiratory metabolism. There are common to the two metabolic processes, photosynthesis and respiration, many common substances such as ADP, ATP, and intermediate carbon compounds. Though these two systems may be partially isolated by their localization in chloroplasts and mitochondria, the two structures do function in a common cytoplasm. Though the interrelationships between photosynthesis and respiration are beyond the scope of this chapter, one may expect that in green plant tissues there are mechanisms of tight regulatory control of respiration dependent upon the photosynthetic steady state.

V. Epilogue

Our basic concern with cellular respiration is as a mechanism producing intermediate substances and available energy for cellular synthesis, growth, and work. We may digress for a bit to consider it at a fundamental level.

In the inorganic world we recognize that all processes proceed toward equilibrium. This experience is summarized in the second law of thermodynamics; this law is a statement that reactions proceed toward maximum entropy. Entropy can be considered as a measure of probability, of randomness, or of disorganization, where an increase in entropy means a more probable state, and a decrease in entropy a gain in organization.

The second law is a statistical law, and is valid for systems of large numbers of molecules, but it cannot be used to predict the behavior of a few molecules observed over a short time. Probability considerations make it clear that in a large system observed over a long time there will be individual fluctuations leading to local temporal decreases in entropy, that is, areas of a higher degree of organization and order than that of the system as a whole.

Though it is difficult to prove that the laws of thermodynamics apply to living systems, we will assume that they do so. Plants and animals are highly organized systems, containing intricate large molecules, macromolecular complexes, cell organelles, differentiated cells and organs. In other words, living systems have a low entropy level. The mere existence of living organisms means that their improbable structures have to be maintained through time, and cannot drift toward equilibrium and death. As we shall see below, this drift can be prevented only by a continuous flow of energy and materials through the cells.

In growth we see the relatively unorganized cell or cells undergo a most orderly process of division and differentiation leading to the more complex organizational level of the adult organism. Simultaneously, a whole chain of biosynthetic pathways is operating in an orderly and regulated manner, resulting in the synthesis of cell walls, proteins, nucleic acids, and other complex molecular and macromolecular structures. As biologists, we recognize that, however improbable all this appears thermodynamically, it proceeds with such regularity and order that we may chart out in advance the course and time sequence with which growth will proceed from a specific zygote or spore.

We cannot discuss here how the highly improbable event of first life had its origin, nor how through a billion years of evolution the simplest living forms gave rise to modern organisms. But we are forced to recognize that once life had its origin, the paradox of highly organized forms increasing in degree of organization in evolution or maturation to still more improbable structures, in the face of thermodynamic laws that predict death and decay, is more an apparent paradox than a real one. The existence of life, growth, and evolution makes it clear that these processes are consistent with the laws of thermodynamics and must proceed with a constant increase in entropy of the whole system. The problem is resolved when we recognize the system.

If the cell or organism is considered as an isolated system, its growth or evolution appears to occur with a decrease in entropy. Living organisms are not closed thermodynamic systems but open ones, exchanging materials and energy across their boundaries, and, when we consider the energy system of which life is but a part, then we see that the system as a whole proceeds toward equilibrium, with a decrease in free energy and an increase in entropy. This system includes the sun and the nuclear reactions occurring within it, resulting in the continuous radiation of energy to the earth. A small part of this energy is trapped by the pigment systems of plants and stored as the potential energy of carbohydrates. These carbohydrates are part of the thermodynamic system to which organisms belong.

Therefore, it is meaningless to discuss the thermodynamic aspects of life, growth, and reproduction apart from organic food and atmospheric oxygen or, in the final analysis, from photosynthesis and the nuclear reactions of the sun. For the decrease in entropy of growth and synthesis is more than compensated for by the increase in entropy from the respiration of organic foods, with the result that the entropy of the whole system increases. From the point of view of the energy balance of the solar system, life is merely a highly improbable fluctuation of microscopic magnitude, but one which possesses the unique property of propagation of this unstable state through time.

Most plants are aerobic and fail to grow in the absence of oxygen gas. Therefore, cellular growth is largely dependent upon cellular respiration. The work of the cell, then, is dependent upon trapping some of the energy flow along the potential gradient from substrate to molecular oxygen.

An examination of cellular respiration and synthesis leads one to the conclusion that cells are molecular engines, where the energy in chemical bonds may be exchanged between molecules without degradation to heat. This is illustrated by transglycosidations and phosphorylations. We have no chemical models for these systems, but must work out each one on the basis of isolated enzymes and identified substrates.

Part of the energy released in respiration is built into ATP by oxidative phosphorylation, part is present in such molecules as acetyl-CoA. This energy is readily exchanged with IDP, UDP, and GDP in exchange reactions with ATP. The energy in the ATP molecules can be used to synthesize glucosidic and peptide bonds, as well as ribose and deoxyribose nucleic acids.

The localization of the respiratory enzymes in the mitochondria and the fact that oxidative phosphorylation also occurs in the mitochondria are of particular interest. The complexity of the respiratory chain and the high velocity of electron transport through catalysis of high molecular weight make it highly improbable that we are concerned with a homogeneous reaction system. This is particularly apparent when we recognize that an uninjured mitochondrion respires at a very low rate unless a phosphate acceptor is present, while a poisoned (dinitrophenol) or injured one will respire at maximum velocity without reference to oxidative phosphorylation. This leads us to the conclusion that models of cellular respiration must be found in the study of chemical reactions in organized solid state systems.

The problem of cellular respiration is far from solved. The discovery of the details of energy exchange in the mitochondrion lies before us. Of particular importance is the recognition of the complementarity of structure and function. The structure determines the function, and the processes occurring under structural control result in the duplication of the original structure. Currently we state this only in words. The next generation has the challenge of making precise, in operational terms, what is meant by this generalization.

REFERENCES

1. Arnon, D. I. Glyceraldehyde phosphate dehydrogenase of green plants. *Science* **116,** 635–637 (1952).
2. Ball, E. G., and Cooper, O. The oxidation of reduced triphosphopyridine nucleotide as mediated by the transhydrogenase reaction and its inhibition by thyroxine. *Proc. Natl. Acad. Sci. U.S.* **43,** 357–364 (1957).
3. Barker, J. A note on the determination of alcohol in potato tubers. *J. Exptl. Botany* **2,** 238–241 (1951).
4. Belitser, V. A. La regulation de la respiration musculaire par les transformations du phosphagène. *Enzymologia* **6,** 1–8 (1939).
5. Belitser, V. A., and Tsybakova, E. T. The mechanism of phosphorylation as related to respiration. *Biokhimiya* **4,** 516–535 (1939).
6. Bennet-Clark, T. A. The role of organic acids in plant metabolism. Part II. *New Phytologist* **32,** 128–161 (1933).
7. Bensley, R. R., and Hoerr, N. L. Studies on cell structure by the freezing-drying method. *Anat. Record* **60,** 449–455 (1934).
8. Bergmann, M., and Fruton, J. S. The specificity of proteinases. *Advances in Enzymol.* **1,** 63–96 (1941).
9. Blackman, F. F., and Parija, P. Analytic studies in plant respiration. I. The respiration of a population of senescent ripening apples. *Proc. Roy. Soc.* **B103,** 412–445 (1928).
10. Blackman, F. F. "Analytical Studies in Plant Respiration." Cambridge Univ. Press, London and New York, 1954.
11. Blinks, L. R., and Skow, R. K. The time course of photosynthesis as shown by the gas electrode, with anomalies in the acidity changes. *Proc. Natl. Acad. Sci. U.S.* **24,** 413–419 (1938).
12. Bonner, W. D., Jr. Soluble oxidases and their functions. *Ann. Rev. Plant Physiol.* **8,** 427–452 (1957).
13. Brachet, J. "Biochemical Cytology." Academic Press, New York, 1957.
14. Brackett, F. S., Olson, R. A., and Crickard, R. G. Respiration and intensity dependence of photosynthesis in Chlorella. *J. Gen. Physiol.* **36,** 529–561 (1953).
15. Brown, A. H., Nier, A. O. C., and Van Norman, R. W. Measurement of metabolic gas exchange with a recording mass spectrometer. *Plant Physiol.* **27,** 320–334 (1952).
16. Burton, W. G. Studies on the dormancy and sprouting of potatoes. 1. The oxygen content of the potato tuber. *New Phytologist* **49,** 121–134 (1950).

17. Castor, L. N., and Chance, B. Photochemical action spectra of CO inhibited respiration. *J. Biol. Chem.* **217**, 453–465 (1955).
18. Ceithaml, J., and Vennesland, B. The synthesis of tricarboxylic acids by carbon dioxide fixation in parsley root preparations. *J. Biol. Chem.* **178**, 133–143 (1949).
19. Chance, B. The properties of the enzyme-substrate compounds of horseradish and lactoperoxidase. *Science* **109**, 204–208 (1949).
20. Chance, B. Enzyme-substrate compounds. *Advances in Enzymol.* **12**, 153–190 (1951).
21. Chance, B. Interaction of adenosinediphosphate with the respiratory chain. *In* "Enzymes: Units of Biological Structure and Function" (O. H. Gaebler, ed.), pp. 447–463. Academic Press, New York, 1956.
22. Chance, B. Techniques for the assay of the respiratory enzymes. *In* "Methods in Enzymology" (S. P. Colowick and N. O. Kaplan, eds.), Vol. 4, pp. 273–329. Academic Press, New York, 1957.
23. Chance, B., and Williams, G. R. The respiratory chain and oxidative phosphorylation. *Advances in Enzymol.* **17**, 65–134 (1956).
24. Colowick, S. P., Kalckar, H. M., and Cori, C. F. Glucose phosphorylation and oxidation in cell-free tissue extracts. *J. Biol. Chem.* **137**, 343–356 (1941).
25. Conn, E. E., and Vennesland, B. Glutathione reductase of wheat germ. *J. Biol. Chem.* **192**, 17–28 (1951).
26. Crook, E. M., and Hopkins, F. G. Further observations on the system ascorbic acid-glutathione-ascorbic acid-oxidase. *Biochem. J.* **32**, 1356–1363 (1938).
27. Cunningham, B., and Kirk, P. A new form of differential microrespirometer. *J. Gen. Physiol.* **24**, 135–149 (1940); The oxygen consumption of single cells of *Paramecium caudatum* as measured by a capillary respirometer. *J. Cellular Comp. Physiol.* **20**, 119–134 (1942).
28. Davies, P. W., and Brink, F. Microelectrodes for measuring local oxygen tension in animal tissues. *Rev. Sci. Instr.* **13**, 524–533 (1942).
29. Dawson, C. R., and Tarpley, W. B. *In* "The Enzymes" (J. B. Sumner and K. Myrbäck, eds.), Vol II, Pt. 1, p. 492. Academic Press, New York, 1951.
30. de Saussure, T. Recherches chimiques sur la végétation, Paris, 1804.
31. Devaux, M. H. Atmosphère intèrne des tubercules et racines tuberculeuses. *Bull. soc. botan. France* **37**, 273–279 (1890).
32. Devaux, M. H. Étude expèrimentale sur l'aeration des tissus massife. *Ann. sci. nat. Botan. et biol. végétale* [7] **14**, 297–395 (1891).
33. Devaux, M. H. Porasité du fruit des cucurbitacées. *Rev. gen. botan.* **3**, 49–56 (1891).
34. Dickens, F. Yeast fermentation of pentose phosphoric acids. *Biochem. J.* **32**, 1645–1653 (1938).
35. Dixon, K. C. The Pasteur effect and its mechanism. *Biol. Revs. Cambridge Phil. Soc.* **12**, 431–460 (1937).
36. Dixon, M. "Manometric Methods." Cambridge Univ. Press, London and New York, 1951.
37. Ehrenberg, A. D., and Ludwig, G. Free radical formation in reaction between old yellow enzyme and reduced triphosphopyridine nucleotide. *Science* **127**, 1177–1178 (1958).
38. Erickson, R. O., and Goddard, D. R. An analysis of root growth in cellular and biochemical terms. *Growth* (Symp. Vol.) **10**, 87–116 (1951).
39. Erickson, R. O., and Sax, K. B. Rates of cell division and cell elongation in the

growth of the primary root of *Zea mays*. *Proc. Am. Phil. Soc.* **100**, 499–514 (1956).
40. Fenn, W. O. The oxygen consumption of frog nerve during stimulation. *J. Gen. Physiol.* **10**, 767–779 (1927).
41. Fenn, W. O. A new method for the simultaneous determination of minute amounts of carbon dioxide and oxygen. *Am. J. Physiol.* **84**, 110–118 (1928); The gas exchange of nerve during stimulation. *Ibid.* **80**, 327–346 (1927).
42. Gerard, R. W. Oxygen diffusion into cells. *Biol. Bull.* **60**, 245–268 (1931).
43. Gibbs, M. Triosephosphate dehydrogenase and glucose 6-phosphate dehydrogenase in the pea plant. *Nature* **170**, 164–165 (1952).
44. Gibbs, M., and Beevers, H. Glucose dissimilation in the higher plant, effect of age of tissue. *Plant Physiol.* **30**, 343–347 (1955).
45. Goddard, D. R. Anaerobic respiration or fermentation. *Science* **101**, 352–353 (1945).
46. Goddard, D. R., and Stafford, H. A. Localization of enzymes in the cells of higher plants. *Ann. Rev. Plant Physiol.* **5**, 115–132 (1954).
47. Godlewski, E. Beiträge zur Kenntniss der Pflanzenathmung. *Jahrb. wiss. Botan.* **13**, 491–543 (1882).
48. Haas, E. TPNH cytochrome c reductase from yeast. *In* "Methods in Enzymology" (S. P. Colowick and N. O. Kaplan, eds.), Vol. 2, pp. 699–703. Academic Press, New York, 1955.
49. Haas, E., Harrer, C. J., and Hogness, T. R. Cytochrome reductase; II. Improved method of isolation; inhibition and inactivation; reaction with oxygen. *J. Biol. Chem.* **143**, 341–349 (1942).
50. Hackett, D. P. Recent studies on plant mitochondria. *Intern. Rev. Cytol.* **4**, 143–196 (1955).
51. Hackett, D. P., and Haas, D. W. Oxidative phosphorylation and functional cytochromes in skunk cabbage mitochondria. *Plant Physiol.* **33**, 27–32 (1958).
52. Harden, A. "Alcoholic Fermentation." Longmans, Green, London. 1932.
53. Harden, A., and Young, W. J. The alcoholic ferment of yeast-juice. Pt. III. The function of phosphates in the fermentation of glucose by yeast-juice. *Proc. Roy. Soc.* **B80**, 299–311 (1908).
54. Hartree, E. F. Haematin compounds. *In* "Modern Methods of Plant Analysis" (K. Paech and M. V. Tracey, eds.), Vol. IV, pp. 197–245. Springer, Berlin, 1955.
55. Hartree, E. F. Cytochrome in higher plants. *Advances in Enzymol.* **18**, 1–64 (1957).
56. Hill, R. Oxidation-reduction potentials. *In* "Modern Methods of Plant Analysis" (K. Paech and M. V. Tracey, ed.), Vol. I, pp. 393–414. Springer, Berlin, 1956.
57. Hill, R., and Bhagvat, K. Cytochrome oxidase in flowering plants. *Nature* **143**, 726 (1939).
58. Hill, R., and Bhagvat, K. Cytochrome oxidase in higher plants. *New Phytologist* **50**, 112–120 (1951).
59. Hill, R., and Hartree, E. F. Hematin compounds in plants. *Ann. Rev. Plant Physiol.* **4**, 115–150 (1953).
60. Hogeboom, G. H. Fractionation of cell components of animal tissues. *In* "Methods in Enzymology" (S. P. Colowick and N. O. Kaplan, eds.), Vol. 1, pp. 16–19. Academic Press, New York, 1955.
61. Holzer, H., and Holzer, E. Bestimmung stationärer Triosephosphat-Konzentra-

tionen in lebender Hefe Ein Beitrag zum Mechanismus des Pasteur Effectes. *Z. Physiol. Chem., Hoppe-Seyler's* **292,** 232–239 (1953).
62. Horecker, B. L. TPNH cytochrome c reductase (liver). *In* "Methods in Enzymology" (S. P. Colowick and N. O. Kaplan, eds.), Vol. 2, pp. 704–706. Academic Press, New York, 1955.
63. Horecker, B. L., Smyrniotis, P. Z., and Seegmiller, J. E. The enzymatic conversion of 6-phospho-gluconate to ribulose-5-phosphate and ribose-5-phosphate. *J. Biol. Chem.* **193,** 383–396 (1951).
63a. Humphreys, T. E., and Stumpf, P. K. Fat metabolism in higher plants IV. Preparation of soluble fatty acid oxidases from peanut microsomes. *J. Biol. Chem.* **213,** 941–949 (1955).
64. Hunter, F. E., Jr. Oxidative phosphorylation during electron transport. Ch. V. *In* "Phosphorus Metabolism" (W. D. McElroy and B. Glass, eds.), Vol. **I,** pp. 297–330. Johns Hopkins Press, Baltimore, Maryland, 1951.
65. Johannsen, W. Ueber den Einfluss hoher Säuerstoffspannung auf die Kohlensaüreausscheidung einiger Keimpflanzen. *Untersuchungen aus dem bot. Inst. zu Tübingen* **I,** 686–717 (1885).
66. Johnson, M. J. The role of aerobic phosphorylation in the Pasteur effect. *Science* **94,** 200–202 (1941).
67. Kalcker, H. M. Phosphorylation in kidney tissue. *Enzymologia* **2,** 47–52 (1937).
68. Kaplan, N. O. Thermodynamics and mechanism of the phosphate bond. *In* "The Enzymes" (J. B. Sumner and K. Myrbäck, eds.), Vol. 2, Pt. 1, pp. 55–113. Academic Press, New York, 1951.
69. Keilin, D. On cytochrome: a respiratory pigment common to animals, yeast and higher plants. *Proc. Roy. Soc.* **B98,** 312–339 (1925).
70. Keilin. D. *In* "Great Experiments in Biology" (M. L. Gabriel and S. Fogel, eds.), pp. 31–38. Prentice-Hall, New York, 1955.
71. Keilin, D., and Hartree, E. F. Cytochrome and cytochrome oxidase. *Proc. Roy. Soc.* **B127,** 167–191 (1939).
72. Keilin, D., and Hartree, E. F. Purification and properties of cytochrome c. *Biochem. J.* **39,** 289–292 (1945).
73. Keilin, D., and Mann, T. On the haematin compound of peroxidase. *Proc. Roy. Soc.* **B122,** 119–133 (1937).
74. Keilin, D., and Slater, E. C. Cytochrome. *Brit. Med. Bull.* **9,** 89–96 (1953).
75. Keilin, D., and Wang, Y.-L. Haemoglobin in the root nodules of leguminous plants. *Nature* **155,** 227–229 (1945).
76. Kenten, R. H., and Mann, P. J. B. The oxidation of certain dicarboxylic acids by peroxidase systems in presence of manganese. *Biochem. J.* **53,** 498–505 (1953).
77. Knoop, F. Zur Oxydation von Fettsäuren *Beitr. chem. Physiol. Pathol.* **11,** 411–414 (1908).
78. Kostychev, S. "Plant Respiration" (C. J. Lyons, transl.). Blakiston, Philadelphia, Pennsylvania, 1927.
79. Krebs, H. A. The intermediary stages in the biological oxidation of carbohydrate. *Advances in Enzymol.* **3,** 191–252 (1943).
80. Krebs, H. A., and Johnston, W. A. The role of citric acid in intermediate metabolism in animal tissues. *Enzymologia* **4,** 148–156 (1937).
81. Kubowitz, F. Uber die chemische Zusammensetzung der Kartoffeloxidase. *Biochem. Z.* **292,** 221–229 (1937); Spaltung und Resynthese der Polyphenoloxidase und des Hämocyanins. **299,** 32–57 (1938).

82. Kubowitz, F., and Haas, E. Ausbau der photochemischen Methoden Zur Untersuchung des säuerstoff-übertragenden Ferments; Anwendung auf Essigbakterien und Hefezellen. *Biochem. Z.* **255,** 247–277 (1932).
83. Kuhn, R., Hand, D. B., and Florkin, M. Über die Natur der Peroxidase. *Z. Physiol. Chem., Hoppe-Seyler's* **201,** 255–266 (1931).
84. Laties, G. G. The physical environment and oxidative and phosphorylative capacities of higher plant mitochondria. *Plant Physiol.* **28,** 557–575 (1953).
85. Leloir, L. F. Enzymic isomerization and related processes. *Advances in Enzymol.* **14,** 193–218 (1953).
86. Liakowski, N. Chemische Untersuchungen über die Keimung Von Kürbissamen, 1874.
87. Lichstein, H. C. Function of the vitamin B_6 group: pyridoxal phosphate (codecarboxylase) in transamination. *J. Biol. Chem.* **161,** 311–320 (1945).
88. Linossier, L. G. Contribution à l'étude des ferments oxydants sur la péroxydase du pus. *Compt. rend. soc. biol.* **50,** 373–375 (1898).
89. Lipmann, F. Pasteur effect. *In* "A Symposium on Respiratory Enzymes," pp. 48–73. Univ. of Wisconsin Press, Madison, Wisconsin, 1942.
90. Lipmann, F. Acetylation of sulfanilamide by liver homogenates and extracts. *J. Biol. Chem.* **160,** 173–190 (1945).
91. Loew, O. Catalase, a new enzyme of general occurrence, with special reference of the tobacco plant. *U.S. Dept. Agr. Rept. No.* **68,** 1–47 (1901).
92. Lohmann, K., and Schuster, P. Untersuchungen über die Cocarboxylase. *Biochem. Z.* **294,** 188–214 (1937).
93. Longmuir, I. S. Respiration rate of bacteria as a function of oxygen concentration. *Biochem. J.* **57,** 81–87 (1954).
94. Loomis, W. F., and Lipmann, F. Reversible inhibition of the coupling between phorphorylation and oxidation. *J. Biol. Chem.* **173,** 807–808 (1948).
95. Lynen, F. Über den aeroben Phosphatbedarf der Hefe Ein Beitrag zur Kenntnis der Pasteur'schen Reaktion. *Ann. Chem., Liebigs* **546,** 120–141 (1941).
96. Lynen, F., and Koenigsberger, R. Zum Mechanismus der Pasteur'schen Reaktion: Der Phosphat-Kreislauf in der Hefe und seine Beeinflussung durch 2,4-Dinitrophenol. *Ann. Chem., Liebigs* **573,** 60–84 (1951).
97. McAlister, E. D. Time course of photosynthesis for a higher plant 1–17. *Smithsonian Misc. Collections* **95,** *Spec. Publ.* 3410 (1937).
98. MacMunn, C. A. Researches on myohaematin and histohaematins. *Phil. Trans. Roy. Soc. London* **177,** 267–298 (1886).
99. Mahler, H. R., Sorkar, N. K., Vernon, L. P., and Alberty, R. A. Studies on diphosphopyridine nucleotide-cytochrome c reductase II. Purification and properties. *J. Biol. Chem.* **199,** 585–597 (1952).
100. Mallette, M. F. The nature of the copper enzymes involved in tyrosine oxidation. *In* "Copper Metabolism" (W. D. McElroy and B. Glass, eds.), pp. 48–75. Johns Hopkins Press, Baltimore, Maryland, 1950.
101. Mapson, L. W., and Goddard, D. R. The reduction of glutathione by plant tissues. *Biochem. J.* **49,** 592–601 (1951).
102. Mason, H. G., Fowlks, W. L., and Peterson, E. Oxygen transfer and electron transport by the phenolase complex. *J. Am. Chem. Soc.* **77,** 2914–2915 (1955).
103. Mason, H. S. Mechanisms of oxygen metabolism. *Advances in Enzymol.* **19,** 79–233 (1957).
104. Meeuse, B. J. D., in Goddard, D. R. Metabolism in relation to growth. Growth symp. XII. *Growth, Suppl.* **12,** 17–45 (1948).

05. Meeuse, B. J. D. "Handbook of Plant Physiology" (W. Ruhland, ed.), Vol. 9, pp. 190–203. Springer, Heidelberg, 1958.
06. Melnick, J. L. The photochemical absorption spectra of the Pasteur enzyme and the respiratory ferment in yeast. *J. Biol. Chem.* **141,** 269–281 (1941).
07. Melnick, J. L. The photochemical spectrum of cytochrome oxidase. *J. Biol. Chem.* **146,** 385–390 (1942).
08. Meyerhof, O. Über den Einfluss des Säuerstoff auf die alcoholische Gärung der Hefe. *Biochem. Z.* **163,** 43–86 (1926).
09. Meyerhof, O. The origin of the reaction of Harden and Young in cell-free alcoholic fermentation. *J. Biol. Chem.* **157,** 105–119 (1945); Further studies of the Harden-Young effect in alcoholic fermentation of yeast preparations. *J. Biol. Chem.* **180,** 575–586 (1949).
10. Meyerhof, O., and Lohmann, K. Über die enzymatische Gleichgewichtsreaktion zwischen Hexosediphosphorsäure und Dioxyacetonphosphorsäure. *Biochem. Z.* **271,** 89–110 (1934).
11. Michaelis, L., and Schubert, M. P. The theory of reversible two-step oxidation involving free radicals. *Chem. Revs.* **22,** 437–470 (1938).
12. Millerd, A., Bonner, J., Axelrod, B., and Bandurski, R. S. Oxidative and phosphorylative activity of plant mitochondria. *Proc. Natl. Acad. Sci. U.S.* **37,** 855–862 (1951).
13. Murlin, J. R. The conversion of fat to carbohydrate in the germinating castor bean. I. The respiratory metabolism. *J. Gen. Physiol.* **17,** 283–302 (1933); Daggs, R. G., and Halcro-Wardlaw, H. S. II. The combustion respiratory quotient as determined by a modified oxycalorimeter. *Ibid.* **17,** 303–309 (1933); Pierce, H. B., Sheldon, D. E., and Murlin, J. R. III. The chemical analysis, and correlation with respiratory exchange. *Ibid.* **17,** 311–325 (1933).
13a. Needham, J., Shen, S-C., Needham, D. M., and Laurence, A. S. C. Myosin birefringence and adenylpyrophosphate. *Nature* **147,** 766–768 (1941).
bean. *J. Gen. Physiol.* **17,** 283–302 (1933).
14. Neilands, J. B., and Stumpf, P. K. "Outline of Enzyme Chemistry." Wiley, New York, 1955.
15. Newton, R. G. An improved electrical conductivity method for the estimation of carbon dioxide and other reactive gases. *Ann. Botany* **49,** 381–398 (1935).
16. Ochoa, S. "Coupling" of phosphorylation with oxidation of pyruvic acid in brain. *J. Biol. Chem.* **138,** 751–773 (1941).
17. Ochoa, S. Enzymic mechanisms in the citric acid cycle. *Advances in Enzymol.* **15,** 183–270 (1954).
18. Ochoa, S., Stern, J. R., and Schneider, M. C. Enzymatic synthesis of citric acid. II. Crystalline condensing enzyme. *J. Biol. Chem.* **193,** 691–702 (1951).
19. Okunuki, K. Über den Gaswechesel der Pollen. *Acta Phytochim.* (*Japan*) **11,** 27–64 (1939); II. Über den Gaswechsel der Pollen. III. Weitere Untersuchungen über die Dehydrasen aus den Pollenkörnern. *Acta Phytochim.* (*Japan*) **11,** 65–80 (1939).
20. Onslow, M. W. "The Principles of Plant Biochemistry," Pt. I. Cambridge Univ. Press, London and New York, 1931.
21. Osterhout, W. J. V., and Haas, A. An adaptation of Winkler's method to biological work. *J. Biol. Chem.* **32,** 141–146 (1917).
22. Phillips, J. Studies on fermentation in rice and barley. *Am. J. Botany* **34,** 62–72 (1947).

123. Racker, E. Alternate pathways of glucose and fructose metabolism. *Advance in Enzymol.* **15**, 141–182 (1954).
124. Raper, H. S. Tyrosinase. *Ergeb. Enzymforsch.* **1**, 270–279 (1932).
125. Raudnitz, R. Ueber sogenannte Ferment reactionen der Milch. *Zentr. Physiol* **12**, 790–793 (1899).
126. Schönbein, C. F. On ozone and ozonic action in mushrooms. *Phil. Mag.* [4] **1** 132–141 (1856).
127. Schönbein, C. F. Über einige neuen höchst empfindlichen Reagentien auf de Wasserstoff-superoxide. *Verhandl. naturforsch. Ges. Basel* **3**, 339–342 (1863).
128. Schulze, E., Umlauf, W., and Urich, A. Untersuchungen über einige chemisch vorgänge bei der Lupine. *Landwitsch. Jahrb.* **5**, 821–868 (1876).
129. Scott, D. B. McN., and Cohen, S. Enzymatic formation of pentose phosphat from 6-phosphogluconate. *J. Biol. Chem.* **188**, 509–530 (1951).
130. Seifter, E. The occurrence of coenzyme A in plants. *Plant Physiol.* **29**, 403–40 (1954).
131. Singer, T. P., Kearney, E. B., and Massey, V. Newer knowledge of succini dehydrogenase. *Advances in Enzymol.* **18**, 65–111 (1957).
132. Slater, E. C. Respiratory chain phosphorylation. *Proc. Intern. Congr. Biochem 3rd Congr., Brussels, 1955*, pp. 264–277 (1956).
133. Slater, E. C. The constitution of the respiratory chain in animal tissues. *Ad vances in Enzymol.* **20**, 147–199 (1958).
134. Slater, E. C. *In* "Handbuch der Pflanzenphysiologie" (W. Ruhland, ed.), Vol. 12 In press. Springer, Berlin.
135. Smith, L. Bacterial cytochromes. *Bacteriol. Revs.* **18**, 106–130 (1954).
136. Smith, L., and Chance, B. Cytochromes in plants. *Ann. Rev. Plant Physiol.* **9** 449–482 (1958).
137. Stich, C. Die Atmung der Pflanzen bei verminderter Säuerstoffspannung un bei Verletzungen. *Flora (Jena)* **74**, 1–57 (1891).
138. Stumpf, P. K., Bokman, A. H., Newcomb, E. H., and Humphreys, T. E. Fa metabolism in higher plants. II. Oxidation of palmitate by a peanut particulat system. *J. Biol. Chem.* **210**, 941–948 (1954).
139. Sumner, J. B., and Dounce, A. L. Crystalline catalase. *J. Biol. Chem.* **121**, 417- 424 (1937).
140. Sumner, J. B., and Howell, S. F. Haematin and the peroxidase of fig sap *Enzymologia* **1**, 133–134 (1936).
141. Szent-Györgyi, A. On the function of hexuronic acid in the respiration of th cabbage leaf. *J. Biol. Chem.* **90**, 385–393 (1931).
142. Tewfik, S., and Stumpf, P. K. Carbohydrate metabolism in higher plants. V The distribution of aldolase in plants. *Am. J. Botany* **36**, 567–571 (1949).
143. Tewfik, S., and Stumpf, P. K. Carbohydrate metabolism in higher plants. IV Observations on triosephosphate dehydrogenase. *J. Biol. Chem.* **192**, 519–53 (1951).
144. Theorell, H. Reversible splitting of a peroxidase. *Arkiv. Kemi, Mineral. Geol* **14B** (20), pp. 1–3 (1940).
145. Theorell, H. The iron-containing enzymes B. Catalases and Peroxidases "Hydroperoxidases." *In* "The Enzymes" (J. B. Sumner and K. Myrbäck, eds.) Vol. 2, Pt. 1, pp. 397–427. Academic Press, New York, 1951.
146. Thunberg, T. Mikro-respirometrische Untersuchungen. Der Gasaustausc einiger niederer Thiere in seiner Abhängigkeit von Säuerstoffpartialdruck *Zentr. Physiol.* **18**, 553–556 (1904).

147. Thunberg, T. Gasautausch einiger niederer Thiere in seiner Abhangigheit von Sauerstoffpartiardruck. *Skand. Arch. Physiol.* **17,** 133–195 (1905).
148. Thunberg, T. Über die vitale Dehydrierung der Bernsteinsaüre bei Abwesenheit von Sauerstoff. *Zentr. Physiol.* **31,** 91–93 (1917); Zur Kenntnis der Einwirkung tierischer Gewebe auf Methylenblau. *Skand. Arch. Physiol.* **35,** 163–195 (1917).
149. Tobias, J. M. Microrespiration techniques. *Physiol. Revs.* **23,** 51–75 (1943).
150. Tsou, C.-L., and Wu, C.-Y. Studies on the codehydrogenase cytochrome c reductase enzyme systems II. *Sci. Sinica (Peking)* **5,** 263–270 (1956).
151. Umbreit, W. W., Burris, R. H., and Stauffer, J. F. "Manometric Techniques." Burgess, Minneapolis, Minnesota, 1957.
152. Utter, M. F. Carbohydrate metabolism. *Ann. Rev. Biochem.* **27,** 245–284 (1958).
153. Vennesland, B. Some applications of deuterium to the study of enzyme mechanisms. *Discussions Faraday Soc., No.* **20,** 240–248 (1955).
154. Vennesland, B. Ceithaml, J., and Gollub, M. C. The fixation of carbon dioxide in a plant. Tricarboxylic acid system. *J. Biol. Chem.* **171,** 445–446 (1947).
154a. Vickery, H. B. The capacity of leaves of *Bryophyllum calycinum* to recover from prolonged exposure to darkness or light. *Plant Physiol.* **31,** 455–464 (1956).
155. Wang, T.-Y., Tsou, C.-L., and Wang, Y.-L. Studies on succinic dehydrogenase. I. Isolation, purification and properties. *Sci. Sinica (Peking)* **5,** 73–90 (1956).
156. Wang, T.-Y., Tsou, C.-L., and Wang, Y.-L. Studies on succinic dehydrogenase. II. Further observation on the properties of the enzyme and its prosthetic group. *Sci. Sinica (Peking)* **6,** 174–184 (1957).
157. Warburg, O. Versuche an überlebendem Carcinomgewebe. (Methoden). *Biochem. Z.* **142,** 317–333 (1923).
158. Warburg, O. "Heavy Metal Prosthetic Groups and Enzyme Action." Oxford Univ. Press, London and New York, 1949.
159. Warburg, O. *In* "Great Experiments in Biology" (M. L. Gabriel and S. Fogel, eds.), pp. 39–50. Prentice-Hall, New York, 1955.
160. Warburg, O., and Christian, W. Über ein neues Oxidationsferment und sein Absorptionsspektrum. *Biochem. Z.* **254,** 438–458 (1932); Pyridin, der wasserstoffüberbragende Bestandteil von Gärungsfermenten (Pyridin-Nucleotid). *Biochem. Z.* **287,** 291–328 (1936); Abbau von Robisonester durch Triphospho-Pyridin-Nucleotid. *Biochem. Z.* **292,** 287–295 (1937).
161. Wieland, H. Über Hydrierung und Dehydrierung. *Ber.* **45,** 484–493 (1912).
162. Wieland, H. Über den Mechanismus der Oxydationsvorgänge. *Ber.* **46,** 3327–3342 (1913).
163. Willstätter, R. Über Isolierung von Enzymen. *Ber.* **55,** 3601–3623 (1922).
164. Willstätter, R., and Pollinger, A. Über Peroxydase. *Ann. Chem., Liebigs* **430,** 269–319 (1923).
165. Willstätter, R., and Stoll, A. Über Peroxydase. *Ann. Chem., Liebigs* **416,** 21–64 (1918); Willstätter, R. IV. Über Peroxydase. *Ann. Chem., Liebigs* **422,** 47–73 (1921).
166. Wilson, W. P. Atmung der Pflanzen. *Flora (Jena)* **65,** 93–96 (1882).
167. Wolf, J. M., Brown, A. H., and Goddard, D. R. An improved electrical conductivity method for accurately following changes in the respiratory quotient of a single biological sample. *Plant Physiol.* **27,** 70–80 (1952).
168. Wu, C.-Y., and Tsou, C.-L. Studies on the codehyrdogenase cytochrome c enzyme systems I. *Sci. Sinica (Peking)* **4,** 137–155 (1955).

169. Yemm, E. W., and Folkes, B. F. The metabolism of amino acids and proteins in plants. *Ann. Rev. Plant Physiol.* **9**, 245–280 (1958).
170. Zaleski, W. Über die Verbreitung der Carboxylase in den Pflanzen. *Ber. deut. botan. Ges.* **31**, 349–353 (1913).

GENERAL REFERENCES

Advances in Enzymol. Interscience, New York, Vol. 1, 1941. (Published annually.)
Ann. Rev. Biochem. Annual Reviews, Inc., Palo Alto, California, Vol. 1, 1931. (Published annually.)
Ann. Rev. Plant Physiol. Annual Reviews, Inc., Palo Alto, California, Vol. 1, 1950. (Published annually.)
Bray, H. G., and White, K. "Kinetics and Thermodynamics in Biochemistry," 343 pp. Academic Press, New York, 1957.
"Ciba Foundation Symposium on the Regulation of Cell Metabolism" (G. E. W. Wolstenholme and C. M. O'Connor, eds.). Churchill, London, 1959.
Dixon, M., and Webb, E. C. "Enzymes," 782 pp. Academic Press, New York, 1958.
Fulton, J. S., and Simmonds, S. "General Biochemistry," 2nd ed., 1077 pp. Wiley, New York, 1958.
James, W. O. "Plant Respiration," 382 pp. Oxford Univ. Press, London and New York, 1953.

AUTHOR INDEX

Numbers in boldface refer to pages on which the complete reference is listed at the end of a chapter. Numbers in lightface indicate the pages in the text on which the references are cited. Numbers in parentheses are reference numbers and are included to assist in locating the reference in cases where the authors' names are not mentioned in the text.

A

B

M

N

O

P

INDEX TO PLANT NAMES

Numbers in this index designate the pages on which reference is made, in the text, to the plant in question. No reference is made in the index to plant names included in the titles that appear in the reference lists. In general, where a plant has been referred to in the text sometimes by common name, sometimes by its scientific name, all such references are listed in the index after the scientific name; cross-reference is made, under the common name, to this scientific name. However, in a few instances when a common name as used cannot be referred with certainty to a particular species, the page numbers follow the common name.

E

F

G

H

J

K

L

M

N

O

P

Q

R

SUBJECT INDEX

D

Q

R

S